Vedic Mathematics
For Schools

Vedic Mathematics
For Schools

JAMES T. GLOVER

Preface by

H.E. DR. L.M. SINGHVI

Formerly High Commissioner for India in the UK

BOOK 3

MOTILAL BANARSIDASS PUBLISHERS
PRIVATE LIMITED • DELHI

First Edition: Delhi, 2002
Reprint: Delhi, 2003

© J.T. GLOVER
All Rights Reserved.

ISBN: 81-208-1819-9

Also available at:
MOTILAL BANARSIDASS
41 U.A. Bungalow Road, Jawahar Nagar, Delhi 110 007
8 Mahalaxmi Chamber, 22 Bhulabhai Desai Road, Mumbai 400 026
120 Royapettah High Road, Mylapore, Chennai 600 004
236, 9th Main III Block, Jayanagar, Bangalore 560 011
Sanas Plaza, 1302 Baji Rao Road, Pune 411 002
8 Camac Street, Kolkata 700 017
Ashok Rajpath, Patna 800 004
Chowk, Varanasi 221 001

Printed in India
BY JAINENDRA PRAKASH JAIN AT SHRI JAINENDRA PRESS,
A-45 NARAINA, PHASE-I, NEW DELHI 110 028
AND PUBLISHED BY NARENDRA PRAKASH JAIN FOR
MOTILAL BANARSIDASS PUBLISHERS PRIVATE LIMITED,
BUNGALOW ROAD, DELHI 110 007

Preface by
His Excellency Dr L.M.Singhvi
High Commissioner for India in the UK

Vedic Mathematics for Schools is an exceptional book. It is not only a sophisticated pedagogic tool but also an introduction to an ancient civilisation. It takes us back to many millennia of India's mathematical heritage. Rooted in the ancient Vedic sources which heralded the dawn of human history and illumined by their erudite exegesis, India's intellectual, scientific and aesthetic vitality blossomed and triumphed not only in philosophy, physics, ecology and performing arts but also in geometry, algebra and arithmetic. Indian mathematicians gave the world the numerals now in universal use. The crowning glory of Indian mathematics was the invention of zero and the introduction of decimal notation without which mathematics as a scientific discipline could not have made much headway. It is noteworthy that the ancient Greeks and Romans did not have the decimal notation and, therefore, did not make much progress in the numerical sciences. The Arabs first learnt the decimal notation from Indians and introduced it into Europe. The renowned Arabic scholar, Alberuni or Abu Raihan, who was born in 973 A.D. and travelled to India, testified that the Indian attainments in mathematics were unrivalled and unsurpassed. In keeping with that ingrained tradition of mathematics in India, S.Ramanujan, "the man who knew infinity", the genius who was one of the greatest mathematicians of our time and the mystic for whom "a mathematical equation had a meaning because it expressed a thought of God", blazed many new mathematical trails in Cambridge University in the second decade of the twentieth century even though he did not himself possess a university degree.

The real contribution of this book, *Vedic Mathematics for Schools*, is to demonstrate that Vedic mathematics belongs not only to an hoary antiquity but is any day as modern as the day after tomorrow. What distinguishes it particularly is that it has been fashioned by British teachers for use at St James Independent Schools in London and other British schools and that it takes its inspiration from the pioneering work of the late Bharati Krishna Tirthaji, a former Sankaracharya of Puri, who reconstructed a unique system on the basis of ancient Indian mathematics. The book is thus a bridge across centuries, civilisations, linguistic barriers and national frontiers.

Vedic mathematics was traditionally taught through aphorisms or *Sutras*. A *Sutra* is a thread of knowledge, a theorem, a ground norm, a repository of proof. It is formulated as a proposition to encapsulate a rule or a principle. A single *Sutra* would generally encompass a wide and varied range of particular applications and may be likened to a programmed chip of our computer age. These aphorisms of Vedic mathematics have much in common with aphorisms which are contained in

Panini's *Ashtadhyayi*, that grand edifice of Sanskrit grammar. Both Vedic mathematics and Sanskrit grammar are built on the foundations of rigorous logic and on a deep understanding of how the human mind works. The methodology of Vedic mathematics and of Sanskrit grammar help to hone the human intellect and to guide and groom the human mind into modes of logical reasoning.

I hope that *Vedic Mathematics for Schools* will prove to be an asset of great value as a pioneering exemplar and will be used and adopted by discerning teachers throughout the world. It is also my prayer and hope that the example of St James Independent Schools in teaching Vedic mathematics and Sanskrit may eventually be emulated in every Indian school.

London
13th March 1995

Introduction

This book is intended as the sequel to *Vedic Mathematics For Schools Book 2*. It assumes that most of the basic methods have been mastered although many are reintroduced or revised.

The methods are based on the system of Vedic mathematical sutras or rules as they are called in the text. There are said to be sixteen of these sutras and about thirteen sub-sutras. They are to be found in the text of *Vedic Mathematics* by Sri Bharati Krishna Tirthaji. Due to flexibility in both meaning and application, no distinction is made here between a sutra and a sub-sutra.

The sutras embody laws, principles or methods of working and do not always easily succumb to rigid classification. Some of them have many applications. *Transpose and adjust* is one such rule. It applies to solving equations, division in fractions and dividing numbers close to a base. It has many other uses at later stages in mathematics and indicates, not a single or particular algorithm, but a general mental procedure. There are other sutras, such as, *When the final digits add up to ten*, for which the uses appear to be very limited.

It is because of the many faceted quality of the sutras, and that there are so few of them, that the subject becomes greatly unified and simplified.

As well as developing further the methods for multiplication and division using *All from nine and the last from ten* there are also further special methods particularly suited to mental computation. New topics are also introduced. These are equations of straight lines, approximations, parallel lines, compound arithmetic, indices, construction of formulae, brackets, factorisation, decimal conversions, direct and inverse proportion, percentage increase and decrease, pie charts, recurring decimals and the geometry of the octahedron.

The text also contains revision chapters and practice examination papers.

Acknowledgements

I would like to thank Penny Moss who, at the time of writing, gave invaluable help by providing feedback on the text. In the preliminary stages Penny and I taught this material to two classes throughout the period of a year. I would also like to thank the children who also provided me with their own kind of feedback as well as letting me know of various necessary corrections. Many thanks are also due to Rajendra Jain who is actively engaged in promoting Vedic mathematics throughout India.

JG September 2000

Contents

List of sutras found in the text with their applications

Chapter 1 Simple arithmetic

The study of number begins at one which is an expression of unity.

The simplest form of arithmetic is $1 + 1 = 2$. All addition starts with the addition of 1. But there are only nine numbers, together with a zero, and so the numbers repeat themselves after 9. This is where place value comes into play.

Place value is the name we give to the digits having a value according to the columns in which they are placed. For example, with 243, the 2 is in the hundreds column and so has a value of two hundred. Similarly, the 4 has a value of four tens and the 3 has a value of three units. When performing arithmetic this place value system is extremely useful. We can add, subtract, multiply and divide numbers easily by carrying numbers into different columns where necessary.

The following exercises give practice in the basic processes of arithmetic.

Addition

Exercise 1a

1.	53 75 143 + 98	**4.**	273 367 497 + 214	**7.**	122 476 8928 + 2435	**10.**	322 543 8790 + 324
2.	18 184 23 + 241	**5.**	825 1436 2546 + 5087	**8.**	6473 5578 45 + 9802	**11.**	88 657 3541 + 878
3.	66 35 90 + 871	**6.**	87 647 7231 + 4705	**9.**	628 5757 327 + 5688	**12.**	8786 2134 5546 + 7007

Add the following mentally:

13. $3 + 6 + 7 + 9$

14. $13 + 10 + 7 + 2$

15. $14 + 7 + 5 + 2 + 3$

16. $23 + 12 + 11 + 30$

17. $54 + 32 + 21$

18. $44 + 21 + 36 + 12$

19. $65 + 34 + 87$

20. $32 + 32 + 45 + 71$

21. $56 + 38 + 99 + 4$

22. $46 + 33 + 68 + 17$

23. $156 + 722$

24. $324 + 568 + 721$

Subtraction

Here is a reminder of how to do subtraction using the *All from 9 and the last from 10* sutra.

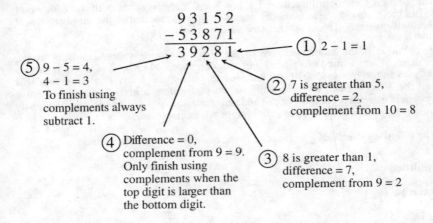

$$
\begin{array}{r}
9\ 3\ 1\ 5\ 2 \\
-\ 5\ 3\ 8\ 7\ 1 \\
\hline
3\ 9\ 2\ 8\ 1
\end{array}
$$

① 2 – 1 = 1

⑤ 9 – 5 = 4,
4 – 1 = 3
To finish using
complements always
subtract 1.

② 7 is greater than 5,
difference = 2,
complement from 10 = 8

④ Difference = 0,
complement from 9 = 9.
Only finish using
complements when the
top digit is larger than
the bottom digit.

③ 8 is greater than 1,
difference = 7,
complement from 9 = 2

The basic procedure is always to find the difference between the two numbers in any given column. Following this, there are one of four things to do according as to which digit is larger.

If the top digit is larger then write down the difference (see step 1 above).
If the bottom digit is larger write down the complement of the difference. When starting with complements use the complement from 10 (step 2) otherwise the complement from 9 is used (steps 3 and 4).

When the top digit is larger you can finish using complements and this requires 1 to be subtracted from the difference (step 5).

Exercise 1b Subtraction

1. 467 – 232	**4.** 738 – 316	**7.** 723 – 435	**10.** 846 – 559	**13.** 2567 – 1334
2. 764 – 143	**5.** 879 – 256	**8.** 653 – 278	**11.** 309 – 122	**14.** 6324 – 2878
3. 429 – 217	**6.** 764 – 430	**9.** 732 – 377	**12.** 462 – 291	**15.** 3112 – 1234

16. 8405 − 5802	**18.** 21134 − 15439	**20.** 53238 − 13239	**22.** 75881 − 36190	**24.** 236572 − 8765
17. 7442 − 3918	**19.** 75430 − 35431	**21.** 60043 − 3877	**23.** 33956 − 9173	**25.** 735812 −146924

Subtract the following mentally:

26. $40 - 7$	**31.** $100 - 23$	**36.** $110 - 11$	**41.** $587 - 134$
27. $30 - 17$	**32.** $200 - 75$	**37.** $101 - 56$	**42.** $746 - 223$
28. $66 - 33$	**33.** $71 - 37$	**38.** $235 - 98$	**43.** $671 - 599$
29. $48 - 29$	**34.** $82 - 48$	**39.** $316 - 79$	**44.** $423 - 124$
30. $90 - 67$	**35.** $93 - 36$	**40.** $400 - 21$	**45.** $540 - 277$

Multiplication

Exercise 1c

1. 78 × 5	**6.** 57 × 4	**11.** 645 × 4	**16.** 3243 × 4	**21.** 96042 × 8
2. 24 × 4	**7.** 83 × 9	**12.** 783 × 6	**17.** 2067 × 5	**22.** 73645 × 2
3. 63 × 6	**8.** 76 × 7	**13.** 467 × 8	**18.** 3146 × 3	**23.** 87428 × 3
4. 33 × 3	**9.** 23 × 11	**14.** 216 × 9	**19.** 4572 × 7	**24.** 65743 × 9
5. 87 × 8	**10.** 453 × 3	**15.** 248 × 8	**20.** 2276 × 4	**25.** 98367 × 7

Multiply the following mentally:

26. 23×2	**32.** 28×2	**38.** 21×7	**44.** 600×3
27. 54×3	**33.** 6×13	**39.** 111×3	**45.** 99×7
28. 102×4	**34.** 4×16	**40.** 623×3	**46.** 500×60
29. 51×5	**35.** 14×3	**41.** $6 \times 7 \times 2$	**47.** 25×6
30. 33×3	**36.** 123×3	**42.** $3 \times 4 \times 5$	**48.** 250×8
31. 41×6	**37.** 34×5	**43.** 20×40	**49.** 125×16

3

Division

Exercise 1d Divide:

1. 4⟌72	**6.** 6⟌84	**11.** 6⟌132	**16.** 7⟌5705	**21.** 6⟌11148
2. 5⟌65	**7.** 9⟌171	**12.** 8⟌512	**17.** 3⟌8796	**22.** 4⟌9948
3. 7⟌91	**8.** 6⟌144	**13.** 4⟌356	**18.** 9⟌4626	**23.** 7⟌32095
4. 4⟌96	**9.** 9⟌144	**14.** 5⟌755	**19.** 8⟌7832	**24.** 8⟌43544
5. 3⟌54	**10.** 4⟌132	**15.** 6⟌942	**20.** 8⟌6352	**25.** 9⟌243873

Mentally,

26. $24 \div 3$	**31.** $81 \div 3$	**36.** $125 \div 5$	**41.** $345 \div 3$	**46.** $1000 \div 8$
27. $68 \div 2$	**32.** $75 \div 5$	**37.** $96 \div 6$	**42.** $963 \div 3$	**47.** $1208 \div 4$
28. $44 \div 2$	**33.** $51 \div 3$	**38.** $122 \div 2$	**43.** $824 \div 4$	**48.** $2727 \div 9$
29. $45 \div 3$	**34.** $91 \div 7$	**39.** $200 \div 5$	**44.** $60 \div 20$	**49.** $3521 \div 7$
30. $99 \div 3$	**35.** $68 \div 4$	**40.** $124 \div 2$	**45.** $150 \div 15$	**50.** $900 \div 30$

Exercise 1e Mixed

1. From the sum of 69 and 35 subtract 48.

2. Find the sum of 45, 55 and 65.

3. From 325 subtract the sum of 46 and 72.

4. What is the difference between 546 and 712?

5. What is the difference between 38 and the sum of 46 and 73?

6. What is the product of 768 and 6?

7. Divide 369 by 9.

8. From 174 subtract the difference between 95 and 57.

9. From the sum of 39 and 45 subtract the product of 7 and 8.

10. From the product of 3, 4 and 5 subtract the product of 2, 3 and 4.

Simplify:

11. $14 + 3 - 8$	**16.** $43 + 14 - 17 - 5$	**21.** $24 \div 8 + 9$
12. $16 + 8 - 3$	**17.** $62 + 23 - 7 - 15$	**22.** $48 \div 24 + 3$
13. $23 - 5 + 7$	**18.** $12 \times 3 + 7$	**23.** $4 \times 5 + 2 \times 3$
14. $32 - 5 - 2 + 3$	**19.** $6 \times 8 + 9$	**24.** $120 \div 6 - 19$
15. $27 - 6 - 2 + 5 + 8$	**20.** $8 \times 4 - 7$	**25.** $24 \times 3 + 4$

Exercise 1f Problems

1. One merchant has seven ships and another has sixteen ships. How many do they have altogether?

2. If one leg of an aeroplane flight takes 13 hours and another takes 8 hours how long do both take?

3. The Old Testament has 39 chapters and the New Testament has 27 chapters; how many chapters are there altogether?

4. Each verse in the Bhagavad Geeta has thirty-two syllables. In chapter 12 there are twenty verses. How many syllables are there in chapter 12?

5. If Ahmed has seven sons and each son has eight sons, how many grand-children does Ahmed have?

6. How many seconds are there in an hour?

7. Sir Winston Churchill was born in 1874 and died in 1965. How old was he when he died?

8. There are 10 chains in a furlong and a furlong is an eighth of a mile. How many chains are there in a mile?

9. If school starts at 8:45 and Amanda was 29 minutes early, at what time did she arrive?

10. There are 112 pounds in a hundredweight and 20 hundredweight in a ton. How many pounds are there in a ton?

11. A tanker carries 125,000 tons of oil in 25 compartments. How much oil is in each compartment?

12. A child is reckoned to be half their adult height at the age of two and a half. If Sam is 96 cm tall at this age, how tall will he be when he has grown up?

13. On a shopping spree a lady spends £265.55 out of her £300 savings. How much does she have left?

14. In four successive weeks a junior doctor was required to work 72 hours, 67 hours 98 hours and 86 hours?. For how many hours did he work during this period?

15. From a weekly wage packet of £235, Joseph Ryan spends £98 on rent, £88.50 on food and £25.75 on fuel bills. How much does he have left anything else?

16. If 457 is written as 547 by mistake, by how much is it wrong?

17. How many 30 cm lengths of string can be cut from a piece 6 m long?

18. When 5 is divided into a certain number the answer is 13 remainder 2. What is the number?

19. Find the number which, when divided by 9 gives the answer 132 with 7 remaining.

20. For eight hours work a man is paid £184. How much does he earn in one hour?

21. Using the numbers 3, 4, 6 and 9, find the product of the smallest and the largest and subtract the product of the other two from the answer.

22. How many 5 ml spoons of medicine can be obtained from a bottle containing 280 ml?

23. What must be added to 6425 so that it can be divided exactly by 64?

24. The distance round the Earth is about 40,000 km and the distance to the moon is about 380,000 km. How much shorter it to travel to the moon and back than to travel twenty times round the Earth.?

25. Find the difference between the products, 432×9 and 256×8.

Rules for signs in addition and subtraction

When adding a minus number it may be treated as increasing a deficiency. For example, 8 is deficient of 10 by 2. To increase this deficiency by 3 you would have to subtract 3. This is written as $8 + (-3) = 5$.

When subtracting a minus number it may be thought of as decreasing a deficiency. To decrease a deficiency a number must be added. For example, when decreasing the deficiency of 8 (from 10) you would have to add 2. This may be written as $8 - (-2) = 10$.

To distinguish between plus or minus as an operation and the plus or minus of a number you use brackets.

The rules for signs are very simple:

When the signs are the same then add,
when the signs are different then subtract.

$$6 + (-4) = 2$$

$$6 - (-4) = 10$$

The signs are different and so we subtract, $6 - 4$.

The signs are the same and so we add, $6 + 4 = 10$.

When a number does not have a sign before it then it is taken as being positive.

Some people are fearful of minus numbers because they cannot think of something being less than nothing. It is perfectly true that you cannot have something less than nothing but with numbers you can imagine that there is.

This is why when someone has a debt at a bank then that person's bank balance is recorded as being negative. To get rid of a debt you have to add money. Furthermore, when money is owed to a bank you always have to pay back more than was borrowed. This is how the banks make their money. Shakespeare gave good advice in Hamlet when he said,

Neither a borrower nor a lender be;
For loan oft loses both itself and friend,
And borrowing dulls the edge of husbandry.

[Hamlet 1:iii]

Exercise 1g

1. $5 + (-3)$	**6.** $5 + (-3)$	**11.** $8 + (-1)$	**16.** $0 - (-6)$	**21.** $1 + (+8)$
2. $2 - (1)$	**7.** $2 - (1)$	**12.** $6 - (-1)$	**17.** $5 - (4)$	**22.** $2 + (-1)$
3. $7 + (-3)$	**8.** $5 - (-4)$	**13.** $9 + (-9)$	**18.** $6 + (-6)$	**23.** $8 - (-5)$
4. $8 - (+1)$	**9.** $2 + (-3)$	**14.** $7 - (-9)$	**19.** $3 - (+3)$	**24.** $9 - (+7)$
5. $3 - (-3)$	**10.** $11 + (+3)$	**15.** $6 - (+3)$	**20.** $5 - (-5)$	**25.** $8 + (-7)$

26. $(-4) + (-2)$ **31.** $(-5) - (-6)$ **36.** $(-6) - (-8)$ **41.** $(+3) + (-2)$

27. $(-1) + (-1)$ **32.** $(-2) - (+8)$ **37.** $(-7) - (+5)$ **42.** $(+8) + (-9)$

28. $(-3) - 2$ **33.** $(-1) - (-1)$ **38.** $(-9) + (+6)$ **43.** $6 - 22$

29. $(-6) - (+3)$ **34.** $(+4) + (-9)$ **39.** $(-3) + (-3)$ **44.** $(-11) - (-12)$

30. $(-7) + (-3)$ **35.** $3 + (-7)$ **40.** $(-2) - (-2)$ **45.** $(+4) - (-9)$

Rules for signs in multiplication and division

The rules for multiplying or dividing positive and negative numbers are very easy:

> *When the signs are the same then the answer is plus,*
> *when the signs are different the answer is minus.*

Some examples are set out below.

$$(+3) \times (+4) = 12$$
$$(-3) \times (-4) = 12$$
$$(+3) \times (-4) = -12$$
$$(-3) \times (+4) = -12$$

$$(+15) \div (+3) = 5$$
$$(-15) \div (-3) = 5$$
$$(+15) \div (-3) = -5$$
$$(-15) \div (+3) = -5$$

$$(+a) \times (+b) = ab$$
$$(-2) \times (-b) = 2b$$
$$(+a) \times (-3) = -3a$$
$$(-a) \times (+a) = -a^2$$

$$(+a) \div (+b) = \frac{a}{b}$$
$$(-2) \div (-b) = \frac{2}{b}$$
$$(+a) \div (-3) = -\frac{a}{3}$$
$$(-a) \div (+a) = -\frac{a}{a} = -1$$

Exercise 1h Simplify:

1. $2 \times (-4)$ **6.** $(-8) \div (-4)$ **11.** $(-a) \times (+d)$ **16.** $(+y) \times (+6)$

2. $(-3) \times 3$ **7.** $(-30) \div (+10)$ **12.** $(+m) \times (-n)$ **17.** $(-x) \div (+x)$

3. $(-5) \times (-2)$ **8.** $(+28) \div (-7)$ **13.** $(-a) \div (+b)$ **18.** $(-ab) \div (-c)$

4. $(-8) \times (+6)$ **9.** $(-48) \div (+4)$ **14.** $(-3) \times (-x)$ **19.** $(-x) \times (+x)$

5. $(+7) \times (-9)$ **10.** $(-2) \div (-2)$ **15.** $(+c) \div (-d)$ **20.** $(-5) \div (-a)$

21. $(-4) \times (+6) \times (-2)$

22. $2 \times (+2) \times (-2)$

23. $(-1) \times (-1) \times (-1)$

24. $(+2) \times (-3) \times (+4)$

25. $(+6) \times (+5) \times (-3)$

26. $(+12) \div (+3) \times (-4)$

27. $(+32) \div (+16) \times (-15)$

28. $(-20) \div (+4) \times (-7)$

29. $(-7) \times (-8) \div (+2)$

30. $(-60) \div (-2) \div (-5)$

31. $(-5) \times (+a) \times (+b)$

32. $(-a) \times (+b) \times (-c)$

33. $(+x) \times (-2) \div (+x)$

34. $(+y) \times (+z) \div (+y)$

35. $(-x) \times (-3) \times (-x)$

Exercise 1i Answers only. See if you can complete this in 10 minutes.

1. $12 + 13 + 14$

2. $100 - 76$

3. $285 - 101$

4. 25×8

5. 35×4

6. $60 \div 4$

7. $23 + 49$

8. $75 \div 3$

9. $123 - 99$

10. 23×2

11. $2.4 \div 3$

12. $3 - 0.1$

13. $105 \div 3$

14. $244 + 199$

15. $1000 \div 4$

16. $78 + 56$

17. $98 - 42$

18. $450 \div 5$

19. 48×3

20. $12 \times 12 \times 2$

21. $64 + 36$

22. $200 - 123$

23. $360 \div 9$

24. 60×60

25. 49×2

26. $102 - 95$

27. 45×0

28. $240 \div 8$

29. 199×5

30. $546 + 99$

31. $5 + 7 + 9 + 11$

32. $34 - 17 + 3$

33. $68 \div 2$

34. 1.2×6

35. 0.15×3

36. $10 - 0.1$

37. $100 - 23 + 3$

38. $2.3 - 1.7$

39. $1 - 0.65$

40. $358 + 298$

41. 198×2

42. $1999 + 2$

43. $2000 \div 4$

44. $160 \div 8$

45. $3.6 + 4.9$

46. $19 + 19 + 19$

47. 17×5

48. $125 \div 5$

49. 324×3

50. $642 \div 3$

51. $581 - 295$

52. $12100 \div 11$

53. 4.62×100

54. $76 \div 10$

55. $340 \div 20$

56. $645 + 250 - 51$

57. $64 \div 16$

58. 21×7

59. $4 \times 5 \times 6$

60. $10,000 \div 250$

Chapter 2 Multiplication by *All from 9 and the last from 10*

Multiplying below the base

For multiplying two numbers together which are both close to a base of 10, 100, 1000, etc., the quick method using the *All from nine and the last from ten* sutra should be used.

All from nine and the last from ten, when applied to any number gives the complement of that number. For example, for 875, the complement is 125, that is, 8 from 9 = 1, 7 from 9 = 2 and 5 from 10 = 5. 125 is the complement of 875 because when added together these two numbers make 1000. Note that when the number ends with a zero then the sutra is applied to the last *number*. For example, with 790, the last number is 9, since 0 is not a number. The *All from nine* sutra should be taken as, *All from nine and the last number from ten*. Any final zeros are placed at the end. The complement of 790 is then 210.

Multiplying numbers using complements requires only one line of easy working.

$87 \times 97.$

The two numbers are set down and their complements are written down to the right, that is 13 and 03. The minus sign indicates that 87 is 13 less than 100 and 97 is 3 less than 100.

$$\begin{array}{r} 87 - 13 \\ \times\, 97 - 03 \\ \hline 84\ /\ 39 \end{array}$$

The answer comes in two parts and the stroke is placed to show this.

For the right, multiply the two complements together $13 \times 3 = 39$.

For the left, cross-subtract, either $97 - 13 = 84$ or $87 - 3 = 84$.

The answer is then 8439.

There is one important point to remember.

> *The number of digits to the right of the remainder stroke must be equal to the number of zeros in the base.*

In the example above, the base, to which the numbers are related is 100 with two zeros, and so there are two places for digits to the right. Sometimes the product can exceed the number of digits allowed and so there will be a carry digit to the left. The next example shows this.

671 × 992.

The complements are 329 and 008 and the product of
these two numbers is 2632. There is only space for
632 and so 2 must be carried.

$$671 - 329$$
$$\times\ 992 - 008$$
$$\overline{665\ /\ 632}$$
$$2\quad 27$$

For the cross-subtraction we have 671 − 8 + 2 = 665
The answer is then 665632.

Exercise 2a

1. 89 × 98	**8.** 67 × 94	**15.** 997 × 995	**22.** 9999 × 9999
2. 76 × 99	**9.** 36 × 98	**16.** 987 × 994	**23.** 9787 × 9997
3. 96 × 92	**10.** 47 × 97	**17.** 899 × 995	**24.** 9996 × 9465
4. 82 × 94	**11.** 28 × 99	**18.** 998 × 879	**25.** 8675 × 9998
5. 97 × 83	**12.** 61 × 91	**19.** 997 × 865	**26.** 3425 × 9999
6. 91 × 81	**13.** 94 × 72	**20.** 453 × 997	**27.** 99989 × 99945
7. 90 × 96	**14.** 92 × 65	**21.** 521 × 996	**28.** 95324 × 99996

Multiplying above the base

With two numbers a little above the same base the method alters slightly because
instead of deficiencies, as with the complements, there are excesses or surpluses. For
example, with 106, the surplus is 06. Instead of cross-subtracting we cross-add to
obtain the left-hand part of the answer. Before beginning each sum it is important to
see which base to use. This is because, when working above the base, the number of
digits in the numbers to be multiplied is one more than the number of surplus digits.

1004 × 1112.

The base is 1000, with three zeros and the
surpluses are 004 and 112. Plus signs are written
to show that the numbers are more than the base.

$$1004 + 004$$
$$\times 1112 + 112$$
$$\overline{1116\ /\ 448}$$

For the right-hand portion, 4 × 112 = 448.

For the left, cross-add to give 1116.
The answer is then 1116448.

Exercise 2b

1. 102×103	**8.** 14×13	**15.** 1003×1006	**22.** 1654×1001
2. 107×109	**9.** 15×17	**16.** 1001×1002	**23.** 1005×1189
3. 112×105	**10.** 16×16	**17.** 1006×1008	**24.** 1645×1010
4. 132×102	**11.** 181×102	**18.** 1010×1002	**25.** 10007×10008
5. 101×189	**12.** 104×177	**19.** 1012×1011	**26.** 11134×10006
6. 162×107	**13.** 156×103	**20.** 1123×1004	**27.** 10009×13243
7. 125×105	**14.** 186×109	**21.** 1015×1005	**28.** 12345×10005

Multiplying above and below the base

Where one number is above the base and the other is below there is *a* deficiency and a surplus. On the **right-hand side there will be a plus multiplied by a minus and this will give a vinculum number.**

106×93.

With 106 there is a surplus of 06 and with 93 there is a complement of 07. When these two are multiplied together the answer is $\overline{42}$.

On the left, either cross-add to give $93 + 6 = 99$ or cross-subtract to give $106 - 7 = 99$.

$$
\begin{array}{r}
106+06 \\
\times\ \ 93-07 \\
\hline
99\ /\overline{42} \\
\hline
98\ /58
\end{array}
$$

To *devinculate* $99\overline{42}$, take 1 away from the digit immediately to the left of the vinculum digits, $9 - 1 = 8$, and apply the *All from nine* sutra to those vinculum digits, 4 from 9 is 5, and 2 from 10 is 8. This gives the answer 9858.

Exercise 2c

1. 102×96	**8.** 108×91	**15.** 1002×998	**22.** 990×1045
2. 108×95	**9.** 88×105	**16.** 997×1004	**23.** 989×1111
3. 8×14	**10.** 67×101	**17.** 993×1012	**24.** 1237×995
4. 9×16	**11.** 113×98	**18.** 978×1005	**25.** 10006×9998
5. 7×13	**12.** 142×96	**19.** 1112×996	**26.** 11232×9997
6. 96×105	**13.** 94×133	**20.** 1230×994	**27.** 9992×10676
7. 97×109	**14.** 145×90	**21.** 999×1786	**28.** 9832×10003

Squaring numbers close to a base

There is a sub-sutra for *All from nine and the last from ten* which is used for squaring numbers which are close to a base. The sub-sutra reads *Whatever the extent of the deficiency lessen it still further to that very extent, and also set up the square of that deficiency*. The following example shows how it works.

Find the square of 96, that is, 96^2 or 96×96. $96^2 = 92/16$

The deficiency of 96 is 4 because it is 4 less than 100. The sub-sutra tells us to lessen 96 still further by that same number, $96 - 4 = 92$. This gives us the left-hand part of the answer. The square of the deficiency is $4 \times 4 = 16$, and this is the right-hand part of the answer.

The working can be done mentally and the answer, 9216, written straight down.

Exercise 2d Write answers only (Remember that the right-hand part of each answer must contain the same number of digits as there are noughts in the base.

1. 97^2	7. 90^2	13. 996^2	19. 9996^2	25. 99993^2
2. 98^2	8. 91^2	14. 993^2	20. 9994^2	26. 99997^2
3. 95^2	9. 89^2	15. 997^2	21. 9991^2	27. 99990^2
4. 92^2	10. 88^2	16. 999^2	22. 9998^2	28. 99994^2
5. 93^2	11. 9^2	17. 991^2	23. 9995^2	29. 999993^2
6. 94^2	12. 8^2	18. 990^2	24. 9992^2	30. 999998^2

The same method may be applied to squaring numbers above the base. Instead of finding the deficiency and decreasing the number by that amount we find the surplus and increase to that very extent.

Find 103^2. $103^2 = 106/09$

The surplus is 3. Increase 103 by 3, gives 106. This gives the left-hand part. The square of the surplus is $3 \times 3 = 09$ and this is the right-hand part of the answer. The base has two zeros and so the right-hand part is 09 and not just 9.

Exercise 2e Write answers only

1. 104^2	**7.** 112^2	**13.** 1005^2	**19.** 1007^2	**25.** 11^2
2. 102^2	**8.** 107^2	**14.** 1008^2	**20.** 1003^2	**26.** 12^2
3. 106^2	**9.** 110^2	**15.** 1004^2	**21.** 1012^2	**27.** 13^2
4. 101^2	**10.** 108^2	**16.** 1001^2	**22.** 1010^2	**28.** 14^2
5. 109^2	**11.** 111^2	**17.** 1006^2	**23.** 1009^2	**29.** 15^2
6. 105^2	**12.** 100^2	**18.** 1002^2	**24.** 1011^2	**30.** 16^2

Squaring numbers ending in 5

A special case of squaring numbers occurs when the number ends in 5 and the sub-sutra for this is *By one more than the one before* which has already been used in connection with recurring decimals.

Find 35^2. $35^2 = 12/25$

The answer comes in two parts. For the first part, the *one before* the final digit is 3 and one more than this is 4. We multiply these two together to obtain 12 as the left-hand part of the answer. For the right-hand part we just put down the square of 5, that is 25. So the answer is 12/25.

$$\text{Similarly,} \quad 85^2 = 72/25,$$
$$850^2 = 72/2500$$
$$8.5^2 = 72.25,$$
$$0.85^2 = 0.7225$$

Exercise 2f Write answers only

1. 45^2	**7.** 85^2	**13.** 650^2	**19.** 6.5^2	**25.** 0.25^2
2. 55^2	**8.** 25^2	**14.** 950^2	**20.** 1.5^2	**26.** 0.15^2
3. 75^2	**9.** 115^2	**15.** 150^2	**21.** 7.5^2	**27.** 0.65^2
4. 15^2	**10.** 450^2	**16.** 550^2	**22.** 9.5^2	**28.** 0.35^2
5. 95^2	**11.** 250^2	**17.** 750^2	**23.** 11.5^2	**29.** 0.45^2
6. 105^2	**12.** 350^2	**18.** 2.5^2	**24.** 5.5^2	**30.** 0.95^2

When the final digits add up to 10

A further extension to this process is found when two numbers to be multiplied have their final digits adding up to 10. The sub-sutra for this is *Antyayor-Dasakepi* and simply means *When the two finals add up to 10*.

This sub-sutra is used in conjunction with By one more than the one before and has a limited application for the case where the two numbers are the same except for the final digits which add up to 10, for example, 36×34.

36×34 $36 \times 34 = 1224$

Again the answer comes in two parts.

The left-hand part is found, as before, by multiplying the penultimate digit by one more than itself, that is $3 \times 4 = 12$.

The right-hand part is just the product of the two final digits, that is, $6 \times 4 = 24$.

The answer is then 1224

Similarly, $3.6 \times 3.4 = 12.24$

and $0.36 \times 0.34 = 0.1224$

Exercise 2g Write answers only

1. 26×24	**9.** 18×12	**17.** 83×87	**24.** 9.2×9.8
2. 37×33	**10.** 21×29	**18.** 31×39	**25.** 0.41×0.49
3. 72×78	**11.** 27×23	**19.** 64×66	**26.** 0.62×0.68
4. 51×59	**12.** 22×28	**20.** 77×73	**27.** 0.71×0.79
5. 63×67	**13.** 56×54	**21.** 5.7×5.3	**28.** 0.52×0.58
6. 17×13	**14.** 74×76	**22.** 6.9×6.1	**29.** 0.93×0.97
7. 19×11	**15.** 48×42	**23.** 8.6×8.4	**30.** 0.88×0.0082
8. 14×16	**16.** 99×91		

Exercise 2h Mixed examples

1. 77×98
2. 85×95
3. 889×994
4. 99989×99965
5. 104×106
6. 115×107
7. 10007×10542
8. 12345×10011

9. 88×106
10. 115×93
11. 9994×10253
12. 9988×11676
13. 87^2
14. 991^2
15. 9997^2
16. 9988^2

17. 1012^2
18. 1015^2
19. 43×47
20. 17^2
21. 111^2
22. 950^2
23. 0.75^2
24. 6.2×6.8

Exercise 2i (Oral)

1. 99×98
2. 97×96
3. 96×92
4. 99×99
5. 91×93
6. 94×95
7. 93×97
8. 98×92
9. 96×96
10. 98×98

11. 101×103
12. 102×104
13. 106×104
14. 102×102
15. 101×101
16. 107×108
17. 109×108
18. 104×107
19. 109×109
20. 110×110

21. 997×999
22. 996×998
23. 994×996
24. 992×993
25. 999×999
26. 1003×1002
27. 1004×1005
28. 1007×1008
29. 1005×1005
30. 1010×1010

The type of multiplication you have been dealing with in this chapter is clearly for special cases. Both the numbers to be multiplied have to be close to a base. When the numbers are not close to a base then you should use *Vertically and crosswise*. This is described in Book 1.

Chapter 3 Division

It should be remembered that the four parts of any division sum are:- divisor, dividend, quotient and remainder. Here is a rhyme to help remember which is which.

The divisor is the number that divides the dividend,
The answer is the quotient with the remainder at the end.

Simple division

This is where the divisor consists of a single digit. To be consistent with other types, the answers are written underneath.

$$6 \overline{)7 \,_1 3 \,_1 8 \, 4}$$
$$\quad 1 \ 2 \ 3 \ 0 \ r \ 4$$

6 into 7 = 1 remainder 1,
6 into 13 = 2 remainder 1,
6 into 18 = 3,
6 into 4 = 0 remainder 4.
The answer is 1230 remainder 4.

Exercise 3a Divide, leaving whole-number remainders.

1. $3\overline{)454}$
2. $5\overline{)629}$
3. $4\overline{)652}$
4. $7\overline{)487}$
5. $2\overline{)502}$
6. $8\overline{)365}$
7. $9\overline{)114}$
8. $3\overline{)781}$
9. $6\overline{)899}$
10. $5\overline{)650}$

11. $4\overline{)5648}$
12. $3\overline{)4112}$
13. $2\overline{)4589}$
14. $8\overline{)3002}$
15. $6\overline{)6599}$
16. $5\overline{)5487}$
17. $3\overline{)1652}$
18. $4\overline{)9258}$
19. $7\overline{)9292}$
20. $3\overline{)6501}$

21. $8\overline{)1254}$
22. $9\overline{)9852}$
23. $5\overline{)9699}$
24. $6\overline{)6332}$
25. $7\overline{)5004}$
26. $4\overline{)8017}$
27. $8\overline{)5609}$
28. $6\overline{)7455}$
29. $9\overline{)1827}$
30. $4\overline{)8456}$

31. $7\overline{)15441}$
32. $8\overline{)26590}$
33. $4\overline{)78428}$
34. $9\overline{)45698}$
35. $5\overline{)51423}$
36. $7\overline{)74111}$
37. $3\overline{)78005}$
38. $6\overline{)96058}$
39. $9\overline{)54871}$
40. $8\overline{)23654}$

Exercise 3b Problems

1. Divide 3253 by 6.

2. How many times does 8 go into 17263, and what is the remainder?

3. What is the remainder when 634 is divided by 50?

4. Alice shares £2.40 amongst three of her friends. How much does each receive if she leaves none for herself?

5. How many 6p stamps can be bought for £2.82?

6. If one breath takes eight seconds, how many breaths do you make in a day of 86400 seconds?

7. 7 apples weigh 686 g find the average weight of one apple.

8. At £6 per ticket a concert-hall box office received £4428. How many tickets were sold?

9. How many nines are there in 1,000,000?

10. Divide 20529936 by 6, divide the answer by 7, the answer to this by 8 and this answer by 9.

11. I wish to tile a front path measuring 3.44 m by 1.04 m. The tiles are 8 cm squares. How many are required?

Division by 9

This is a special case of division by *All from nine and the last from ten*. It is a special case because the base for the divisor is 10 and 9 is 1 less than 10. This 1 has no effect on the division whereas when the deficiency is some other number there is an effect.

In order to divide any number by 9 sum the digits, one by one, writing down that· sum at each step. For example, $1241 \div 9 = 137$ rem. 8. How to proceed with this is shown in the next example.

$1241 \div 9$

$$9 \overline{\smash{\big)}\, 1\ 2\ 4\ /\ 1}$$
$$1\ 3\ 7\ /\ 8$$

Section off the last digit of the dividend for the remainder portion of the answer.

The first digit, 1 is set down as the first answer digit.

Take this 1 and add the next digit 2, $1 + 2 = 3$, and this is the next answer digit. Working in the same way, $3 + 4 = 7$ and $7 + 1 = 8$, the remainder. The answer is 137 rem.8.

Exercise 3c Write answers only

1. $9 \overline{\smash{\big)}\, 21}$

2. $9 \overline{\smash{\big)}\, 32}$

3. $9 \overline{\smash{\big)}\, 43}$

4. $9 \overline{\smash{\big)}\, 71}$

5. $9 \overline{\smash{\big)}\, 52}$

6. $9 \overline{\smash{\big)}\, 231}$

7. $9 \overline{\smash{\big)}\, 112}$

8. $9 \overline{\smash{\big)}\, 421}$

9. $9 \overline{\smash{\big)}\, 5101}$

10. $9 \overline{\smash{\big)}\, 1000}$

11. $9 \overline{\smash{\big)}\, 1221}$

12. $9 \overline{\smash{\big)}\, 1022}$

13. $9 \overline{\smash{\big)}\, 2141}$

14. $9 \overline{\smash{\big)}\, 3140}$

15. $9 \overline{\smash{\big)}\, 42110}$

16. $9 \overline{\smash{\big)}\, 121101}$

17. $9 \overline{\smash{\big)}\, 121031}$

18. $9 \overline{\smash{\big)}\, 121211}$

19. $9 \overline{\smash{\big)}\, 111110}$

20. $9 \overline{\smash{\big)}\, 500011}$

In the addition process it is possible for there to be a number larger than 9. The sum can continue as before but there will be carrying to do at the end. Also, if the remainder is larger than the divisor then it should be redivided.

$1654 \div 9$

$$9 \overline{\smash{\big)}\, 1\ 6\ 5\ /\ 4}$$
$$1\ 7\ 12/16$$
$$1\ 8\ 3\ /\ 7$$

The first digit is brought down into the answer line.

$1 + 6 = 7$, $7 + 5 = 12$. The 12 is set down in the answer line, *squeezed* into one column. $12 + 4 = 16$ gives the remainder.

There are two adjustments which have to be made: firstly, the 1 of 12 is carried to the left, and secondly, the remainder 16 is larger than the divisor and so is divided by 9 giving 1 remainder 7. The 1 is carried to the left, giving 3, and the 7 is left as the final remainder.

Exercise 3d Leave spaces between dividend digits when setting out.

1. 9⌋1155	**6.** 9⌋5301	**11.** 9⌋213244	**16.** 9⌋6001152
2. 9⌋1327	**7.** 9⌋2166	**12.** 9⌋214091	**17.** 9⌋1230402
3. 9⌋1338	**8.** 9⌋1618	**13.** 9⌋233111	**18.** 9⌋3211118
4. 9⌋2417	**9.** 9⌋3421	**14.** 9⌋160132	**19.** 9⌋3240115
5. 9⌋1426	**10.** 9⌋6128	**15.** 9⌋420317	**20.** 9⌋2222222

Division by *All from nine and the last from ten*

This method of division may be used where the divisor is close to a power of ten such as 10, 100 or 1000 but is less than that base.

Divide 12123 by 879

879 is close to the base 1000. Since 1000 has three zeros the remainder stroke is placed with three digits to its right. The two digits to the left of the remainder stroke indicate two lines to be left before the horizontal line is drawn for the answer.

$$879 \underline{|1\,2\,/\,1\,2\,3}$$
$$121$$
$$\overline{1}$$

The complement of 879 is found using the *All from nine* sutra and set down below the divisor. The first answer digit is the same as the first dividend digit, 1.

This first answer digit is multiplied by the complement, that is, $1 \times 121 = 121$, and these digits are set out in the next three columns.

$$879 \underline{|1\,2\,/\,1\,2\,3}$$
$$121 \quad 1 \ 21$$
$$\overline{13}$$

The second column is added, $2 + 1 = 3$, and this is set down as the next answer digit.

$3 \times 121 = 363$, which is written in the next three columns of the dividend. Since the last digit of 363 comes under the final digit of 12123, the sum is completed except for summing the remainder. The final answer is then 13 remainder 696.

$$879 \underline{|1\,2\,/\,1\,2\,3}$$
$$121 \quad 1 \ 21$$
$$\qquad\quad 3\,6\,3$$
$$\overline{13\,/\,6\,9\,6}$$

Exercise 3e

1. $88 \lfloor 112$	**6.** $73 \lfloor 128$	**11.** $677 \lfloor 2000$	**16.** $892 \lfloor 21381$
2. $76 \lfloor 131$	**7.** $779 \lfloor 1121$	**12.** $867 \lfloor 2132$	**17.** $971 \lfloor 21031$
3. $83 \lfloor 102$	**8.** $866 \lfloor 1254$	**13.** $982 \lfloor 4231$	**18.** $975 \lfloor 20111$
4. $79 \lfloor 105$	**9.** $8877 \lfloor 12074$	**14.** $999 \lfloor 6754$	**19.** $884 \lfloor 12055$
5. $83 \lfloor 143$	**10.** $8907 \lfloor 13193$	**15.** $887 \lfloor 2342$	**20.** $950 \lfloor 23410$

Division by *Transpose and Adjust*

Where the divisor is a little more than the base then you use a method very similar to *All from 9* division. The sutra is *Transpose and adjust*. This method of division takes the divisor and transposes all the numbers greater than the base into vinculum numbers.

$23689 \div 112$

The base of the divisor is 100 and since this has two zeros we allow two digits after the remainder stroke. The surplus of 12 is transposed to $\overline{1}\overline{2}$ and this is written below 112.
There are three digits to the left of the remainder stroke and this provides the number of lines needed for working.
2 is brought down as the first answer digit.
$2 \times \overline{1}\overline{2} = \overline{2}\,\overline{4}$.

$$
\begin{array}{c|cc}
112 & 2\,3\,6\,/\,8\,9 \\
\overline{1}\overline{2} & \quad \overline{2}\,\overline{4} \\
\hline
 & \\
 & 2 \\
\end{array}
$$

The second column is added, that is, $3 + \overline{2} = 1$ to give the next answer digit.
$1 \times \overline{1}\overline{2} = \overline{1}\overline{2}$ which is put below the 6 and 8. The sum of the third column is $6 + \overline{4} + \overline{1} = 1$, and this is the third answer digit.
$1 \times \overline{1}\overline{2} = \overline{1}\overline{2}$, which is set down below the last two dividend digits.
The remainder is added up, and the answer is 211 remainder 57.

$$
\begin{array}{c|cc}
112 & 2\,3\,6\,/\,8\,9 \\
\overline{1}\overline{2} & \quad \overline{2}\,\overline{4} \\
 & \quad\;\; \overline{1}\;\,\overline{2} \\
 & \qquad\;\; \overline{1}\,\overline{2} \\
\hline
 & 2\,1\,1\,/\,5\,7 \\
\end{array}
$$

Exercise 3f

1. 112 $\lfloor$ 1233	**9.** 123 $\lfloor$ 2584	**17.** 113 $\lfloor$ 13696	**25.** 1212 $\lfloor$ 243813
2. 123 $\lfloor$ 1377	**10.** 131 $\lfloor$ 2653	**18.** 112 $\lfloor$ 23766	**26.** 1212 $\lfloor$ 13545
3. 131 $\lfloor$ 1481	**11.** 121 $\lfloor$ 2683	**19.** 112 $\lfloor$ 13565	**27.** 11202 $\lfloor$ 2578787
4. 132 $\lfloor$ 1366	**12.** 122 $\lfloor$ 2684	**20.** 123 $\lfloor$ 36951	**28.** 1122 $\lfloor$ 13888
5. 121 $\lfloor$ 1473	**13.** 111 $\lfloor$ 2577	**21.** 104 $\lfloor$ 1258	**29.** 1003 $\lfloor$ 321987
6. 112 $\lfloor$ 1496	**14.** 121 $\lfloor$ 3791	**22.** 121 $\lfloor$ 13445	**30.** 111 $\lfloor$ 79999
7. 121 $\lfloor$ 2573	**15.** 111 $\lfloor$ 3786	**23.** 1121 $\lfloor$ 24789	**31.** 112 $\lfloor$ 34884
8. 113 $\lfloor$ 2388	**16.** 161 $\lfloor$ 1781	**24.** 1121 $\lfloor$ 137987	**32.** 1126 $\lfloor$ 24772

This chapter has dealt with three types of division: simple division, *All from 9* division and *Transpose and adjust* division. When the divisor is a single digit or an easy number like 12 use simple division. When the divisor has large digits and is close to a base of 10, 100, etc., use *All from 9 and the last from 10*. When the divisor has small digits a little more than a base then use *Transpose and adjust*. For divisors not close to a base the Straight division method is used and this is to be found in chapter 12.

Exercise 3g Mixed practice

1. 4356 ÷ 3	**9.** 3276 ÷ 8	**17.** 12879 ÷ 1032
2. 1002 ÷ 98	**10.** 10343 ÷ 102	**18.** 125 ÷ 15
3. 6574 ÷ 8	**11.** 8976 ÷ 12	**19.** 6880 ÷ 20
4. 21908 ÷ 4	**12.** 12445 ÷ 999	**20.** 700 ÷ 25
5. 14657 ÷ 111	**13.** 3412 ÷ 99	**21.** 3423332 ÷ 4
6. 654 ÷ 9	**14.** 13008 ÷ 121	**22.** 26543 ÷ 9999
7. 3278 ÷ 11	**15.** 45974 ÷ 6	**23.** 102345 ÷ 112
8. 20034 ÷ 997	**16.** 14386 ÷ 9989	**24.** 26473 ÷ 11

Chapter 4 Algebra

First principles

Algebra is used to express the universal laws of mathematics.

In algebra, letters are used to represent numbers. The letters used are usually those of the English alphabet. A letter either stands for a particular number or for any number in general. If a letter is given a particular value, it is understood that in the same piece of work it keeps the same value. For, if we say "let $x = 1$", we do not mean that x must always have the same value 1, but only in the particular example we are considering.

The sign, $\times$, is not used much in algebra. When letters are placed next to letters or numbers next to letters, with no sign between them, it is to be understood that they are joined by multiplication.

For example, $a \times b$ is written as ab

$8 \times b$ is written as $8b$

If $a = 8$ and $b = 5$, then $ab = 8 \times 5 = 40$

As in arithmetic, so in algebra, when one number is placed over another number with a line between them it is to be understood that the numbers are joined by division; the upper number being divided by the lower.

For example, $a \div b$ is written as $\frac{a}{b}$. If $a = 12$ and $b = 3$, then $\frac{a}{b} = \frac{12}{3} = 4$.

Exercise 4a If $a = 4$, $b = 3$, $c = -2$ and $d = 0$, find the value of the following:

1. $5 + a$
2. $5b$
3. $6 + c$
4. $7 - d$
5. $10 - a$

6. $b + 2$
7. $a + 2b$
8. $ab + a$
9. $b + d$
10. $a + b + c$

11. $6a + bc$
12. $ad + 2b$
13. $a + 2c + bd$
14. $ad - bc$
15. $12d - c$

16. $a + b - cd$
17. $4b - 3c$
18. $abcd$
19. $5 - c + a$
20. $7a - 3b + c - d$

21. $4 - 4c + 8ab$

22. $\frac{a}{b}$

23. $\frac{b}{a}$

24. $\frac{ab}{2}$

25. $\frac{3 + a + b}{5}$

26. $\frac{a - c}{b}$

27. $\frac{4b + 5c}{a}$

28. $1 - \frac{1}{ab}$

Solving equations

An equation is a sentence expressing an equality. In mathematics, we use the equals symbol, =, and always have something on both sides. So $2 \times 4 = 8$ is an equation. If we have $2p = 8$, where p is a letter standing for a number, we can solve the equation by simply looking at it and realising that the number which fits is 4.

Many simple equations can be solved in this way and the sutra involved is by *Mere inspection*.

Exercise 4b Solve by *Mere inspection*

1. $4x = 12$	**8.** $6 = 10 - x$	**15.** $x + 9 = 51$	**22.** $76 = 2x$
2. $5x = 45$	**9.** $18 = 3x$	**16.** $3 = \frac{x}{9}$	**23.** $\frac{12}{x} = 3$
3. $2x = 102$	**10.** $\frac{x}{5} = 2$	**17.** $\frac{1}{4} + x = \frac{1}{2}$	**24.** $24 = x - 6$
4. $x + 5 = 17$	**11.** $\frac{x}{2} = 8$	**18.** $18 - x = 15$	**25.** $\frac{30}{x} = 5$
5. $x - 2 = 19$	**12.** $\frac{x}{7} = 1$	**19.** $\frac{x}{3} = 12$	**26.** $22 = 30 - x$
6. $x + 12 = 20$	**13.** $4 = \frac{x}{3}$	**20.** $\frac{x}{10} = 23$	**27.** $35 = x - 15$
7. $3 = x - 1$	**14.** $16 = 2x$	**21.** $5 + x = 88$	**28.** $82 = 100 - x$

Two-stage equations by *Transpose and adjust*

A two-stage equation is one in which two steps are taken in order to obtain the solution. You can pretend that the unknown term has been dressed up with a shirt and a jacket. The shirt is put on first followed by the jacket. To reveal the unknown term by itself, in all its glory, as it were, you have to remove the jacket and *then* the shirt.

For example, with the equation, $3x + 5 = 17$, the unknown term, x, has been dressed up first by multiplying it by 3 and then by adding 5. So you have to remove the jacket of $+ 5$ before removing the shirt of $\times 3$. This order is important and, although many of the equations at this stage can be solved by inspection, the system of how to solve equations must be learnt and practised so that harder examples can be approached.

When setting out an equation and the steps to the solution, always keep the equal signs in a vertical line. This will help keep the steps orderly and clear.

Solve, $3x + 5 = 17$

To remove the 5 from the left-hand side, transpose it to the right and change the sign to minus.

To remove the 3, transpose it to the right and change the sign from × to ÷.

$$3x + 5 = 17$$
$$3x = 17 - 5$$
$$3x = 12$$
$$x = \frac{12}{3}$$
$$\therefore x = 4$$

Exercise 4c Solve by *Transpose and adjust*

1. $5x - 11 = 29$
2. $3x + 3 = 36$
3. $4x - 2 = 26$
4. $2 + 3x = 20$
5. $4 + 9x = 4$

6. $1 + 2x = 3$
7. $6x + 1 = 4$
8. $7 = 3x - 5$
9. $9 = 2x + 1$
10. $16 = 4 + 6x$

11. $67 = 12 + 5x$
12. $3x + 8 = 2$
13. $4x - 5 = -13$
14. $3 = 5x + 18$
15. $-5 = 7 + 3x$

The next type of equation involves the unknown term appearing more than once. Here, you have to collect like terms first. The example shows how this is done.

Solve, $2x + 4x + 1 = 19$

The first step is to simplify the left-hand side by collecting up like terms. The equation can then be solved in the usual way.

$$2x + 4x + 1 = 19$$
$$6x + 1 = 19$$
$$6x = 18$$
$$x = \frac{18}{6}$$
$$\therefore x = 3$$

Exercise 4d Solve by first collecting up like terms

1. $2x + 3x = 15$
2. $4y + 5y + 2y = 22$
3. $2z + 3z - 4z = 17$
4. $7p - 3p = 16$
5. $24 = 2q + 6q$

6. $9d - 5d = 20$
7. $25 = 12a - 7a$
8. $c + c + c = 6$
9. $2h + h + 4h = 28$
10. $36 = 14j - 12j + 4j$

11. $42 = x + x + 3x - x$
12. $2n + 4n - 5n = 0.1$
13. $a + a + a - a - a = 1$
14. $5y - 2y + 7y - 3y = 0$
15. $18x - 19x + 3x = 10$

16. $5y - 3y + 7y + 3 = 30$ **22.** $m + 2m + 3m + 4m = 10$

17. $25 - 2a + 5a - a = 33$ **23.** $3x + 23x - 13 = -13$

18. $4b + 13b + 6 - 9b = 70$ **24.** $12 = 6 + 7z + 8z - 5z$

19. $21 + 3h - 4h - 2h + 12h = 66$ **25.** $36 = 18 - 4p - 3p + p + 12p$

20. $5d - 8d + 21d - 2 = 16$ **26.** $22 = 2x + 5x - 7x + x + 22$

21. $15 - 2r + 6r - r = 9$ **27.** $35 = 7s - 6s + 7s + 12s + 15$

Expanding Brackets

Brackets are used to express multiplication of a collection of terms by one term. The collection is written inside brackets and the multiplying term is placed outside the bracket, usually on the left.

For example, $4(2a + b)$ means 4 times the whole of $2a + b$

Expand $4(2a + b)$ $4(2a + b) = 8a + 4b$

To expand, or multiply out the bracket, multiply each term inside the bracket by the factor outside.

Exercise 4e Expand:

1. $2(3a - 4b)$ **6.** $3(2n - 7)$ **11.** $a(2 + b)$ **16.** $a(a + 2)$

2. $5(4h + 1)$ **7.** $5(a + b + c)$ **12.** $b(2a - 4c)$ **17.** $ab(a - 8)$

3. $3(x + y)$ **8.** $2(2a + 3b - c)$ **13.** $3b(c + 5d)$ **18.** $xy(x - 3y)$

4. $4(2a - 17)$ **9.** $6(12a - 5 + b)$ **14.** $2u(3 + 5v)$ **19.** $x(xy - 3y)$

5. $6(3 + 8k)$ **10.** $4(-3a + b - c)$ **15.** $3p(3q + 4r)$ **20.** $5y(3x + 3xy)$

Expand and simplify, $3(x - 2y) + 5(x + 7y)$ $3(x - 2y) + 5(x + 7y)$

$$= 3x - 6y + 5x + 35y$$

After expanding both brackets like terms are collected up. This is done by counting up the number of terms with x and then terms with y. $= \underline{8x + 29y}$

Exercise 4f Expand and simplify:

1. $2(x + 2) + 3(x + 7)$
2. $3(x - 3) - 4(x + 5)$
3. $5(2 + x) - 2(x + 1)$
4. $3(a + b) + 5(2a + 3b)$
5. $2(a - 2b) + 2(3a - 4b)$

6. $6(2m - 3n) + 2(m - n)$
7. $12(2a + 3b) - 2(3a - 5b)$
8. $6(3p - q) - 2(p + q)$
9. $2(a + b) + 7(a - b) - 4(a - 5b)$
10. $6(x + y - 2z) + 4(2x + 3y - 5z)$

Equations with brackets

Solve, $2(x + 5) + 3 = 19$

There are two methods. The one shown first is to remove the brackets by division, that is, for $2(x + 5) = 16$ in the second line, the multiplying factor, 2, is transposed to the right-hand side.

The second method is to expand the bracket first, simplify and then finish off. This usually takes a little longer.

$$2(x + 5) + 3 = 19$$
$$2(x + 5) = 16$$
$$x + 5 = \frac{16}{2}$$
$$x = 8 - 5$$
$$\therefore x = 3$$

$$2(x + 5) + 3 = 19$$
$$2x + 10 + 3 = 19$$
$$2x = 19 - 13$$
$$2x = 6$$
$$\therefore x = 3$$

Exercise 4g Solve:

1. $2(x + 3) = 20$
2. $3(b - 2) = 9$
3. $4(a - 1) = 20$
4. $6 = 3(a - 1)$
5. $2(d - 5) = 1$
6. $2(x + 5) = 14$
7. $3(y - 2) = 15$
8. $5(2a + 3) = 75$
9. $7(2c - 8) = 42$
10. $4(2 + 3y) = 20$

11. $4 + 2(x - 1) = 7$
12. $3 + 2(x - 5) = 2$
13. $6 + 3(x + 4) = 24$
14. $5y + 3(y + 1) = 14$
15. $6(p + 1) = 9$
16. $7(3 - 9w) = 21$
17. $33 = 3(4p - 1)$
18. $4 = 2(6g - 10)$
19. $18 = 3(t - 4)$
20. $26 = 2(3 + 5a)$

21. $4 + 2(z - 1) = 12$
22. $7x + (x - 2) = 22$
23. $8b - 3(2b + 1) = 7$
24. $4 = 5x - 2(x + 4)$
25. $9x - 7(x - 1) = 0$
26. $3(a + 7) + 1 = 28$
27. $7(b - 2) - 5 = 2$
28. $9(4 + m) - 11 = 34$
29. $8 + 3(3 - x) = 11$
30. $15 = 3 + 2(q - 9)$

Making up expressions

In algebra there are two basic types of statement; an equation and an expression. An expression is a series of one or more terms connected together with signs. An equation is a statement expressing an equality and so has an equals sign. When composing an expression or equation always read the question carefully twice. Decide which operation is involved, such as multiplication, division, addition or subtraction. For division you must be clear as to which number is being divided by which and for subtraction, which number is being subtracted from which.

Exercise 4h Writing algebraic expressions

1. John is x years old. If his brother, James, is 5 years older, how old is James in terms of x?

2. A piece of string is 8 ft long. If I cut off y ft, how much is left, in terms of y?

3. A rectangular picture measures 42 cm by x cm. In terms of x, what is its area?

4. Find an expression for the perimeter of the picture in question 3.

5. Angle ABD = $x°$. Find, in terms of x, angle CBD.

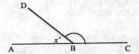

6. Sarah is x years old. Her mother is a year younger than twice her age. In terms of x, how old is her mother?

7. I have n biscuits and share them out amongst three friends. How many biscuits does each receive?

8. In sharing a collection of model cars among four boys, each receives p cars. How many cars are there altogether?

9. A certain train journey takes x minutes. After 5 minutes of the journey, how many minutes are left, in terms of x?

10. Clara is reading a book containing y pages. If she has read 46 pages, how many pages does she have left?

11. Two numbers are a and b. Find an expression for the average of these two numbers.

12. n is a number. In terms of n, what is the number which is, (a) one less, and (b) one more than n?

13. Three numbers are a, b and c. Find an expression for their average.

14. A certain number is x. If I double it and add 2 the answer is 14.
(a) Write down an equation from this information.
(b) Solve the equation to find the value of x.

15. An orange costs x pence. What is the cost of 15 such oranges?

16. Find an expression for the cost of the oranges in the previous question in pounds instead of in pence.

17. If pears cost 24p, what is the cost of y such pears?

18. If h pens cost £12.68, write down an expression for the cost of one pen.

19. From a piece of wood, 235 cm long, a cabinet maker cuts off two pieces each x cm long. How much of the original piece is left?

20. A land owner shares his y acres equally amongst his four sons. How much land does each son receive?

21. A paper-boy delivers 45 newspapers a day. How many does he deliver in d days if he delivers the same number every day?

22. Anna is t years old. Her father is five years older than three times Anna's age. Find an expression for her father's age.

23. On his birthday Robert received £x from one uncle, £y from his other uncle and £z from his aunt. How much did he receive altogether?

24. At the greengrocer one box contains a kilos of beans and another contains three times that amount. How many kilos are there altogether?

25. A lady has £p in her purse. She spends £q in one shop and £r in another shop. How much does she have left?

Dealing with minus signs

When simplifying expressions or solving equations there are times when unwanted minus signs are present. The operation of multiplying by -1 can be used to eliminate these. Since a minus times a minus is a plus and a plus times a minus is a minus, the effect of multiplying any number or term by -1 is simply to change the sign.

Multiply $2x - 3y^2 + 4xy$ by -1

This is done by multiplying each coefficient by -1, in other words, by changing the sign, $+$ to $-$, or $-$ to $+$

The answer is therefore $-2x + 3y^2 - 4xy$

Sometimes a minus sign appears immediately outside a bracket. In such cases, treat the bracket as being multiplied by -1.

Simplify $4 -(3x - 2y + 3)$

This is the same as $4 -1(3x - 2y + 3)$ and so we can first expand the bracket in the usual way. The only like terms to be collected are 4 and -3.

$4 -(3x - 2y + 3)$

$= 4 -3x + 2y - 3$

$= 1 -3x + 2y$

Exercise 4i

Multiply each of the following expressions by -1

1. $4a - 2b + 3c$
2. $-5x + y - 2z$
3. $6m - 3n + 14$
4. $7 + 3i -2j + k$
5. $-9 - 2p - 3p^2$
6. $2 - 3x - 6x^2$
7. $-11 + 3y - x - z$
8. $-2a - b + b^2$
9. $a - b + c - d - e$

Simplify:

10. $4 -(5 - 2)$
11. $17 -2(3 - 7)$
12. $17 -(4 + 1)$
13. $12 - (5 - 2) + 18$
14. $-6 + (13 + 3)$
15. $10 + (3 - 4)$
16. $14 - (6 - 2)$
17. $13a - (2a + 1)$
18. $15b - (c + d)$
19. $3c - (2a + b)$
20. $14g - (2g + 3h)$
21. $12a - (3b - 2a)$
22. $13m - (3n - m)$
23. $3x + (2x - 3y)$
24. $24s - (3s + 4t)$
25. $a + (- c + b)$
26. $-c - (b - a)$
27. $a - (b + c)$
28. $3a^3 - (2a^3 - a^3)$
29. $12a - (3a - a + 4a - a)$
30. $4ab - (3ab - 56)$

Solving equations with minus signs

When the unknown term has a negative coefficient there are a number of different ways of dealing with it. One way is to multiply each term by −1, thereby clearing the offending character. Another way is to transpose the negative term to the other side of the equal sign and adjusting its sign to plus. The equation in the example below is solved in three different ways all using *Transpose and adjust*.

Solve, $25 - 2x = 3$

This can be done by transposing the $-2x$ over to the right and then transposing the 3 over to the left. This leaves $22 = 2x$ and so $x = 11$.

$$25 - 2x = 3$$
$$25 = 3 + 2x$$
$$25 - 3 = 2x$$
$$\frac{22}{2} = x$$
$$\therefore x = 11$$

Alternatively, 25 can be transposed to the right followed by −2. The final step is $-22 \div -2$, which by the rules of signs, gives 11 as the answer.

$$25 - 2x = 3$$
$$-2x = 3 - 25$$
$$-2x = -22$$
$$x = \frac{-22}{-2}$$
$$\therefore x = 11$$

Another method is frequently useful and that is to multiply, at some stage, all the terms by −1.

Whenever a negative term is multiplied by −1 the effect is to change the sign to a plus and vice versa for positive terms.

$$25 - 2x = 3$$
$$-2x = -22$$
$$2x = 22$$
$$x = \frac{22}{2}$$
$$\therefore x = 11$$

Exercise 4j Solve:

1. $24 - 3y = 18$
2. $6 - 4x = 2$
3. $17 - 3a = 5$
4. $54 - 9d = 0$
5. $20 - 7b = -1$
6. $7 = -3c + 4$
7. $17 = 35 - 6e$
8. $2 = -9p + 38$

9. $-2x + 18 = 26$
10. $27 - 4z = -5$
11. $2(3 - y) = 4$
12. $3(2 - x) = 4$
13. $4(3 - y) = 7$
14. $-2(x + 1) = 8$
15. $-(a + 3) = -5$
16. $-6(2b - 5) = 24$

17. $-5(y - 2) = -10$
18. $-4(8 + d) = 16$
19. $-(x - 2) = -6$
20. $-3(4x + 2) = 18$
21. $4 - (3 + x) = 12$
22. $(3 - 2y) + 7 = -36$
23. $2(8 - z) + 1 = 0$
24. $2 - 3(4 - 6b) = 44$

Exercise 4k Revision

1. Solve by *Mere inspection*, (a) $\dfrac{15}{x} = 3$ (b) $42 = x - 7$

2. Solve by *Transpose and adjust*,

   (a) $11 = 4x - 1$

   (b) $70 = 6 + 8x$

   (c) $5x + 13x - 14 = 40$

   (d) $2t + 5t - 8t + 4t + 11 = 50$

3. Expand, (a) $3(2a - 4b)$ (b) $5x(xy - 4x)$

4. Expand and simplify,

   (a) $2(2m - 3n) + 3(m - n)$

   (b) $7(a + b) + 3(a - b) - 4(a - 3b)$

5. Solve,

   (a) $7x - 3(2x - 1) = 0$

   (b) $20 = 6 + 2(q - 9)$

   (c) $9(2c - 5) = 19$

6. Jemima is y years old. Her father is two years older than three times her age. How old is her father in terms of y?

7. Four numbers are a, b, c and d. Find an expression for the average of these four numbers.

8. In sharing a collection of postcards among six girls, each receives m postcards. How many postcards are there altogether?

9. If nectarines cost 23p each, what is the cost of x nectarines?

10. Simplify $19 - 5(3 - 5)$

11. Solve: $3(4y - 2) = -12$

12. Solve: $-6(3 + w) = 10$

Chapter 5 Coordinate geometry

Coordinate geometry has to do with graphs and equations represented on graphs in the form of lines and curves. Much of the pioneering work in this topic was done by a French philosopher and mathematician called Rene Descartes (1596 - 1650). When he was twenty-three years old, Descartes was employed by the Bavarian army as a soldier and, so the story goes, used to lie in bed until late in the morning thinking about mathematical problems. It is said that whilst considering ,the position of a fly on the ceiling of his room he realised the system of using coordinates and graphs to represent equations as lines or curves.

Descartes is most famous for his method of philosophy which was a search for truth of the first cause, that is, God. His was the famous statement, *Cogito ergo sum*, which means, *I think, therefore I am.* Unfortunately, this statement seems to suggest that because he thinks therefore he exists which implies that if someone stops thinking then they stop existing. He might have been better served by turning the statement round to *Sum ergo cogito, I am, therefore I think.*

In a plane, the position of a point can be specified using two measurements called **coordinates**. The lines along which they are measured are called **axes.** Each axis begins at 0 and this point is called the **origin**. The horizontal axis is called the *x*-axis and the vertical axis is called the *y*-axis.

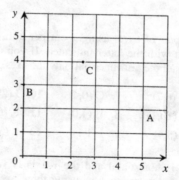

The position of a point is specified by two coordinates; the first indicates the distance along the *x*-axis and the second gives the distance along the *y*-axis. Both numbers are placed in brackets with a comma placed between them. In the diagram above, the position of A is (5,2), that of B is (0,3) and C lies at $\left(2\frac{1}{2}, 4\right)$.

When giving the position of a point the *x*-coordinate is written first and the *y*-coordinate follows. This is in alphabetical order.

Exercise 5a Give the coordinates for points A to N.

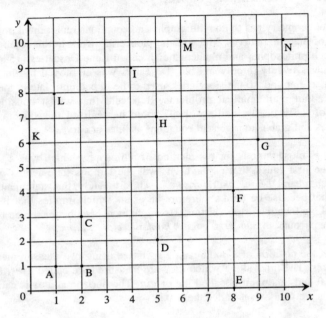

Exercise 5b Draw a pair of axes, using 1 cm per unit, and plot the following points. Label each point with the letter indicated. If you are using squared paper you do not need to draw all the grid-lines but only the axes.

1. A (1,3)	**4.** D (6,7)	**7.** G (0,4)	**10.** J (2,2)	**13.** M (5,6)
2. B (4,2)	**5.** E (10,1)	**8.** H (4,0)	**11.** K (6,10)	**14.** N (3,0)
3. C (5,7)	**6.** F (8,4)	**9.** I (1,1)	**12.** L (3,4)	**15.** P (2,9)

In a plane, the x-axis is horizontal and the y-axis is vertical. There are other systems of axes and coordinates, such as using three axes to cover the whole of space, but for now we will be using this system called Cartesian after Rene Descartes.

By drawing the axes on the other side of the origin we can also have negative coordinates. So the x-axis is extended to the left of the origin and the y-axis is extended downwards below the origin.

Exercise 5c Give the coordinates of the points A to U (O is omitted because it is already the origin)

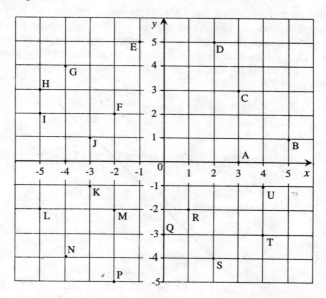

Exercise 5d Draw a pair of axes from −10 to +10 on both, using 5 mm per unit, and plot the following points:

1. A (−2,4)	**4.** D (6,−4)	**7.** G (−4,−4)	**10.** J (−6,−5)	**13.** M (−6,−2)
2. B (8,3)	**5.** E (3,−7)	**8.** H (−7,8)	**11.** K (−8,0)	**14.** N (3,−4)
3. C (−1,2)	**6.** F (7,−7)	**9.** I (5,−3)	**12.** L (4,−6)	**15.** P (8,−10)

Exercise 5e Draw a pair of axes from −10 to +10 for each question, using 5 mm per unit. Points A, B and C are three corners of a square. Plot and label these points and then complete the square to find the coordinates of the fourth corner, D. Write down the coordinates of D.

1. A (1,1)	B (5,3)	C (5,−1)	**6.** A (−8,6)	B (−4,−8)	C (10,−4)
2. A (2,2)	B (2,−1)	C (−1,−1)	**7.** A (0,4)	B (−2,1)	C (1,−1)
3. A (0,3)	B (−2,1)	C (0,−1)	**8.** A (1,0)	B (3,2)	C (1,4)
4. A (−4,2)	B (−3,−2)	C (1,−1)	**9.** A (−2,−1)	B (2,−2)	C (3,2)
5. A (−4,3)	B (−2,−4)	C (5, −2)	**10.** A (−3,−2)	B (−5,2)	C (−1,4)

35

Straight lines on graphs

A line drawn on a graph with x and y axes represents a relationship between x and y. In the graph below, the line drawn cuts in half the right-angle formed by the axes. For every point on the line, the x-coordinate is equal to the corresponding y-coordinate. This means that every x value is equal to every y value. This is expressed as $x = y$ and is the simplest possible relationship. $x = y$ is the equation of the line shown.

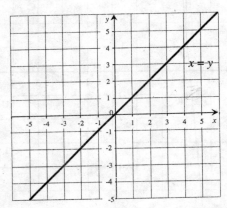

With the line drawn perpendicular to the line $x = y$, the y-coordinates of each point are simply the negative, or minus, values of their corresponding x-coordinates. This is shown on the graph and table below.

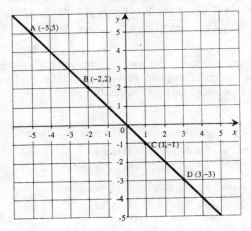

	A	B	C	D
x coordinate	−5	−2	1	3
y coordinate	5	2	−1	−3

The equation of this line is therefore $y = -x$

Exercise 5f Problems involving *Proportionately*

1. Draw a pair of axes with 1 cm per unit and −6 to +8 on both. Plot the points, A (2,8), B (−1,−4), and C (1,4). Join the points with a straight line.

   (a) Give the coordinates of another two points on the line.

   (b) For each point, what is the relationship between the x-coordinate and its corresponding y-coordinate?

   (c) From your answer to (b) what is the equation of the line ?

2. Draw a y-axis from −4 to 10 and an x-axis from −2 to 4 using 1 cm per unit. Plot the points, P (−1,−3), Q (1,3) and R (3,9). Join the points to form a straight line.

   (a) Give the coordinates of another two points on the line.

   (b) If the point S has x-coordinate $\frac{1}{2}$, what is its y-coordinate?

   (c) If the point T has y-coordinate 12, what is its x-coordinate?

   (d) For each point, what is the relationship between the x-coordinate and its corresponding y-coordinate?

   (e) From your answer to part (d), what is the equation of this line?

3. Make a copy of the following graph.

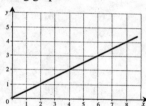

   (a) Mark on the line three points. Label these points A, B and C and write down their coordinates.

   (b) For each point, what is the relationship between the x-coordinate and its corresponding y-coordinate?

   (c) From your answer to part (b), what is the equation of this line?

4. Choosing your own set of axes, plot the points A (−2,4), B (2,−4) and C (−1,2). Draw the straight line which passes through these points.

   (a) One point on the line has x-coordinate 2. What is its y-coordinate?

   (b) From your answer to (a) what is the equation of this line?

Coordinates which satisfy an equation

If the x and y values given for the coordinates of a point "fit" a given equation then those values are said to *satisfy* that equation. For example, with an equation such as, $y = 3x + 4$, the question may arise as to whether the point with coordinates, $(2,10)$ lies on the line with that equation.

The point with coordinates, $(2,10)$, has x and y values, $x = 2$ and $y = 10$. Since y is the subject of the equation we substitute 2 for x and find the value for y.

$$y = 3 \times 2 + 4 = 6 + 4 = 10$$

Therefore when $x = 2$, $y = 10$ and so the point $(2,10)$ does satisfy the equation.

Do the values $x = 4$, $y = 5$ satisfy the equation,
$y = 6x - 2$

$y = 6x - 2$
$= 6 \times 4 - 2$
$y = 22$, No!

Exercise 5g Do the values for x and y satisfy the given equations?

1. $y = 3x$ $x = 2$ $y = 6$ 6. $y = x - 12$ $x = 21$ $y = 7$

2. $y = \frac{3}{4}x$ $x = 12$ $y = 9$ 7. $y = 2x - 1$ $x = -3$ $y = -7$

3. $y = x + 2$ $x = 6$ $y = 7$ 8. $y = 4x + 2$ $x = -2$ $y = -8$

4. $y = x - 6$ $x = 2$ $y = -3$ 9. $y = 3x + 5$ $x = 0$ $y = 5$

5. $y = 3x + 1$ $x = 4$ $y = 13$ 10. $y = 7x - 9$ $x = -1$ $y = -16$

Find the value of y when $x = 4$ in the equation,
$y = 3x + 5$.

$y = 3x + 5$
$y = 3 \times 4 + 5$
$y = 17$

Find the value of x when $y = 2$ in the equation,
$y = 3x - 4$.
By placing the value $y = 2$ into the equation we then have the equation, $2 = 3x - 4$ to solve.

$y = 3x - 4$
$2 = 3x - 4$
$2 + 4 = 3x$
$x = 2$

Exercise 5h In 1 - 5 solve the equations for y given the value of x. In 5 -10 solve the equations for x from the given y values.

1. $y = 5x$	$x = 3$	**6.** $y = x - 9$	$y = 7$
2. $y = \frac{3}{4}x - 2$	$x = 20$	**7.** $x + y = 6$	$y = -7$
3. $y = 2x + 7$	$x = 6$	**8.** $y = 4x + 2$	$y = 14$
4. $y = 5x - 6$	$x = 1$	**9.** $3x - y = 5$	$y = 7$
5. $y = 3x + 4$	$x = 0$	**10.** $y = 7x - 9$	$y = -16$

Plotting a straight line from a given equation

Given an equation involving x and y, such as $y = 2x - 4$, it is possible to draw the graph of the line which this equation represents. To do this you need at least two points whose coordinates "fit" the equation. Plot them on a graph and then draw the line through those points. To draw the line in the correct position use three points and check that they are all in line.

To draw a straight line from its equation the following table shows the steps:

1. Choose three x values
2. Find the corresponding y values
3. Make a table of values
4. Plot the points
5. Draw the line through the points

A table of values consists of at least three pairs of x-coordinates and their corresponding y-coordinates relating to a given equation. In practice, the x-coordinates are chosen and the corresponding y-coordinates are found from the equation. For example, suppose we wanted to obtain three points which lie on the line whose equation is $y = 2x$. You could choose three x-coordinates such as 2, 3 and 5 and make a table as shown below.

x	2	3	5
y			

From the equation, when $x = 2$, $y = 4$; when $x = 3$, $y = 6$ and when $x = 5$, $y = 10$. These results are shown in the table.

x	2	3	5
y	4	6	10

39

Plot the line whose equation is $y = 2x - 4$.

Choosing three values for x, say 0, 2 and 7, we first make a table of values as shown below.

Having chosen three values for x, the corresponding y values have to be found. This is done by placing each x value, in turn, into the equation and solving it for y. With a good choice of x values the equation can be solved by *Mere inspection.*

x	0	2	7
y			

At $x = 0$, $y = 2 \times 0 - 4 = -4$
At $x = 2$, $y = 2 \times 2 - 4 = 0$
At $x = 7$ $y = 2 \times 7 - 4 = 10$

x	0	2	7
y	–4	0	10

The table of values can then be completed.

This table gives three points, $(0,-4)$, $(2,0)$ and $(7,10)$ and these can then be plotted on a graph. Once the points are plotted then a straight line can be drawn through them.

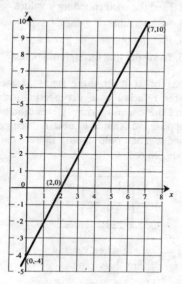

Exercise 5i For each question use a scale of $\frac{1}{2}$ cm per unit.

1. A line has equation, $y = x + 1$. Draw an x-axis from −4 to 5 and a y-axis from −3 to 6. Using the equation, copy and complete the table of values.

x	−3	0	4
y			

Plot the three points given in the table of values and draw a straight line through them.

2. A line has equation, $y = x - 2$. Draw an x-axis from −2 to 7 and a y-axis from −4 to 5. Using the equation, copy and complete the table of values.

x	0	−1	6
y			

Plot the three points given in the table of values and draw a straight line through them

3. Copy and complete the table of values below for the equation $y = \frac{1}{2}x$

x	−2	2	6
y			

Using an x-axis from −2 to 7 and a y-axis from −2 to 5, plot the three points and draw the line which passes through them.

4. Draw axes for x from −2 to 6 and for y from −7 to 6. Construct your own table of values using the equation, $y = 2x - 5$, by choosing values of x which are suitable for the axes drawn. Plot the points from the table of values and hence draw the line whose equation is $y = 2x - 5$.

For each of the following equations choose your own values to construct a table of values. Use the table of values to choose the size of each axis, plot the points and then draw the line.

5. $y = -x + 4$

6. $y = -\frac{1}{2}x + 2$

7. $y = x - 3$

8. $y = \frac{1}{3}x - 1$

9. $y = -2x + 5$

10. $y = -2x + 3$

Chapter 6   Approximations

Rounding off

In many practical calculations only an approximation is required rather than an exact answer. To do this numbers are rounded off to a given place value of ten, a hundred, a thousand, and so on.

Round off 34,259 to the nearest (a) ten, (b) hundred and (c) thousand.

(a) Locate the ten's digit and look at the one following, that is, 9. If it is less than 5 we round down and if it is 5 or more then we round up. 9 is more than 5 and so we round 59 up to 60. The answer is then 34,260.
(b) Locate the hundred's digit and look at the following one, that is, 5. It is customary to round 5 upwards. The answer is then 34,300.
(c) Locate the thousand's digit and look at the one following. 4 is the thousands digit but does not need to be rounded up because the following digit is a 2. The answer is therefore 34,000

Exercise 6a Round off each number to the nearest a) 10, b) 100, c) 1000

1. 3428	**4.** 7813	**7.** 16,719	**10.** 23,981	**13.** 30,499
2. 6202	**5.** 8194	**8.** 24,187	**11.** 14,592	**14.** 28,458
3. 5623	**6.** 72,981	**9.** 92,396	**12.** 26,755	**15.** 96,509

Decimal places

The same method is used for rounding off to a given number of decimal places.

Write 21.0491 correct to a) 3 decimal places, b) 2 decimal places and c) 1 decimal place

    a) 21.049   b) 21.05   c) 21.0

Note that, to 1 decimal place, 21.0491 is 21.0

Exercise 6b Write each number correct to a) one, b) two, c) three decimal places.

1. 8.2362	**5.** 0.2376	**9.** 213.0015	**13.** 0.0274
2. 9.0166	**6.** 21.6714	**10.** 65.8818	**14.** 0.6192
3. 43.2131	**7.** 1.8795	**11.** 3.4992	**15.** 5.9997
4. 35.6571	**8.** 45.3517	**12.** 8.9853	**16.** 121.38976

Significant figures

Approximating a number to a given number of significant figures follows the same procedure as for rounding off. The figures are counted from the left starting with the first digit. For example, 239 to one significant figure is 200. This is because the 2 in 239 is the first significant figure and so we round off this number to the nearest hundred. 239 to two significant figures is 240 because 3, being the second figure and in the ten's column, the number is rounded off to the nearest ten.

For decimal fractions, the figures are counted from the left-hand most number, that is, any left-hand zeros are not counted. This is shown in the table below with two examples.

Number	1 s.f.	2 s.f.	3 s.f.	4 s.f.
0.0021859	0.002	0.0022	0.00219	0.002186
0.10398	0.1	0.10	0.103	0.1040

Exercise 6c Write each number correct to a) one, b) two, c) three significant figures.

1. 5124	**5.** 215788	**9.** 2.4512	**13.** 0.1569
2. 46897	**6.** 874956	**10.** 14.59805	**14.** 0.005474
3. 5489	**7.** 646058	**11.** 421.508	**15.** 0.0008798
4. 9482	**8.** 2001549	**12.** 8794.001	**16.** 0.09989

Working to a given number of decimal places

When calculating answers questions may require rounding off to a given number of decimal places. The sutra involved with this is by *Elimination and retention* where the digits required are retained and those not needed are neglected.

For multiplication, the answer is found more quickly by working from the left. The example below shows how this can be done for single-digit multipliers.

Multiply 2.34236 by 7, leaving your answer correct to one decimal place.

Working from the left, the first step is $2 \times 7 = 14$. The decimal point is then brought down in line. The next step is $3 \times 7 = 21$. The 1 is set down in the next column and the 2 is carried to the left and so placed below the 4.

$$
\begin{array}{r}
2.34236 \\
\times \qquad 7 \\
\hline
14.1 \\
2 \\
\hline
\end{array}
$$

$4 \times 7 = 28$, and 8 is written in the next column with 1 carried to the left. In like manner the product is continued until we are certain that no extra figures are going to affect the first decimal place when rounding off. This means that the digits in the second decimal place must be known. The answer is then 16.4

$$
\begin{array}{r}
2.34236 \\
\times \qquad 7 \\
\hline
14.184 \\
2\ 21 \\
\hline
16.4
\end{array}
$$

Exercise 6d Calculate each sum leaving your answers corrected to the number of decimal places given in the brackets.

1. 3.411×3 (1 d.p.)
2. 62.265×2 (1 d.p.)
3. 3.17561×4 (2 d.p.)
4. 0.6237×6 (1 d.p.)
5. 0.21956×7 (2 d.p.)

6. 2.3546×5 (1 d.p.)
7. 34.812×8 (1 d.p.)
8. 0.34251×3 (2 d.p.)
9. 7.0673×9 (1 d.p.)
10. 0.0872×3 (2 d.p.)

11. 0.0054632×4 (2 d.p.)
12. 0.07688×6 (3 d.p.)
13. 54.878×8 (1 d.p.)
14. 52.167×3 (2 d.p.)
15. 2.8725342×9 (3 d.p.)

When dividing to a given number of decimal places the sum is continued to the following digit before rounding off can take place.

Find $32.78096 \div 6$ correct to 1 decimal place.

$$
\begin{array}{r}
6\,|\,\overline{32.\,_27\,_38\,0\,9\,6} \\
\hline
5.\ 4\ 6 \\
\hline
5.\ 5
\end{array}
$$

Exercise 6e In numbers 1-5, give the answer correct to 1 decimal place, in numbers 6-10 correct to 2 decimal places and in 11-15 correct to 3 decimal places.

1. $30 \div 7$	**6.** $2.45364 \div 3$	**11.** $425.564 \div 6$
2. $57 \div 9$	**7.** $0.7213 \div 9$	**12.** $23.0 \div 7$
3. $21 \div 8$	**8.** $23.576 \div 4$	**13.** $18.215273 \div 5$
4. $32.5 \div 6$	**9.** $38.902 \div 7$	**14.** $376.64804564 \div 3$
5. $213.7 \div 8$	**10.** $13.99 \div 8$	**15.** $6574.012765 \div 8$

When multiplying numbers, using *Vertically and crosswise*, to a given number of decimal places it is easier to work from the left. To place the decimal point in the correct position in the answer it should be remembered that it is placed after the step involving the multiplication of the units digits.

Multiply 0.31236 by 4.6132, leaving your answer
correct to one decimal place.

$$
\begin{array}{r}
0.31236 \\
\times 4.6132 \\
\hline
0.227 \\
1\ 2\ 1 \\
\hline
1.4
\end{array}
$$

$0 \times 4 = 0$
$0 \times 6 + 3 \times 4 = 12$
$0 \times 1 + 3 \times 6 + 1 \times 4 = 22$
$0 \times 3 + 3 \times 1 + 1 \times 6 + 2 \times 4 = 17$

We now have all the digits in the second decimal place
and can round off the answer to 1.4.

Exercise 6f In numbers 1 - 5, give the answer correct to the nearest whole number, in numbers 6 - 10 correct to 1 decimal place and in 11 - 15 correct to 2 decimal places.

1. 1.23×2.42	**6.** 0.354×9.111	**11.** 0.23142×0.34253
2. 3.44×6.12	**7.** 1.3645×8.3526	**12.** 1.2765×4.3253
3. 0.76×21.48	**8.** 32.54105×11.3524	**13.** 0.06574×0.7321
4. 7.15×8.32	**9.** 0.546×0.23111	**14.** 6.8213×2.334
5. 32.7×12.4	**10.** 3.241523×0.0345	**15.** 0.756547×0.53643

Chapter 7 Practice and revision 1

Revision for chapter 1

Exercise 7a

1. $2.3 + 4.8$	**6.** 45×8	**11.** $5 + (-2)$	**16.** $7 + (-8)$
2. $6.4 - 3.7$	**7.** 3.5×6	**12.** $(-3) + (-4)$	**17.** $(-5) - 12$
3. $34 + 58 + 79$	**8.** $584 \div 4$	**13.** $(-2) - (-7)$	**18.** $5468 - 1891$
4. $1245 - 844$	**9.** $1001 \div 7$	**14.** $8 \times (-7)$	**19.** $48712 \div 8$
5. $23.12 - 19.45$	**10.** $1001 \div 11$	**15.** $(-14) \div 2$	**20.** 4.087×7

Revision for chapter 2

Exercise 7b

1. 98×97	**11.** 102×93	**21.** 45^2
2. 82×95	**12.** 106×96	**22.** 35^2
3. 96×47	**13.** 102×99	**23.** 115^2
4. 997×992	**14.** 1014×997	**24.** 0.65^2
5. 9995×9993	**15.** 12342×9998	**25.** 0.025^2
6. 8165×9998	**16.** 10003×8796	**26.** 47×43
7. 103×104	**17.** 98^2	**27.** 36×34
8. 112×109	**18.** 96^2	**28.** 62×68
9. 1132×1007	**19.** 102^2	**29.** 71×79
10. 12132×10005	**20.** 108^2	**30.** 92×98

Revision for chapter 3

Exercise 7c

1. $112 \div 9$	**5.** $113 \div 88$	**9.** $1234 \div 998$
2. $10221 \div 9$	**6.** $112 \div 96$	**10.** $24351 \div 9997$
3. $112 \div 8$	**7.** $1012 \div 88$	**11.** $12123 \div 987$
4. $10342 \div 9$	**8.** $1123 \div 89$	**12.** $132042 \div 989$

13. $21432 \div 979$

14. $1213233 \div 99$

15. $210321 \div 999$

16. $2344 \div 101$

17. $1346 \div 102$

18. $1489 \div 112$

19. $1239 \div 111$

20. $12567 \div 113$

21. $236 \div 9$

22. $48647 \div 987$

23. $37667 \div 988$

24. $120262 \div 89$

Revision for chapter 4

Exercise 7d Simplify:

1. $5b + 4b - 3b$

2. $n + n + n + t$

3. $k + k + m + m + \mathrm{m}$

4. $3k + 2n + 2k + n$

5. $d + 1 + d + 3$

6. $7h + 5g - 6h$

7. $2n + 3p - 2n - p$

8. $2 \times b \times 4$

9. $h \times k \times 4$

10. $3c \times 2 \times 3d$

11. $3m \times 4 \times p$

12. $3v \times 5x \times 2w$

Expand the brackets:

13. $3(c + d)$

14. $7(e + f)$

15. $6(n - p)$

16. $a(b + c)$

17. $d(e - f)$

18. $a(b + 3)$

19. $g(5 - h)$

20. $4(2c - 3)$

21. $6(3 + 2h)$

22. $2a(b + 5)$

23. $2n(7t + 3u)$

24. $2p(p - 5)$

25. $m(m + 1)$

26. $x(4x - 8y)$

27. $2a(4 - 3b)$

Expand and simplify:

28. $2(x + 4) + 3(x + 1)$

29. $4(y - 2) + 2(3 + y)$

30. $5(a - 4) + 2(3 - a)$

31. $5(x + 7) - 2(x + 1)$

32. $7(2 - z) - 2(z + 3)$

33. $8(a + b) + 2(a - b)$

34. $5(x + 2y) - 3(x - 1)$

35. $9(2a + 1) - 4(3b + 6)$

36. $3(3a + 4b) + (7a - 5b)$

37. $2(3x - 5y) - (4x - 9y)$

Exercise 7e Solve:

1. $x + 3 = 8$

2. $n + 4 = 9$

3. $y - 3 = 8$

4. $p - 9 = 3$

5. $3 + b = 7$

6. $7k = 35$

7. $3p = 15$

8. $3x - 7 = 11$

9. $2x - 5 = 7$

10. $4a + 3 = 11$

11. $3y - 2 = 10$

12. $5k + 3 = 33$

13. $1 = 8 + 5b$

14. $7 = 3d + 7$

15. $2 = 77w + 2$

16. $2(x + 7) = 18$

17. $4(y + 3) = 24$

18. $2 + (d - 1) = 4$

19. $(h - 4) + 2 = 5$

20. $3 = 2(2x - 7) - 19$

21. $4k + 3 + k - 2 = 11$

Revision for chapter 5

Exercise 7f

1. Draw axes, using 1 cm per unit, for x and y from 0 to 8 on each. Plot the points A(2,1), B(6,1), C(6,7) and D(2,7). Join, with straight lines, AB, BC, CD and DA.
   (a) What name is given to the shape ABCD?
   (b) What is the area of ABCD?

2. Draw axes as in question 1. Plot the points, P(6,1), Q(6,7) and R(1,7). Draw triangle PQR. Find the area of this triangle.

3. Draw axes as in question 1. Plot the points, A(6,0), B(8,2), C(2,8), D(0,6), P(8,0), Q(8,8) and R(0,8)
   (a) Draw the rectangle ABCD and the square OPQR.
   (b) Find the area of OPQR.
   (c) Find the areas of triangles OAD and APB.
   (c) What is the area of the rectangle ABCD?

4. A line has equation $y = 2x - 3$. Copy and complete the following table of values.

x	0	2	6
y			

   Draw suitable axes and plot the points given in the table. Hence draw the line whose equation is $y = 2x - 3$.

5. By making up your own table of values and drawing suitable axes draw the line whose equation is $y = -2x + 5$
   (a) Find the y-coordinate of the point on the line whose x-coordinate is 3.
   (b) Find the x-coordinate of the point on the line whose y-coordinate is 4.
   (c) Write down the coordinates of the two points where the line passes through the axes.

6. A certain line has equation $y = 4x - 3$. Without drawing the line but showing your working,
   (a) Does the point (8,29) lie on the line?
   (b) Does the point (2,-3) lies on the line?
   (c) Rearrange the equation to make y the subject.

Chapter 8   Geometry

Revision of basic constructions

Constructions 1 to 6 are revisions of some of the more important drawing skills contained in book 1.

Construction 1   To draw the perpendicular bisector of a straight line.

To bisect means to cut something into two equal parts and perpendicular means *at right angles to*. The following construction divides any given line into two equal parts with a perpendicular line.

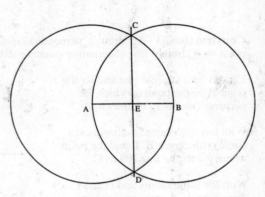

Let AB be the given line.

With radius AB and centre A draw a circle.

With the same radius and centre B draw another circle. Let the points where these two circles cut one another be C and D.

Join C to D and let the point where CD cuts AB be E.

CD is perpendicular to AB and cuts AB in half at E. E is the centre of AB.

Construction 2   To draw a perpendicular at a given point on a straight line.

Begin with a straight line and let A be the point at which the perpendicular is to be drawn. Choose a point B above the line and not vertically above the point A.

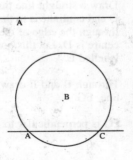

With centre B and radius AB draw a circle. Let the point where the circle cuts the straight line again be C. This is the only circle we need for the construction.

Draw the diameter of the circle through B and C. Let the other end of the diameter be D.

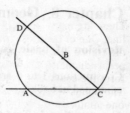

Join AD. AD is perpendicular to the straight line.

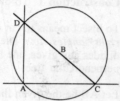

Construction 3 To draw a perpendicular at a given point on a straight line (alternative construction).

Let AB be a straight line and let the point B be the point at which the perpendicular is to be drawn.

With any convenient radius draw a circle with centre B. Label the point where it cuts the line AB as C.

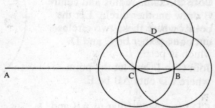

With the same radius and centre C draw a circle. Let the point above the straight line where these two circles cut one another be called D. Draw a third circle with the same radius and with centre at D.

Draw a straight line through C and D and continue it so that it passes through the edge of the circle whose centre is D. Let this point be labelled E.

Through B and E draw the straight line, FG.

FG is perpendicular to AB.

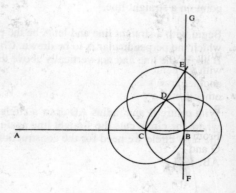

50

There are many ways of drawing a perpendicular at a given point on a straight line. One of the most common is based on Construction 1 above. The only difference is that a circle is first drawn centred at the point where the perpendicular is required. The points at which this circle cuts the straight line form the centres of two equal circles.
The points where the circles intersect one another are used to draw the

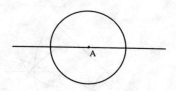

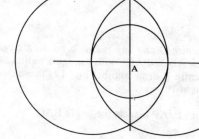

perpendicular.

Construction 4 To drop a perpendicular from a point to a given straight line.

Let P be the point and AB the given straight line. The problem is to draw a line from P which is perpendicular to AB.

.P

A   B

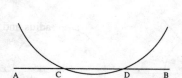

With centre P set the compasses to such a size as will pass through the straight line twice. Draw the arc and let the points where it cuts the line AB be C and D.

With any radius and centre C draw an arc and with the same radius but with centre D draw another arc so that the two arcs cut each other. Let the points where they cut be Q and R.

From P draw a straight line passing through Q and R. The line PQR is perpendicular to AB.

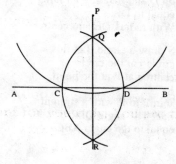

51

Construction 5 To bisect a given angle.

Let the two lines AB and AC form an angle.

With centre A and any suitable radius draw an arc cutting AB in D and AC in E.

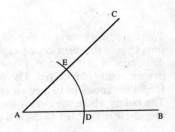

With centre D and any radius draw an arc lying between AB and AC. With the same radius but with centre E draw another arc. Let these two arcs cut at P.

Join A to P. AP bisects the angle BAC

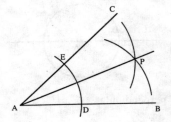

Construction 6 To copy a given angle

Let angle ABC be any given angle and let P be the point on the line PQ at which the angle ABC is to be copied.

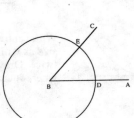

With centre B draw a circle. Let the points where the circle cuts AB and BC be D and E.
With the same radius draw a circle with centre P. Let this circle cut the straight line PQ at S.
Place your compass point on D and measure a radius equal to DE.
With radius DE and centre

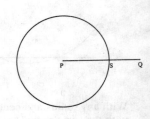

S draw a circle. Let this circle cut the circle centred at P at the point R.
Join P to R with a straight line. The angle QPR is equal to the angle ABC.

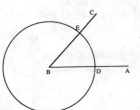

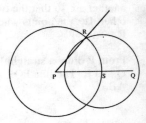

Angles in relation to a circle

Definition 1 A **plane angle** is the divided part of a circle where the two lines making the angle meet at the centre. When the lines are straight the angle is called **rectilinear**.

The *one* from which angles begin is the whole circle. For purposes of measure, the angle at the centre of a whole circle may be divided into 4 right angles or 360 degrees (360°).

Definition 2 A **right angle** is a quarter part of the angle at the centre of a whole circle.

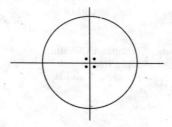

It follows that when a line stands upright on another line so that the angles on either side are equal then those angles are right angles.

When a circle is divided into 360 parts each part is called a degree. There are 360° in a whole circle and 90° in a right angle. From this it follows that angles about a point add up to 360°, or 4 right angles, and angles on a straight line add up to 180° or 2 right angles.

Definition 3 A **rectangle** is a plane figure with four straight sides such that opposite sides are equal and parallel. At each corner is a right angle.

From this definition it follows that a rectangle has four right angles.

Proposition 1 The angles within any right-angled triangle taken together make two right angles.

For let ABCD be any rectangle and let the diagonal BD be drawn within it. By observation the diagonal divides the rectangle into two equal halves each of which are right-angled triangles. Then since the rectangle has four right-angles it follows that each right-angled triangle has two right angles.

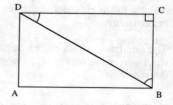

This is equally true for all right-angled triangles.

Construction 7 To draw a rectangle within a circle.

Draw any circle with a pair of compasses. Within the circle draw a horizontal straight line which meets the circumference at two points, A and B.

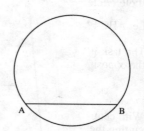

From B and through the centre of the circle draw a diameter, BD.
Lay the ruler so that a diameter could be drawn from A through the centre but instead of drawing it mark a point at the other end. Let this point be C.

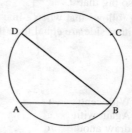

Draw the lines BC, CD and AD to complete the rectangle.

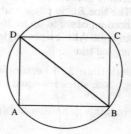

Proposition 2 Any triangle may be divided into two right-angled triangles.

This may be done by drawing a perpendicular from one corner to the opposite side. If the triangle has an obtuse angle (greater than 180°) then the perpendicular should be drawn from the corner with that angle.

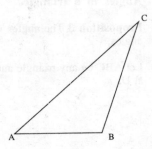

Construction 8 To construct a perpendicular from one corner of a triangle to the opposite side.

Let ABC be any triangle and let the angle at B be obtuse.

The task is to construct a perpendicular from B to the opposite side AC.

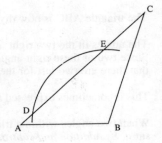

With centre B and any suitable radius draw an arc cutting the side AC at D and E. The radius must be sufficiently large so as to pass through AC but not so big that the arc does not cut AC twice.

With centre D and any radius draw an arc. Again with centre E but with the same radius draw another arc. Let these two arcs cut at F. Join B to F cutting AC in G. The line BG is perpendicular to AC, on account of the symmetry of the arcs, and so triangle ABC has been divided into two right-angled triangles, ABG and BGC.

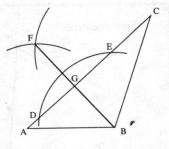

55

Angles in a triangle

Proposition 3 The angles within any triangle taken together make two right angles.

Let ABC be any triangle and let the perpendicular be drawn from C meeting AB at D.

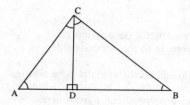

The triangle ABC is now divided into two right-angled triangles, ADC and BDC.

The angles in the two right-angled triangles together make four right angles. Since two of these right angles are at the foot of the perpendicular, D, it follows that there are two left for the three angles in triangle ABC.

This is sometimes expressed as, *angles in a triangle add up to 180°.*

When two angles within a triangle are known the third may be found using the sutra, *By addition and subtraction.*

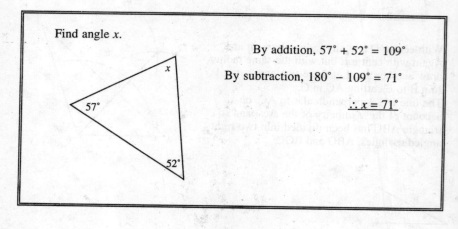

Find angle x.

By addition, $57° + 52° = 109°$

By subtraction, $180° - 109° = 71°$

$$\therefore x = 71°$$

Exercise 8a Find the angles denoted by each of the letters.

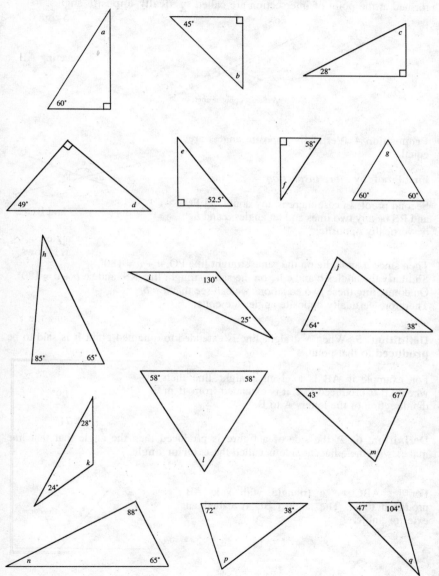

Definition 4 Whenever two straight lines cross the angles opposite one another formed at the point of intersection are called **vertically opposite** angles.

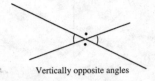

Vertically opposite angles

Proposition 4 Vertically opposite angles are equal.

First Proof: by *Mere inspection*

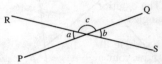

Second proof: In case there is any doubt, let PQ and RS be any two lines and let angles a and b be vertically opposite.

Then since a and c lie on the same straight line PQ, $a + c = 180°$.
Similarly the angles b and c lie on the same straight line RS, and so $b + c = 180°$.
On comparing these two equations we can see that $a = b$.
Therefore vertically opposite angles are equal.

Definition 5 When a straight line is extended to a named point it is said to be **produced** to that point.

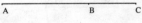

For example if AB is a given straight line then when AB is produced to C it is extended from B in the direction of the letters A to B.

Definition 6 If the side of a figure is produced then the angle that that line makes with the adjacent side is called the **exterior angle**.

For let ABC be a triangle with side AB produced to D. The angle CBD is called an exterior angle.

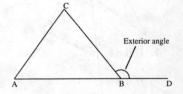

Exterior angle

Proposition 5 The exterior angle of a triangle is equal to the sum of the two interior opposite angles.

Let ABC be a triangle and let AB be produced to D. Let s be an exterior angle and let p and r be the interior opposite angles.

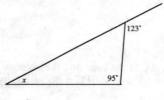

Since the angles within a triangle add up to 180°, $p + r + q = 180°$.
But angles on a straight line also add up to 180°, and so $s + q = 180°$.
On comparing these two equations it can be seen that $s = p + r$.
The exterior angle is therefore equal to the sum of the two interior opposite angles.

Exercise 8b Where the problem is given without a diagram it is often useful to draw your own so that the question is clear.

1. Find angle x.

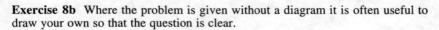

2. Find the value of y.

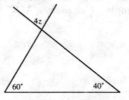

3. Calculate the value of z.

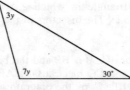

4. If the angles of a triangle are equal, how large is each angle?

5. If a triangle has two of its angles equal to 50°, what type of triangle is it?

6. A triangle has one angle of 20° and another angle of 80°. What is the size of the third angle?

7. In ΔABC, ∠A = 73°, ∠B = 54°; find ∠C.

8. In a right-angled triangle, one angle is 37°; find the third angle.

9. In the ΔPQR, ∠P = 103°, ∠Q = 22°; find the ∠R.

10. In ΔXYZ, ∠X = 27°, the exterior angle at Z = 97°; find the ∠Y.

11. Calculate the angles of a triangle if they are in the ratio 1 : 2 : 3.

12. In the diagram, PM bisects ∠QPR. Find ∠PQR and ∠PMQ

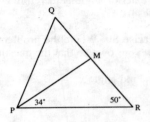

13. In ΔABC, AC is the base and the bisector of ∠ABC meets AC at P. If ∠ABC = 68° and ∠BPC = 86°, find, by calculation, ∠A and ∠C.

14. ABC is a triangle in which ∠A = 60°, ∠B = 52° and the side BC is produced to D. The bisectors of the ∠ABC and ∠ACD meet at M. Calculate the ∠BMC.

15. The bisector of ∠B is BP and the bisector of ∠C is CQ. BP and CQ meet at O. ∠ABC = 60° and ∠POQ = 110°. Copy the diagram and fill in any necessary angles. Calculate ∠AQC and ∠ACB.

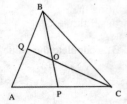

Parallel Lines

Definition 7 Parallel lines are lines which do not meet howsoever long they are drawn.

Note that this does assume that the lines are drawn in a plane and not on any other surface such as lines of longitude on a sphere.

Two arrows running in the same direction are used to indicate that lines are parallel.

Construction 9 To draw a line parallel to a given line through a given point.

Let P be the given point and AB the given line. Here the problem is to draw a line through P which is parallel to AB.

Choose any point on the straight line and label it C. With centre C and radius CP make a circle cutting the line AB at M and N. With radius NP but with centre M draw an arc cutting the circle at Q. Draw a straight line from P through Q.

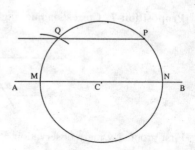

PQ is parallel to AB.

Definition 8 When a straight line falls across parallels the angles on the interior of the parallels but on opposite sides of the straight line are called **alternate**.

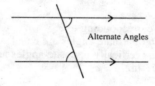

Alternate Angles

Proposition 6 Alternate angles are equal

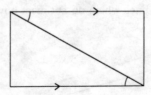

From the definition of a rectangle, opposite sides are parallel. Furthermore, a diagonal of a rectangle divides it into two equal halves.
Therefore alternate angles are equal.

Definition 9 Whenever a straight line falls across parallels the interior angle formed on one side of the straight line on one parallel is **corresponding** to the exterior angle on the same side of the straight line on the other parallel.

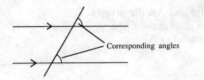

Corresponding angles

Proposition 7 Corresponding angles are equal.

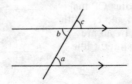

First proof: By mere observation.

Second proof:

[The reason for each statement is given in brackets and refers back to a previous proposition.]

In the diagram,

a is corresponding to c.
$a = b$ (alternate angles are equal)
$b = c$ (vertically opposite angles are equal)
Therefore $a = c$

Definition 10 Whenever a straight line falls across parallels the angles formed on the inside of the parallels are called **interior** angles.

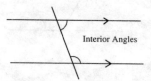

Interior Angles

Proposition 8 Interior angles add up to 180°.

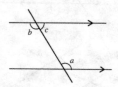

In the diagram,

$b + c = 180°$ (Angles on a straight line)
But $b = a$ (Alternate angles)
Therefore $a + c = 180°$

To sum up:

Alternate angles are equal

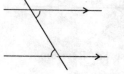

Corresponding angles are equal

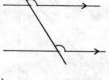

Interior angles add up to 180°

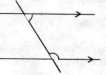

Exercise 8c Find the missing angles

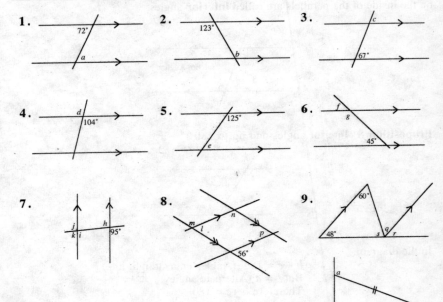

Exercise 8d Revision

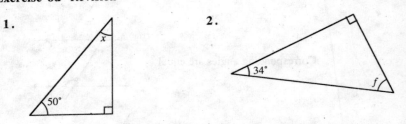

3. If the angles of a triangle are equal, how large is each angle?

4. If two sides of a right-angled triangle are equal, how large is each of the three angles?

5.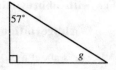

6.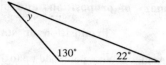

7.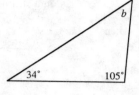

8.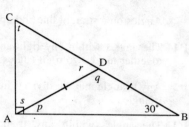

9. A triangle has one angle of 40° and another angle of 75°. What is the size of the third angle?

10. Calculate the angles of a triangle if they are in the ratio 2 : 3 : 4.

11. Find the size of angle *s*. **12.** Find *t* and then *u*.

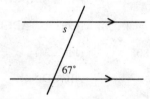
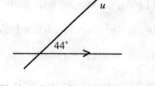

13. Find *x*, *y* and *z*. **14.** Find *a*, *b*, *c*, *d*, *e*, *f* and *g*.

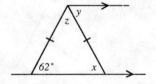
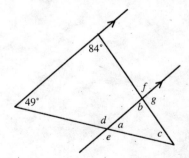

Summary of propositions and other facts together with abbreviations

Proposition or statement	Abbreviation
Angles about a point add up to 360°	($\angle$'s about a pt.)
Angles on a straight line add up to 180°	($\angle$'s on a st. line)
P1 The angles within any right-angled triangle taken together make two right angles.	
P2 Any triangle may be divided into two right-angled triangles.	
P3 The angles within any triangle taken together make two right angles.	($\angle$'s sum in $\triangle$)
P4 Vertically opposite angles are equal.	(Vert. opp.$\angle$'s)
P5 The exterior angle of a triangle is equal to the sum of the two interior opposite angles.	(Ext. $\angle$ in $\triangle$)
P6 In parallel lines alternate angles are equal	(Alt.$\angle$'s ABCD)*
P7 In parallel lines corresponding angles are equal.	(Corr.$\angle$'s ABCD)*
P8 In parallel lines interior angles add up to 180°	(Int. $\angle$'s)
The line AB is parallel to the line CD.	AB//CD
The line AB is perpendicuar to the line CD.	AB$\perp$CD

Chapter 9 Arithmetic practice

Exercise 9a Tuning up practice - work mentally and write answers only:

1. $25 + 26$	**9.** $276 + 198$	**17.** $92 - 29$	**25.** $5000 - 1$
2. $17 + 19$	**10.** $210 + 299$	**18.** $76 - 39$	**26.** $40500 - 32$
3. $34 + 34$	**11.** $12 + 13 + 14$	**19.** $234 - 99$	**27.** $213 + 425$
4. $49 + 50$	**12.** $56 - 24$	**20.** $433 - 199$	**28.** $1232 + 5432$
5. $36 + 29$	**13.** $34 - 17$	**21.** $820 - 398$	**29.** $3984 - 1111$
6. $45 + 99$	**14.** $98 - 62$	**22.** $1000 - 765$	**30.** $625 - 293$
7. $324 + 199$	**15.** $101 - 76$	**23.** $500 - 234$	**31.** $474 + 688$
8. $523 + 399$	**16.** $102 - 35$	**24.** $400 - 276$	**32.** $2365 - 78$

Exercise 9b Tuning up practice - work mentally and write answers only:

1. 23×2	**9.** 412×9	**17.** 0.421×9	**25.** 516.7×7
2. 48×3	**10.** 342×7	**18.** 23.147×7	**26.** 148241×8
3. 61×4	**11.** 2168×2	**19.** 68.12×8	**27.** 94284×6
4. 217×2	**12.** 3421×3	**20.** 3.1415×9	**28.** 1148.12×9
5. 332×4	**13.** 67144×4	**21.** 2.067×8	**29.** 6.0287×8
6. 211×8	**14.** 6281×7	**22.** 31.112×7	**30.** 0.4041×7
7. 345×5	**15.** 3214×8	**23.** 0.461×5	**31.** 0.063×5
8. 236×6	**16.** 6.248×6	**24.** 321.4×8	**32.** 2.37×9

Exercise 9c Tuning up practice - work mentally and write answers only:

1. $248 \div 2$	**9.** $2346 \div 3$	**17.** $3.126 \div 3$	**25.** $31.75 \div 5$
2. $246 \div 3$	**10.** $8564 \div 4$	**18.** $448 \div 7$	**26.** $0.2016 \div 4$
3. $464 \div 2$	**11.** $4836 \div 6$	**19.** $315 \div 9$	**27.** $10.24 \div 8$
4. $524 \div 4$	**12.** $3542 \div 7$	**20.** $504 \div 8$	**28.** $15.03 \div 9$
5. $924 \div 6$	**13.** $6448 \div 8$	**21.** $4938 \div 6$	**29.** $4.361 \div 7$
6. $7314 \div 3$	**14.** $7209 \div 9$	**22.** $1072 \div 8$	**30.** $114.768 \div 6$
7. $1465 \div 5$	**15.** $1.236 \div 2$	**23.** $2611 \div 7$	
8. $9842 \div 2$	**16.** $423 \div 5$	**24.** $3.68 \div 4$	

Exercise 9d Write answers only:

1. 216×20	**9.** 852×80	**17.** 14829×20	**25.** 62.1×90
2. 311×40	**10.** 554×90	**18.** 52041×40	**26.** 27.8×60
3. 682×30	**11.** 1624×30	**19.** 12387×30	**27.** 3.142×40
4. 191×60	**12.** 3215×40	**20.** 34620×80	**28.** 8.92×30
5. 318×20	**13.** 9624×60	**21.** 2.81×20	**29.** 0.618×80
6. 427×70	**14.** 1267×90	**22.** 4.34×40	**30.** 0.4211×70
7. 691×30	**15.** 3287×70	**23.** 6.28×70	
8. 724×20	**16.** 4289×60	**24.** 0.24×50	

$336 \div 70$

Divide 336 by 7 to give 48 and then divide 48 by 10
to give 4.8. This may also be done by first dividing
by 10 to give 33.6 and then dividing by 7.

$$7 \overline{\smash{\big)}\ 33_56}$$
$$4.8$$

Exercise 9e Write answers only:

1. $480 \div 20$	**9.** $42 \div 60$	**17.** $489 \div 40$	**25.** $2763 \div 90$
2. $480 \div 40$	**10.** $81 \div 30$	**18.** $627 \div 60$	**26.** $6144 \div 80$
3. $480 \div 30$	**11.** $63 \div 70$	**19.** $723 \div 30$	**27.** $3261 \div 30$
4. $360 \div 90$	**12.** $28 \div 40$	**20.** $128 \div 40$	**28.** $3780 \div 40$
5. $9810 \div 30$	**13.** $45 \div 50$	**21.** $1284 \div 20$	**29.** $62954 \div 20$
6. $48 \div 20$	**14.** $72 \div 90$	**22.** $7434 \div 70$	**30.** $728469 \div 30$
7. $56 \div 70$	**15.** $180 \div 20$	**23.** $6192 \div 40$	**31.** $6454 \div 70$
8. $64 \div 80$	**16.** $564 \div 20$	**24.** $8215 \div 50$	**32.** $32480 \div 160$

Multiplying and dividing by powers of ten

This is largely a case of adding or subtracting zeros or moving the decimal point.
When moving the decimal point, move it to the left for division and to the right for
multiplication.

$$1\ 2\ 3\ 5\ 4\ .\ 6\ 0\ 7\ 6$$

Division $\longleftarrow$ $\longrightarrow$ *Multiplication*

The following examples illustrate the effects of multiplying and dividing by 10, 100, 1000, etc.

$23 \times 10 = 230$	Add a zero.
$0.234 \times 10 = 2.34$	When the number has a decimal point then move it one place to the right.
$2.654 \times 1000 = 2654$	Move the decimal point 3 places to the right.
$4500 \div 10 = 450$	Remove a zero.
$67 \div 10 = 6.7$	Move the decimal point one place to the left, remembering that $67 = 67.0$ and $6.70 = 6.7$.
$866.2 \div 100 = 8.662$	Move the point 3 places to the left.

Exercise 9f Write answers only:

1. 45×10
2. 7.6×10
3. 67.7×10
4. $680 \div 10$
5. 0.003×10
6. $0.072 \div 10$
7. 0.123×10
8. 34.52×10
9. 0.4×100
10. 0.576×100
11. 45.7×100
12. $12.9 \div 100$
13. $4890 \div 100$
14. 0.3×100
15. $0.3 \div 100$
16. 0.02×100
17. 57×1000
18. 354×1000
19. $7000 \div 1000$
20. $6500 \div 1000$
21. 0.2×1000
22. $384.7 \div 1000$
23. 23.99×1000
24. 0.075×1000

Using the *Proportionately* sutra

$1456 \div 50$	$1456 \times 2 = 2912$
Since 50 is one half of 100 the easy way to divide by 50 is to divide by 100 and multiply by 2. This gives 29.12 as the answer.	$2912 \div 100 = 29.12$

Exercise 9g Write answers only:

1. $72 \div 5$	**7.** $426 \div 50$	**13.** 48×25	**19.** 804×250
2. $43 \div 5$	**8.** $1288 \div 50$	**14.** 88×25	**20.** 420×250
3. $37 \div 5$	**9.** $3284 \div 50$	**15.** 40×25	**21.** 248×250
4. 46×5	**10.** 46×50	**16.** $121 \div 25$	**22.** $1342 \div 250$
5. 84×5	**11.** 284×50	**17.** $312 \div 25$	**23.** $8130 \div 250$
6. 234×5	**12.** 371×50	**18.** $611 \div 25$	**24.** $61941 \div 250$

Further use of *Proportionately*

We can perform division sums by treating the numbers as in a fraction and reducing to lowest terms.

$2088 \div 24$

Since both numbers are divisible by 4, divide them both to give 522 on top and 6 underneath. For 6 into 522, 6 into 52 = 8 remainder 4 and 6 into 42 = 7.

$$\frac{2088}{24} = \frac{522}{6} = 87$$

$1152 \div 27$

Since 27 is divisible by 3 and 9, sum the digits of 1152 to see if it is divisible by 3 or 9. $1 + 1 + 5 + 2 = 9$, and so it is divisible by 9. 9 into $1152 = 128$ and 9 into $27 = 3$. 3 into $128 = 42$ remainder 2, and so the answer is $42\frac{2}{3}$

$$\frac{1152}{27} = \frac{128}{3} = 42\frac{2}{3}$$

Exercise 9h Simplify by first reducing to lowest terms:

1. $\frac{75}{125}$	**4.** $\frac{960}{30}$	**7.** $\frac{144}{36}$	**10.** $\frac{500}{75}$	**13.** $\frac{950}{75}$
2. $\frac{150}{5}$	**5.** $\frac{375}{15}$	**8.** $\frac{180}{36}$	**11.** $\frac{2400}{180}$	**14.** $\frac{2000}{150}$
3. $\frac{640}{20}$	**6.** $\frac{960}{20}$	**9.** $\frac{840}{120}$	**12.** $\frac{256}{12}$	**15.** $\frac{360}{72}$

16. $\dfrac{180}{22\frac{1}{2}}$ **21.** $\dfrac{480}{25}$ **26.** $\dfrac{1296}{32}$ **31.** $360 \div 144$ **36.** $28500 \div 75$

17. $\dfrac{560}{160}$ **22.** $\dfrac{2400}{30}$ **27.** $\dfrac{522}{24}$ **32.** $861 \div 56$ **37.** $1295 \div 35$

18. $\dfrac{900}{48}$ **23.** $\dfrac{1600}{640}$ **28.** $\dfrac{812}{12}$ **33.** $1278 \div 18$ **38.** $12000 \div 48$

19. $\dfrac{640}{128}$ **24.** $\dfrac{720}{144}$ **29.** $\dfrac{160}{15}$ **34.** $2400 \div 35$ **39.** $11224 \div 24$

20. $\dfrac{1500}{75}$ **25.** $\dfrac{351}{21}$ **30.** $\dfrac{130}{125}$ **35.** $1562 \div 33$ **40.** $6872 \div 16$

Exercise 9i Use *Vertically and crosswise*. Remember that for decimal multiplication, the number of decimal digits in the answer is equal to the number of decimal digits in the two numbers to be multiplied.

1. 11×13 **9.** 23×12 **17.** 31.2×12.1 **25.** 1212×1321

2. 14×11 **10.** 21×11 **18.** 22.3×11.1 **26.** 10.03×23.11

3. 14×12 **11.** 24×13 **19.** 1.2×4.03 **27.** 2.133×2.005

4. 20×24 **12.** 31×21 **20.** 2.10×1.04 **28.** 214.2×132.5

5. 15×16 **13.** 41×22 **21.** 320×110 **29.** 1520×1100

6. 21×21 **14.** 43×23 **22.** 2.04×10.8 **30.** 3212×1587

7. 22×22 **15.** 1.6×5.1 **23.** 5.4×1.26

8. 23×14 **16.** 2.3×5.3 **24.** 119×32

Chapter 10 Compound arithmetic

Any quantities expressed in terms of the same units are said to be of the same **denomination**. If two units are related the larger one is of a higher denomination than the smaller. For example, there are 100 centimetres in 1 metre and so the metre is of a higher denomination then the centimetre. Similarly, there are 12 inches in a foot and so the foot is of a higher denomination than the inch.

Calculations with quantities of the same type with units of different denominations come under the heading of compound arithmetic. The sutra employed is *Transpose and adjust*. With each problem in compound arithmetic the number of units of the smaller denomination contained within one unit of the higher denomination should always be brought to mind.

For historical reasons we have two systems of weights and measures: metric and British. Units for time are the same in both systems. In the metric system the denominations are all based on multiples and sub-multiples of 10. The calculations can all be done with decimal arithmetic. In the British system and for time, the denominations are based on different numbers and this is where compound arithmetic is used.

Addition

To take a simple example, consider adding two periods of time in months and years. Since there are twelve months in one year, the base is 12.

	yr	m
Two men are aged 21 yrs 8 months and 28 yrs 11 months. Find the sum of their ages.	21	8
	+ 28	11
	50	7

Two men are aged 21 yrs 8 months and 28 yrs 11 months. Find the sum of their ages.

The sum is set out in two columns with the unit title above each. Starting with months, 8 + 11 = 19, but this is more than 1 year. Divide 19 months by 12 to give 1 yr 7 m, put down 7 and carry 1.
In the years column, 21 + 28 + 1 = 50.
The answer is then 50 yrs 7 m.

The British measures for weight and length, together with the measures for time, are given below for reference.

Weight

| 16 | ounces (oz) | make | 1 pound (1 lb) |
| 14 | pounds | .... | 1 stone (1 st) |

Linear Measure

12	inches (in)	make	1 foot (ft)
3	feet	....	1 yard (yd)
1760	yards	....	1 mile (mi)

Measures of Time

60	seconds	make	1 minute
60	minutes	....	1 hour
24	hours	....	1 day
7	days	....	1 week
12	months	....	1 year

Exercise 10a Find the sum of:

1.3 yr 7 m, 5 yr 9 m
2.13 yr 8 m, 29 yr 11 m
3.3 min 45 sec, 8 min 38 sec
4.8 min 53 sec, 13 min 27 sec
5.6 hr 23 min, 7 hr 49 min
6.6 hr 13 min, 1 hr 41 min
7.9 hr 44 min, 3 hr 19 min
8.5 d 13 hr, 9 d 17 hr
9.12 d 19 hr, 3 d 21 hr
10.6 d 14 hr, 7 d 7 hr

11.3 ft 4 in, 6 ft 9 in
12.17 ft 8 in, 5 ft 11 in
13.23 ft 7 in, 19 ft 10 in
14.6 yds, 2 ft, 7 yds 2 ft
15.2 lbs 13 oz, 7 lbs 11 oz
16.32 lbs 12 oz, 29 lbs 13 oz
17.4 lbs 8 oz, 8 lbs 15 oz
18.12 st 10 lb, 8 st 9 lb
19.9 st 5 lb, 11 st 11 lb
20.3 mi 754 yd, 6 mi 1324 yd

Subtraction

With compound subtraction it is usually easier to adjust the numbers before setting out. This means that the numbers must be inspected first.

---

17 ft 2 in − 9 ft 8 in

By inspecting the numbers of lower denomination we can see that 8 in is greater than 2 in. Adjust 17 ft 2 in to 16 ft 14 in and then set out the sum.

	ft	in
	16	14
−	9	8
	7	6

The subtraction is done in each column separately. Answer: 7 ft 6 in

---

Exercise 10b

1. 12 ft 4 in − 3 ft 8 in

2. 15 ft 7 in − 12 ft 11 in

3. 72 ft 6 in − 37 ft 9 in

4. 6 st 13 lb − 2 st 15 lb

5. 15 st 3 lb − 7 st 7 lb

6. 4 lb 3 oz − 2 lb 7 oz

7. 9 lb 5 oz − 4 lb 13 oz

8. 55 lb 5 oz − 29 lb 15 oz

9. 3 yr 4 m − 1 yr 9 m

10. 12 yr 2 m − 8 yr 7 m

11. 16 yr 7 m − 9 yr 11 m

12. 7 hr 35 min − 3 hr 48 min

13. 3 hr 23 min − 1 hr 56 min

14. 9 hr 12 min − 4 hr 36 min

15. 23 hr 11 min − 15 hr 49 min

16. 4 d 5 hr − 2 d 12 hr

17. 7 d 13 hr − 2 d 21 hr

18. 16 d 4 hr − 8 d 15 hr

Multiplication of compound quantities

Adjusting the answer in a product requires division.

---

3 ft 8 in × 5

First multiply the separate columns to give 15 ft 40 in. Since 40 in is larger than a foot, divide 40 by 12 to give 3 remainder 4, that is 3 ft 4 in.

The answer is then 18 ft 4 in.

	ft	in
	3	8
×		5
	15	40
	3 /	4
	18	4

Exercise 10c

1. 3 ft 7 in × 3

2. 11 ft 5 in × 6

3. 2 ft 9 in × 8

4. 16 ft 8 in × 4

5. 5 yd 2 ft × 7

6. 4 yd 1 ft × 9

7. 6 lb 9 oz × 2

8. 2 lb 7 oz × 4

9. 3 lb 5 oz × 7

10. 9 lb 4 oz × 8

11. 15 st 3 lb × 5

12. 8 st 5 lb × 4

13. 6 st 7 lb × 7

14. 5 st 4 lb × 5

15. 5 hr 12 min × 5

16. 2 hr 34 min × 3

17. 7 hr 48 min × 7

18. 6 min 25 sec × 9

19. 3 min 40 sec × 6

20. 14 min 23 sec × 8

21. 1 min 15 sec × 40

22. 5 d 11 hr × 3

23. 17 d 14 hr × 7

24. 8 d 3 hr × 11

Exercise 10d

1. How many inches are there in 2 ft, 8 ft, 1 yd, 3 yd, 4 yd?

2. How many feet are there in 48, 60, 72, 90, 100 inches?

3. How many yards in 72, 144, 108 inches?

4. How many feet are there in one mile, half a mile?

5. How many ounces are there in 3 lb, 6 lb, 4 st, 5 st?

6. How many pounds in 48 oz, 80 oz, 8 oz, 4 oz?

7. How many seconds are there in 3 min, 7 min, 10 min, 30 min, 1 hr?

8. How many minutes are there in 2 hr, 4 hr, 12 hrs, 1 day?

9. How many seconds in a day, a week, a year?

Division

23 ft 4 in ÷ 7

$$
\begin{array}{r}
\text{ft} \quad \text{in} \\
7)\overline{21 \quad 28} \\
\overline{3 \quad 4}
\end{array}
$$

The first step is to inspect the first number to see if it is divisible by 7. Since 23 is not divisible by 7 we can adjust it until it is. By subtracting 2 ft from the ft column and adding 24 in to the in column we arrive at 21 ft 28 in, both of which are divisible by 7.
The answer is 3 ft 4 in.

Vinculums may also be used to obtain the answer as shown in the example below.

14 ft 7 in ÷ 5
In this example, it is easier to adjust 14 ft to 15 ft than to 10 ft. By adding 1 ft to 14 ft it becomes 15 ft and 7 in is reduced to $\bar{5}$ in. On completing the division 3 ft $\bar{1}$ in is adjusted to 2 ft 11 in.

$$
\begin{array}{r}
\text{ft} \quad \text{in} \\
5)\overline{15 \quad \bar{5}} \\
\overline{3 \quad \bar{1}} \\
\overline{2 \quad 11}
\end{array}
$$

Exercise 10e

1. 6)<u>18ft 6in</u>	**6.** 9)<u>27hr 54min</u>	**11.** 5)<u>15min 5sec</u>	**16.** 3)<u>6lb 12oz</u>
2. 2)<u>7ft 8in</u>	**7.** 7)<u>16hr 20min</u>	**12.** 3)<u>7min 27sec</u>	**17.** 7)<u>22lb 5oz</u>
3. 3)<u>8ft 9in</u>	**8.** 2)<u>11hr 14min</u>	**13.** 7)<u>22min 24sec</u>	**18.** 2)<u>11lb 7oz</u>
4. 5)<u>18ft 4in</u>	**9.** 3)<u>5hr 21min</u>	**14.** 9)<u>19min 12sec</u>	**19.** 3)<u>14st 2lb</u>
5. 9)<u>23ft 3in</u>	**10.** 4)<u>7hr 52min</u>	**15.** 11)<u>24min 34sec</u>	**20.** 8)<u>21st 10lb</u>

In some cases the whole of the quantity with higher denomination will need to be expressed in terms of the lower denomination.

Reduce 7 ft 5 in to inches. $\qquad$ $7 \times 12 + 5 = 89$ in.

Exercise 10f Express each quantity in terms of the lower denomination.

1. 3 ft 7 in	**6.** 2 m 360 yds	**11.** 5 hr 5 min	**16.** 5 lb 7 oz
2. 7 ft 2 in	**7.** 6 d 14 hr	**12.** 12 min 20 sec	**17.** 9 lb 10 oz
3. 15 ft 11 in	**8.** 3 d 19 hr	**13.** 3 min 47 sec	**18.** 4 st 5 lb
4. 15 yds 2 ft	**9.** 3 hr 23 min	**14.** 15 min 35 sec	**19.** 3 st 2 lb
5. 13 yds 1 ft	**10.** 7 hr 58 min	**15.** 2 lb 3 oz	**20.** 8 st 11 lb

The following example uses this reduction for division.

5 lb 4 oz ÷ 7 $\qquad$ 7)<u>84oz</u>
$\qquad$ 12oz

$5 \times 16 = 80$, $80 + 4 = 84$
7 into 84 oz = 12 oz.

Exercise 10g

1. 2 lb 3 oz ÷ 5

2. 3 lb 6 oz ÷ 9

3. 4 st 4 lb ÷ 6

4. 2 st 7 lb ÷ 7

5. 5 lb ÷ 8

6. 3 ft 6 in ÷ 7

7. 2 ft 6 in ÷ 15

8. 1 ft 8 in ÷ 5

9. 3 yd 2 ft ÷ 11

10. 5 yd 1 ft ÷ 4

11. 2 min 13 sec ÷ 7

12. 4 min 15 sec ÷ 5

13. 3 min 4 sec ÷ 8

14. 2 hr 24 min ÷ 9

15. 2 d 8 hr ÷ 8

Exercise 10h Find:

1. $\frac{1}{4}$ of 1 lb

2. $\frac{1}{4}$ of 1 yd

3. $\frac{1}{6}$ of 1 yd

4. $\frac{3}{8}$ of 1 lb

5. $\frac{1}{2}$ of 1 st

6. $\frac{3}{14}$ of 1 st

7. $\frac{1}{3}$ of 1 ft

8. $\frac{3}{4}$ of 1 yd

9. $\frac{2}{3}$ of 1 ft

10. $\frac{1}{5}$ of 1 min

11. $\frac{2}{4}$ of 1 hr

12. $\frac{5}{12}$ of 1 hr

13. $\frac{3}{20}$ of 1 min

14. $\frac{3}{5}$ of 1 hr

15. $\frac{1}{3600}$ of 1 hr

Compound arithmetic with metric units

Since the metric system of weights and measures is based on powers of 10 and the decimal point, most problems involving units of more than one denomination can be simplified. For example, in adding 3 m 23 cm to 5 m 46 cm we can change both to metres. The problem then becomes 3.23 m + 5.46 m = 8.69 m. Again *Transpose and adjust* is used to convert a quantity given in metres and centimetres into metres. This requires us to know beforehand that 1 cm = 0.01 m or 100 cm = 1 m. The following tables give the metric units for weight, length, area volume and capacity.

Measures of weight

10 milligrams (mg.)	make	1 centigram (cg.)
10 centigrams	....	1 decigram (dg.)
10 decigrams	....	1 GRAM (g.)
10 grams	....	1 decagram (dag.)
10 decagrams	....	1 hectogram (hg.)
10 hectograms	....	1 kilogram (kg.)
100 kilograms	....	1 quintal (q.)
1000 kilograms	....	1 tonne (t.)

Measures of length

10	millimetres (mg.)	make	1 centimetre (cm.)
10	centimetres	....	1 decimetre (dm.)
10	decimetres	....	1 METRE (m.)
10	metres	....	1 decametre (dam.)
10	decametres	....	1 hectometre (hm.)
10	hectometres	....	1 kilometre (km.)

Measures of area

100	sq. millimetres (mm^2)	make	1 sq. centimetre (cm^2)
100	sq. centimetres	....	1 sq. decimetre (dm^2)
100	sq. decimetres	....	1 sq. metre (m^2)
100	sq. metres	....	1 sq. decametre (dam^2) = 1 are
100	sq. decametres	....	1 sq. hectometre (hm^2) = 1 hectare
100	sq. hectometres	....	1 sq. kilometre (km^2)

Measures of volume

1000	cubic millimetres (mm^3.)	make	1 cubic centimetre (cm^3.)
1000	cubic centimetres	....	1 cubic decimetre (dm^3.)
1000	cubic decimetres	....	1 cubic metre (m^3.)

Measures of capacity

10	millilitres (ml.)	make	1 centilitre (cl.)
10	centilitres	....	1 decilitre (dl.)
10	decilitres	....	1 LITRE (l.)
10	litres	....	1 decalitre (dal.)
10	decalitres	....	1 hectolitre (hl.)
10	hectolitres	....	1 kilolitre (kl.)

Exercise 10i Convert:

1. 10.6 cm to mm	**5.** 8.3 km to m	**9.** 700 g to kg
2. 900 mm to cm	**6.** 2500 m to km	**10.** 7.85 kg to g
3. 1.4 m to cm	**7.** 8000 mg to g	**11.** 3.5 tonnes to kg
4. 600 cm to m	**8.** 4.2 g to mg	**12.** 500 kg to tonnes

13. 2.275 l to ml   **17.** 2.9 km to m   **21.** 10,500 kg to tonnes
14. 125 cm to m   **18.** 0.6 kg to g   **22.** 9.5 m to cm
15. 3.64 cm to mm   **19.** 613.5 m to km   **23.** 7 mm to cm
16. 4500 m to km   **20.** 250 mg to g   **24.** 2.4 tonnes to kg

Exercise 10j

1. How many grams are there are there in 2 kg, 0.5 kg, 0.36 kg 4.32 kg?

2. How many centimetres are there 2 m, 0.7 m, 2.05 m, 8 mm 23 mm?

3. How many metres are there in 400 cm, 172 cm, 58 cm, 4 cm?

4. How many centilitres are there in 4 l, 3.68 l, 0.8 l, 0.22 l?

5. How many litres are there in 4000 cl, 385 dl, 386 cl, 1 dl?

6. How many square metres are there in 1 square kilometre?

7. How many square millimetres are there in 1 square centimetre?

8. How many square centimetres are there in 1 square metre?

9. How many square centimetres are there in 1 square kilometre?

Add together 345 m and 879 m leaving the answer in km.

Convert the quantities into the required denomination before carrying out the calculation.

$$\begin{array}{r} \text{km} \\ 0.345 \\ + \ 0.879 \\ \hline 1.224 \text{ km} \end{array}$$

Exercise 10k
Add together the following quantities. Give your answer in the unit in brackets:

1. 8 mm + 9 mm (cm)   **6.** 2.47 m + 65 cm (m)
2. 36 cm + 92 cm (m)   **7.** 15.3 cm + 88 mm (cm)
3. 450 m + 768 m (km)   **8.** 57.5 g + 900 mg (g)
4. 800 mg + 500 mg (g)   **9.** 3500 g + 3.65 kg (kg)
5. 150 kg + 240 kg (tonnes) **10.** 45 cm + 1.2 m (m)

Subtract the following quantities. Give your answer in the unit in brackets:

11.12 cm – 49 mm (cm)

12.3.5 m – 325 cm (m)

13.24.5 cm – 234 mm (cm)

14.7 g – 230 mg (g)

15.5.5 g – 1500 mg (g)

16.7 kg – 4500 g (kg)

17.4 tonnes – 860 kg (tonnes)

18.800 kg – 0.35 tonnes (kg)

19.6 l – 350 ml (l)

20.3.4 l – 756 ml (ml)

Multiply the following quantities by the given number. Leave your answers in the unit in brackets.

21. 8 mm × 12 (cm)

22. 3.4 mm × 7 (cm)

23. 86 cm × 24 (m)

24. 38.9 cm × 6 (m)

25. 340 m × 8 (km)

26. 250 mg × 3 (g)

27. 725 g × 4 (kg)

28. 230 kg × 25 (tonnes)

29. 270 ml × 9 (l)

Divide these quantities by the given number. Give your answer in the unit in brackets.

30. 20.3 cm ÷ 7 (cm)

31. 6 cm ÷ 5 (mm)

32. 37.8 m ÷ 6 (m)

33. 7 m ÷ 4 (cm)

34. 2.45 km ÷5 (m)

35. 13.5 km ÷2 (km)

36. 7.5 tonnes ÷ 15 (kg)

37. 3 l ÷ 20 (ml)

38. 36 m ÷ 72 (cm)

Exercise 10l

1. In a school athletics competition Michael runs 100 m three times, the 200 m twice, a 400m and the 1500 m races. How far does he run altogether in km?

2. Jose has a piece of wood 5.7 m long. Find the remainder, in cm, when he has cut 15 pieces, each 36 cm long, from the original piece.

3. A garden pond holds 21,000 l of water and leaks at a rate of 0.25 l per minute. How many litres will be left after a whole day?

4. A birthday cake weighing 3.4 kg is to be cut and shared amongst 20 children. If it is cut equally, what weight of cake, in grams, does each child receive?

5. A ream of paper is 5 cm thick. Find the thickness of a single sheet in mm. (A ream = 500 sheets.)

6. On a box of lawn fertiliser it states, 'To cover 5 m^2, dissolve 145 g in 5 litres of water'. How many 500 g boxes are needed for a lawn with an area of 75 m^2?

Chapter 11 Indices

Indices

The word *indices* is the plural of *index*. When a number has an index, such as 3^4, it indicates a product (the result of a multiplication) consisting of four factors each of which are 3. That is, $3^4 = 3 \times 3 \times 3 \times 3 = 81$. 3^4 is read as *three to the power of four* or, more briefly, *three to the four*. Sometimes it is said as *three is raised to the power of four*.

When a number is raised to the power of two it is often called the *square* of that number. For example, 5^2 is read as *five squared* or the *square of five*. This relates to the way in which the ancient Greek mathematicians thought of numbers. They did not have our numerical system, which came from India, but thought and represented number by using length or magnitude. One number multiplied by another became an area of a rectangle. If the two numbers were the same then it was a square. The ancient Greeks did most of their calculations using geometrical methods.

In the same way that the word *square* is used to denote one number multiplied by itself so the *cube* of a number is used to denote the third power. For example, four cubed or the cube of four is four to the power of three, that is, 4^3. This may be expressed as, $4^3 = 4 \times 4 \times 4 = 64$.

Simplify using indices, (a) $8 \times 8 \times 8 \times 8$, (b) $x \times x \times x \times x \times x \times y \times y \times y$

(a) $8 \times 8 \times 8 \times 8 = 8^4$

(b) $x \times x \times x \times x \times x \times y \times y \times y = x^4 \times y^3 = x^4 y^3$

Exercise 11a Simplify, leaving answers in index form:

1. $2 \times 2 \times 2 \times 2$
2. $3 \times 3 \times 3$
3. $4 \times 4 \times 4 \times 4$
4. 10×10
5. 2×2
6. $6 \times 6 \times 6 \times 6 \times 6$

7. $7 \times 7 \times 7$
8. $9 \times 9 \times 9 \times 9 \times 9$
9. $2 \times 2 \times 2 \times 5 \times 5$
10. $3 \times 3 \times 7 \times 7 \times 7$
11. $a \times a \times a$
12. $b \times b \times b \times b$

13. $c \times c$
14. $d \times d \times d \times d \times d$
15. $a \times a \times b \times b$
16. $b \times b \times b \times c \times c$
17. $x \times x \times x \times x \times y \times y$
18. $m \times m \times m \times n$

81

19. $\dfrac{5 \times 5 \times 5}{5}$

20. $\dfrac{8 \times 8 \times 8 \times 8}{8 \times 8 \times 8}$

21. $\dfrac{9 \times 9 \times 9 \times 9}{9 \times 9}$

22. $\dfrac{a \times a \times a}{a}$

23. $\dfrac{b \times b \times b \times b}{b \times b}$

24. $\dfrac{x \times x \times x \times x \times x \times x}{x \times x \times x \times x}$

25. $\dfrac{b \times b}{b}$

26. $\dfrac{c \times c \times c}{c \times c}$

27. $\dfrac{y \times y \times y \times y \times y}{y \times y}$

Laws of Indices

The power of one is to take any number to itself and so any number to the power of one is itself. For example, $3^1 = 3$. In general if x is any number, then

$$x^1 = x$$

Express in index notation, $5^2 \times 5^4$

$$5^2 \times 5^4 = (5 \times 5) \times (5 \times 5 \times 5 \times 5)$$
$$= 5 \times 5 \times 5 \times 5 \times 5 \times 5$$
$$= 5^6$$

In this example we can see that the total number of factors of 5 is $2 + 4 = 6$ and therefore, $5^2 \times 5^4 = 5^{2+4} = 5^6$.

The quicker method is to add the indices. This can be summarised by saying that, in general, if x, a and b are three numbers, then

$$x^a \times x^b = x^{a+b}$$

Express in index notation, $3^6 \div 3^4$

$$3^6 \div 3^4 = \frac{3 \times 3 \times 3 \times 3 \times 3 \times 3}{3 \times 3 \times 3 \times 3} = 3 \times 3 = 3^2$$

In this example we can see that $3^6 \div 3^4 = 3^{6-4} = 3^2$ and that the index for the answer may be obtained by subtracting the indices of the numbers to be divided. In general, if x, a and b are three numbers, then

$$x^a \div x^b = x^{a-b}$$

From this law it follows that any number to the power of 0 is 1. For consider the example, $2^3 \div 2^3$. By the subtraction of indices law, this is equal to 3^0. But $2^3 \div 2^3 = 1$. Similarly, if x is any number, then

$$x^0 = 1$$

The power of nought is to take any number back to unity, or one, and so any number to the power of nought is one. Since nought stands for the unmanifest, this may be stated as,

The unmanifest power of a number is one.

This means that within every number, the number 1 lies hidden and since number begins at 1, that 1 is the unmanifest power within all.

Shining yet hidden, Spirit lies in the cavern

[Upanishads]

In summary: The unmanifest power of a number is one;
The first power of a number is itself;
The second power of a number is that number multiplied by itself.

Exercise 11b Simplify, using the laws of indices:

1. $2^3 \times 2^2$
2. $3^3 \times 3^5$
3. $2^3 \times 2^2 \times 2^5$
4. $5^2 \times 5 \times 5^2$
5. $7^4 \times 7^3$
6. $9^8 \times 9$
7. $3^4 \times 3^3 \times 3^7$
8. $2 \times 2^2 \times 2^3 \times 2^4$
9. $6^{18} \times 6^7$

10. $3^7 \div 3^4$
11. $2^3 \div 2$
12. $4^3 \div 4^2$
13. $6^5 \div 6^2$
14. $9^5 \div 9$
15. $8^6 \div 8^6$
16. $4^3 \times 4^2 \div 4^4$
17. $5^5 \times 5^2 \div 5^6$
18. $7^2 \times 7^8 \div 7^{10}$

19. $a^3 \times a^4$
20. $y^2 \times y^6$
21. $x \times x^4$
22. $b^3 \times b^2 \times b$
23. $d^5 \times d^6 \times d^9$
24. $m^2 \times m^2 \times m \times m$
25. $p^7 \div p^5$
26. $z^8 \times z^3 \div z^2$
27. $x^3 \times x^2 \div x^8$

83

Exercise 11c

Copy and complete the following table and then construct two similar tables for the powers of 5 and 10:

Powers of 3

3^5	$=$	$3 \times 3 \times 3 \times 3 \times 3$	$=$	243
3^4	$=$		$=$	
3^3	$=$		$=$	
3^2	$=$		$=$	
3^1	$=$		$=$	
3^0	$=$		$=$	
3^{-1}	$=$	$\dfrac{1}{3^1}$	$=$	$\dfrac{1}{3}$
3^{-2}	$=$	$\dfrac{1}{3^2} = \dfrac{1}{3 \times 3}$	$=$	$\dfrac{1}{9}$
3^{-3}	$=$		$=$	
3^{-4}	$=$		$=$	

Observe what happens as you move down the table step by step. On the left hand side the powers are decreasing by 1 at each level. On the right each step down corresponds to dividing by 3 (in the case of the first table) or 5 (in the case of the second table) and 10 in the case of the third. Using this pattern you can arrive at the meaning for negative indices.

In general, if x and a are numbers, then

$$x^{-a} = \frac{1}{x^a}$$

Express in index notation, $\dfrac{1}{2 \times 2 \times 2}$

$$\frac{1}{2 \times 2 \times 2} = \frac{1}{2^3} = 2^{-3}$$

Exercise 11d Express in index notation:

1. $\dfrac{1}{2 \times 2 \times 2 \times 2}$

2. $\dfrac{1}{3 \times 3}$

3. $\dfrac{1}{5 \times 5 \times 5}$

4. $\dfrac{1}{8 \times 8 \times 8 \times 8}$

5. $\dfrac{1}{4}$

6. $\dfrac{1}{9 \times 9 \times 9 \times 9 \times 9}$

7. $\dfrac{1}{x \times x}$

8. $\dfrac{1}{y \times y \times y}$

9. $\dfrac{1}{a \times a \times a \times a}$

10. $\dfrac{1}{p}$

11. $\dfrac{1}{p \times p \times q \times q}$

12. $\dfrac{1}{a \times a \times b}$

13. $\dfrac{1}{c \times c \times c \times d}$

14. $\dfrac{1}{m \times n \times n \times n}$

15. $\dfrac{2}{x \times x \times x \times y}$

16. $\dfrac{a}{b \times b}$

17. $\dfrac{c \times c}{b \times b}$

18. $\dfrac{x \times x \times x \times x}{y \times y \times y \times z}$

Simplify, $\dfrac{x^2 y^3}{xy^2}$

$$\frac{x^2 y^3}{xy^2} = \frac{x \times \cancel{x} \times y \times y \times y}{\cancel{x} \times y \times y} = \frac{xy}{1} = xy$$

or, by the laws of indices,

$$\frac{x^2 y^3}{xy^2} = x^{2-1}y^{3-2} = x^1 y^1$$

Exercise 11e Simplify:

1. $\dfrac{ab}{a}$

2. $\dfrac{abc}{bc}$

3. $\dfrac{a}{ab}$

4. $\dfrac{a^2}{a}$

5. $\dfrac{a}{a^2}$

6. $\dfrac{x^3}{x}$

7. $\dfrac{x^2}{x^2}$

8. $\dfrac{y^3}{y^2}$

9. $\dfrac{ab}{b^2}$

10. $\dfrac{a^2 b^2}{ab}$

11. $\dfrac{c^2 d}{cd^2}$

12. $\dfrac{a^2 bc^2}{abc}$

13. $\dfrac{mn^3}{n^4 m}$

14. $\dfrac{xy}{x^2 y^3}$

15. $\dfrac{6a^2 b}{3ab}$

16. $\dfrac{12x^3}{8x^2}$

17. $\dfrac{10ab}{15a^3 b}$

18. $\dfrac{24y^5}{16y^6}$

19. $\dfrac{3a^2 b^2 c}{6bc^2}$

20. $\dfrac{4x^2 y^2 z^2}{12x^2 y}$

85

Areas and Volumes

The powers of 2 and 3, that is square and cube, are used for the units measuring areas and volumes.

Common metric units for area are the square millimetre, mm^2, the square centimetre, cm^2, the square metre, m^2, and the square kilometre, km^2. The area of a shape is given by the number of cm^2, etc., which can fit into that shape. Since a cm^2 is square it is easiest if the shapes whose areas are to be found are rectangular. The area of a rectangle is found by multiplying the length of the base by the height.

$$\textbf{Area = base} \times \textbf{height}$$

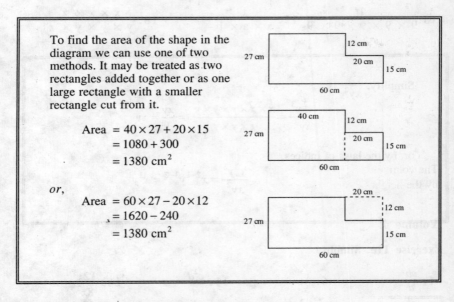

To find the area of the shape in the diagram we can use one of two methods. It may be treated as two rectangles added together or as one large rectangle with a smaller rectangle cut from it.

$$\begin{aligned} \text{Area} &= 40 \times 27 + 20 \times 15 \\ &= 1080 + 300 \\ &= 1380 \text{ cm}^2 \end{aligned}$$

or,

$$\begin{aligned} \text{Area} &= 60 \times 27 - 20 \times 12 \\ &= 1620 - 240 \\ &= 1380 \text{ cm}^2 \end{aligned}$$

Exercise 11f Find the areas of the following shapes:

1. A square with edge length 13 cm.

2. A rectangle with base 8 cm and height 32 cm.

3. The surface of a swimming pool with length 25 m and width 15 m.

4. A postage stamp measuring 24 mm by 21 mm.

5. A rectangular field 54 m by 34 m.

6.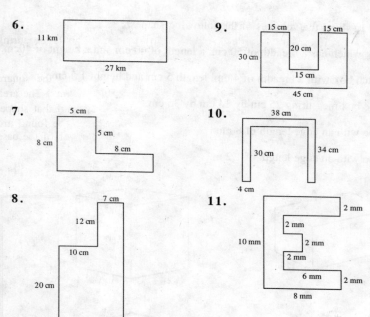

7.

8.

9.

10.

11.

The volume of a cube or cuboid is found by multiplying the length by the breadth by the height. The units are cubic millimetres, mm^3, cubic centimetres, cm^3,etc.

Volume of cuboid = length × breadth × height

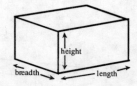

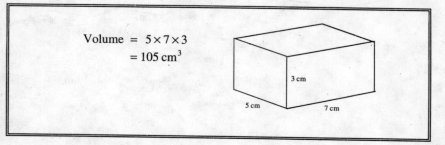

$$\text{Volume} = 5 \times 7 \times 3$$
$$= 105 \, cm^3$$

Exercise 11g Find the volumes of the following shapes:

1. A tank which has a breadth of 50 cm, a length of 60 cm and a height of 40cm.

2. A match box with a breadth of 4 cm, length 5 cm and height 1.5 cm.

3. A shoe box measuring 25 cm by 14 cm by 36 cm.

4. A cube with an edge length of 8 mm.

5. A cube with an edge length of 1.2 m.

6.
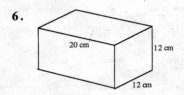

9.
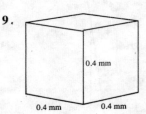

7.
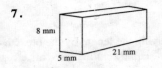

10.
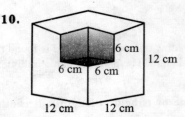

8.
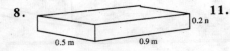

11.
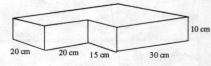

Chapter 12 Further division

Straight division is the general method for all. It can be applied to divisors and dividends of any size.

Two-digit divisors with whole number remainders

When the divisor is written down all its digits, except for the first are hoisted into the flag position. The dividing is then only done by the first digit. With two-digit divisors there will be one flag digit and with three digit divisors there will be two flag digits, and so on. Although the sutra is *Vertically and crosswise*, this does not become apparent until there are at least three digits in the divisor. For the present we will only be dealing with two-digit divisors.

The following example illustrates the method.

---

337 ÷ 24

The sum is set out as shown with the 4 of 24 placed *On top of the flag*. The number of flag-digits indicates the number of digits is the same as the number of remainder digits.

$$\begin{array}{c c} & 4 \\ 2 & \overline{\left| 3 \;\; 3 \;/\; 7 \right.} \end{array}$$

All the dividing is done by the 2 of 24. 2 into 3 is 1 remainder 1. The second dividend number is now 13.

$$\begin{array}{c c} & 4 \\ 2 & \left| \begin{array}{c c c} .3 & 3 \;/\; 7 \\ & 1 \end{array} \right. \\ & \overline{\;1\;} \end{array}$$

From 13 subtract the first quotient digit, 1, multiplied by the flag digit, 4, and divide the answer by 2. This is $13 - (1 \times 4) = 9$, and 2 into $9 = 4$ rem. 1.

$$\begin{array}{c c} & 4 \\ 2 & \left| \begin{array}{c c c} 3 & 3 \;/\; 7 \\ & 1 & 1 \end{array} \right. \\ & \overline{1 \;\; 4 \;/} \end{array}$$

In the remainder portion we do not divide but merely subtract the product of the previous quotient digit and the flag digit. This is $17 - (4 \times 4) = 1$. The answer is then 14 remainder 1.

$$\begin{array}{c c} & 4 \\ 2 & \left| \begin{array}{c c c} 3 & 3 \;/\; 7 \\ & 1 & 1 \end{array} \right. \\ & \overline{1 \;\; 4 \;/\; 1} \end{array}$$

For four or more digits in the dividend the same process is involved. The next example shows this.

$9137 \div 43$

4 into 9 = 2 remainder 1
$11 - 2 \times 3 = 5$, 4 into 5 = 1 remainder 1.
$13 - 1 \times 3 = 10$, 4 into 10 = 2 remainder 2.

```
        3
   4 | 9 1 3 / 7
       1 1 ·
       2 1
```

Once we have reached the remainder portion the
division is finished but the remainder is adjusted as
before, that is, $27 - 2 \times 3 = 21$.

```
        3
   4 | 9 1 3 / 7
       1 1  2
       2 1 2 /21
```

The answer is then 212 remainder 21.

Exercise 12a

1. 32 | 672

2. 41 | 891

3. 21 | 536

4. 63 | 712

5. 72 | 899

6. 81 | 465

7. 22 | 533

8. 34 | 816

9. 92 | 423

10. 83 | 534

11. 43 | 731

12. 51 | 846

13. 13 | 392

14. 74 | 557

15. 62 | 587

16. 54 | 817

17. 24 | 5353

18. 35 | 4585

19. 64 | 7332

20. 71 | 9102

21. 81 | 8819

22. 44 | 6718

23. 53 | 9028

24. 71 | 4354

25. 92 | 1874

26. 75 | 3276

27. 36 | 8696

28. 61 | 4564

29. 64 | 6576

30. 43 | 2188

31. 56 | 9534

32. 33 | 7343

Exercise 12b   Problems

1. Divide 570 by 21.

2. Find the remainder when 2584 is divided by 32.

3. How many 23p rolls can be bought for £5.52? (Calculate in pence.)

4. How many 32 cm pieces of wood can be cut from a piece 5.5 m long and how long will the remaining piece be?

5. A pool can be emitted at a rate of 52 gallons per minute. How long does it take to empty if it has 13,000 gallons of water?

6. A group of 34 soldiers have 1462 rounds of ammunition to share between them. If they are shared equally, how many rounds does each receive?

7. A nature reserve, 27360 acres in area, is thought to have 24 acres for each eland. How many eland live on the reserve?

8. How many times does 49 go into 5439?

9. Divide 77138 by 24

10. A librarian can fit 43 journals of a particular type on a single shelf. How many shelves are needed for 2265?

11. A lady wishes to buy a washing machine for £744 and opts to pay in regular instalments for 24 months. How much does she have to pay each month?

12. A wine manufacturer reckons to produce a bottle of wine every 21 seconds. To the nearest 10, how many bottles can be produced in 8 hours?

13. A piece of embroidery has 1352 stitches with 52 stitches in each row. How many rows are there?

14. How many notepads can be bought for £5.28 if they each cost 44p?

15. A farming company in Brazil can uproot a tree in the rain forest every 32 seconds. How many trees can it uproot in a day of 24 hours?

16. 74 food mixers were sold in a shop in one year. The total takings were £8510. Find the cost of one food mixer.

17. The area of a field is 3822 m^2. If its length is 91 m, find its width.

18. At a garage £6710 was received in three months from the sale of a particular car tyre. If each tyre sold for £55, find the number sold.

19. How many pens at 86p could be bought for £100? (Calculate in pence)

20. The price of a ticket at a concert was £22. The takings for a week were £97,504. How many tickets were sold?

Altered Remainders

To the question "how many two's are there in nine?" the answer comes as 4 remainder 1. But this is not the only answer. You could also say that 2 into 9 goes 3 remainder 3 or 2 remainder 5. The chart below shows various possibilities.

$$
\begin{aligned}
2 \text{ into } 9 &= 4 \text{ r } 1 \\
&= 3 \text{ r } 3 \\
&= 2 \text{ r } 5 \\
&= 1 \text{ r } 7 \\
&= 0 \text{ r } 9
\end{aligned}
$$

In fact , we can take this further in both directions by using vinculum numbers.

$$
\begin{aligned}
2 \text{ into } 9 &= 7 \text{ r } \bar{5} \\
&= 6 \text{ r } \bar{3} \\
&= 5 \text{ r } \bar{1} \\
&= 4 \text{ r } 1 \\
&= 3 \text{ r } 3
\end{aligned}
\qquad
\begin{aligned}
\text{Also } 2 \text{ into } 9 &= 2 \text{ r } 5 \\
&= 1 \text{ r } 7 \\
&= 0 \text{ r } 9 \\
&= \bar{1} \text{ r } 11 \\
&= \bar{2} \text{ r } 13, \text{ etc.}
\end{aligned}
$$

By extending this chart both upwards and downwards we can see that there is no limit to the number of possible answers. There are an infinite number of answers all of which are valid. The answer we usually give is the conventional one and is useful for most purposes but there are occasions when an altered remainder is required for Straight division.

Give the answer together with the next three altered remainders for $31 \div 3$

$$
\begin{aligned}
3)\underline{31} &= 10 \text{ r } 1 \\
&= 9 \text{ r } 4 \\
&= 8 \text{ r } 7 \\
&= 7 \text{ r } 10
\end{aligned}
$$

3 into 31 = 10 remainder 1

By repeatedly subtracting 1 from the quotient, 10, we find the next quotients, 9, 8 and 7.
With each subtraction of 1 we add the divisor 3 to the remainder, that is,
$1 + 3 = 4$, $4 + 3 = 7$ and $7 + 3 = 10$.

Exercise 12c Give the answer together with the next three altered remainders.

1. 4)17	**4.** 5)24	**7.** 3)19	**10.** 3)62	**13.** 5)49
2. 3)16	**5.** 4)25	**8.** 7)32	**11.** 4)53	**14.** 9)67
3. 2)21	**6.** 6)31	**9.** 8)29	**12.** 1)5	**15.** 8)39

Straight division with altered remainders

To master straight division there must be practice involving altered remainders. The key is to look ahead at each stage to see whether or not the remainder needs to be altered.

7818 ÷ 22

Before each answer digit is written down with its remainder, the next step of subtraction must be checked. If the subtraction leads to a minus number then an altered remainder is required at the previous step.

$$\begin{array}{r} 2 \\ 2\,\overline{\smash{)}\,7\ 8\ 1\,/\,8} \\ 1\ 2 \\ \hline 3\ 5 \end{array}$$

2 into 7 = 3 r 1, check 18 − 6, Yes! 18 − 6 = 12
2 into 12 = 6 r 0, check 1 − 12, No!
2 into 12 = 5 r 2, check 21 − 10, Yes! 21 − 10 = 11

$$\begin{array}{r} 2 \\ 2\,\overline{\smash{)}\,7\ 8\ 1\,/\,8} \\ 1\ 2\ \ 1 \\ \hline 3\ 5\ 5\,/\,8 \end{array}$$

2 into 11 = 5 r 1, check 18 − 10, Yes! 18 − 10 = 8
The answer is 355 remainder 8

Exercise 12d

1. 23 | 435
2. 34 | 627
3. 67 | 728
4. 37 | 921
5. 26 | 677
6. 88 | 435
7. 48 | 831
8. 36 | 945

9. 26 | 546
10. 13 | 243
11. 14 | 332
12. 15 | 715
13. 16 | 312
14. 18 | 261
15. 28 | 444
16. 86 | 344

17. 26 | 4209
18. 77 | 3243
19. 38 | 9067
20. 46 | 5405
21. 39 | 212
22. 35 | 8777
23. 86 | 2313
24. 27 | 5463

25. 48 | 8641
26. 94 | 8454
27. 37 | 4230
28. 66 | 2433
29. 54 | 7688
30. 38 | 6290
31. 78 | 3244
32. 17 | 10000

Exercise .12e Problems

1. How many pencils at 23p each can be bought for £7.00?

2. Divide 37 into 1000

3. How many pieces of ribbon each 46 cm long can be cut from a 5 m length?

4. How many days are there in 2000 hours?

5. David shares his 860 football cards equally amongst his 26 class-mates. How many does each receive and how many are left over?

6. Mrs Credit buys a set of book-cases for £672. If she repays at £28 per month, how many months will it take to pay off the debt?

7. A rectangular field has an area of 3450 m^2. If its width is 46 m, find its length.

8. A decorator charges £2760 for a certain job which takes him 23 days. How much does he earn per day?

9. In catering for a party Sarah has £20 to spend on bread. If each loaf costs 78p, how many can she buy?

10. In a factory a worker can pack a box in 14 minutes. At this rate, how many boxes can be packed in 7 hours?

11. A land-owner collects £1058 a week from the 23 cottages on his estate. How much is the rent on each cottage if they are all the same?

12. How many pieces of wood, each 27 cm long, can be cut from a length of

   5 m and how long is the remainder?

13. A director of a company earns £45,000 a year. How much is this per month?

14. A 250,000 ton oil-tanker has 36 oil-tanks. To the nearest whole number many tons does each tank hold?

Chapter 13 Factors and multiples

Summary of definitions

These definitions should be learnt by heart:

DEFINITION	EXAMPLES
1. When two numbers are multiplied together the answer is called the product.	The product of 4 and 6 is 24.
2. Numbers that are multiplied together to give a product are called factors of that product.	3 and 5 are factors of 15.
3. One is a factor of every number.	$1 \times 17 = 17$
4. Any product is a multiple of any one of its factors.	20 is a multiple of 5 since $5 \times 4 = 20$.
5. The highest common factor of two or more numbers is the highest number that can divide those numbers exactly.	Of 12 and 16, 4 is the HCF.
6. Prime numbers are only divisible by one and themselves.	17 is prime because its only factors are 1 and 17.
7. Numbers that are not prime are called composite.	22 is composite because 2 and 11 are factors as well as 1 and 22.
8. Every composite number may be expressed as the product of factors which are primes.	$36 = 2 \times 2 \times 3 \times 3$
9. The lowest common multiple of two or more numbers is the lowest number into which those numbers can divide.	The LCM of 8 and 12 is 24.
10. Two numbers are coprime when their highest common factor is one.	6 and 35 are coprime.
11. Since 1 is a factor of all numbers, every number is related to every other number through 1.	

Divisibility

When one number has another number as one of its factors then it is said to be divisible by that factor. For example, 18 has 6 as one of its factors and so is divisible by 6. This implies that on dividing that number by its factor there is no remainder. For example, 34 is divisible by 2 because 34 ÷ 2 = 17 remainder 0; but 34 is not divisible by 3 because 34 ÷ 3 = 11 remainder 1.

Divisibility rules

Here is a summary of the divisibility rules for 1, 2, 3, 4, 5, 8, 9 and 10:

All numbers are divisible by 1 because 1 is a factor of all. This means that one is contained within every number just as the unity of the Absolute, or God, is present in every aspect of the universe.

2: ends with an even number.
3: when the digital root is divisible by three.
4: when the ultimate and twice the penultimate are divisible by four, or when the number comprising the final two digits are divisible by four.
5: when it ends with nought or five.
8: when the ultimate, twice the penultimate and four times the pen-penultimate is divisible by eight, or when the number comprising the final three digits is divisible by eight.
9: when the digital root (the sum of the digits) is nine.
10: when it ends with a nought.

You can extend these divisibility rules for composite numbers. To obtain a divisibility rule for any composite number, such as 6, 12, 15 and 18, we use combinations of the rules for their factors. For example, 6 = 2 × 3 and so a number which can be divided exactly by 6 must be divisible by 3 and also 2. The various rules for some of the composite numbers are given below.

6: when it is divisible by both 2 and 3.
12: when it is divisible by both 3 and 4.
15: when it is divisible by both 3 and 5.
18: when it is divisible by both 2 and 9.
20: when it ends in nought and the previous digit is even.
24: when it is divisible by both 3 and 8.
30: when it is divisible by both 3 and 10.

For a number to be divisible by one of these composite numbers it must pass the test for both the factors. So when testing a number for its divisibility for say, 24, it must pass the test for 3 and the test for 8.

Test for 11

A number is divisible by 11 if the sum of the digits in the odd places and the sum of the digits in the even places are equal or differ by a multiple of 11.

Is 5234878 divisible by 11?

By the above rule,
5 + 3 + 8 + 8 = 24,
2 + 4 + 7 = 13,
24 − 13 = 11 ∴ yes!

24 − 13 = 11 Yes!

Exercise 13a Which of the following numbers are divisible by the first number:-

1. 2; 235, 456, 850, 333, 48621
2. 3; 721, 531, 6352, 777, 13482
3. 4; 344, 674, 1190, 788, 464
4. 5; 329, 4500, 101, 210, 677
5. 8; 324, 5789, 8264, 5200
6. 9; 2184, 257, 7353, 361368
7. 10; 21, 437, 34000, 564050

8. 6; 34, 612, 426, 572, 12123
9. 12; 5647, 824, 7188, 924
10. 15; 435, 765, 125, 560, 675
11. 18; 2184, 361, 522, 6804
12. 20; 43, 890, 460, 1025
13. 24; 3462, 13152, 1032
14. 30; 450, 890, 3700

15. 11 1331, 45632, 48202, 68435, 4669874, 82345211, 845574323

Prime Factors

When a number is given as a product of numbers which are all prime then it is said to be expressed in terms of prime factors.

For example, $12 = 2 \times 2 \times 3$ is in prime factors because 2, 2 and 3 are all prime. On the other hand, $12 = 6 \times 2$ is not in prime factors because 6 is not prime.

The shorter way of writing $2 \times 2 \times 3$ is $2^2 \times 3$ and this is 12 expressed as prime factors in **index form**.

Index notation is the abbreviation for the product of one number by itself. For example, $2 \times 2 \times 2 = 2^3$, "2 to the power of 3" or "2 cubed"; $2 \times 2 \times 2 \times 2 = 2^4$, "2 to the power of 4". This is dealt with in more detail in the chapter on Indices.

Express a) 24, b) 252 in terms of its prime factors in index form.

Begin with the lowest prime greater than 1 which can divide into 24, that is 2.
2 into 24 = 12.
2 will also divide 12 to leave 6.
2 into 6 = 3.
$24 = 2 \times 2 \times 2 \times 3 = 2^3 \times 3$

$$\begin{array}{r|l} 2 & 24 \\ 2 & 12 \\ 2 & 6 \\ & 3 \end{array} = 2^3 \times 3.$$

2 into 252 = 126, 2 into 126 = 63.
63 is not divisible by 2 and so we turn to the next largest prime, that is 3. Is 63 divisible by 3? Yes!
3 into 63 = 21, 3 into 21 = 7. 7 is a prime and so the division is complete.
$252 = 2^2 \times 3^2 \times 7$

$$\begin{array}{r|l} 2 & 252 \\ 2 & 126 \\ 3 & 63 \\ 3 & 21 \\ & 7 \end{array} = 2^2 \times 3^2 \times 7$$

Exercise 13b Express the following as prime factors in index form:

1. 6	**9.** 49	**17.** 42	**25.** 72	**33.** 102	**41.** 525
2. 9	**10.** 8	**18.** 45	**26.** 80	**34.** 105	**42.** 594
3. 10	**11.** 12	**19.** 16	**27.** 81	**35.** 210	**43.** 612
4. 14	**12.** 18	**20.** 24	**28.** 96	**36.** 231	**44.** 693
5. 21	**13.** 20	**21.** 48	**29.** 102	**37.** 252	**45.** 715
6. 33	**14.** 27	**22.** 56	**30.** 75	**38.** 168	**46.** 840
7. 35	**15.** 28	**23.** 60	**31.** 78	**39.** 315	**47.** 854
8. 38	**16.** 30	**24.** 64	**32.** 98	**40.** 429	**48.** 1089

Harder examples:

49. 1331	**53.** 3675	**57.** 5250	**61.** 28413	**65.** 405769
50. 1430	**54.** 4536	**58.** 7623	**62.** 48510	**66.** 750684
51. 1456	**55.** 4620	**59.** 11025	**63.** 51425	**67.** 750750
52. 3465	**56.** 4851	**60.** 14157	**64.** 89712	**68.** 561924000

Highest common factor

The highest common factor of two or more numbers is the highest number which can divide those numbers exactly.

For example, the highest common factor of 10 and 15 is 5. The factors of 10 are 1, 2, 5 and 10; the factors of 15 are 1, 3, 5 and 15. Of factors which are common to both 10 and 15, 5 is the highest and so it is called the highest common factor.

Where the HCF of two numbers is 1 those numbers are called coprime.

Exercise 13c Find the HCF, by *Mere inspection*. If the HCF of two numbers is 1 write *Coprime* as the answer.

1. 10, 15	**6.** 27, 45, 63	**11.** 14, 35, 56	**16.** 50, 150, 200
2. 12, 30	**7.** 6, 18	**12.** 7, 14, 20	**17.** 6, 54, 21
3. 12, 30, 40	**8.** 10, 21	**13.** 11, 23	**18.** 36, 18, 72
4. 6, 10, 14	**9.** 40, 60, 80	**14.** 16, 24, 36	**19.** 19, 3
5. 21, 35	**10.** 4, 9	**15.** 45, 30, 15	**20.** 75, 100, 150

Using prime factors to find the HCF

By expressing the numbers in terms of prime factors the HCF may be found by taking all those factors which are common to both.

Find the HCF of 420 and 36.

$$
\begin{array}{ll}
2\underline{|420} \quad = 2^2 \times 3 \times 5 \times 7 & 2\underline{|36} \quad = 2^2 \times 3^2 \\
2\underline{|210} & 2\underline{|18} \\
3\underline{|105} & 3\underline{|9} \\
5\underline{|35} & 3 \\
7 &
\end{array}
$$

Common factors are $2 \times 2 \times 3 = 12$
Therefore 12 is the HCF.

Exercise 13d Find the HCF by prime factors.

1. 20, 30	**6.** 27, 45, 63	**11.** 245, 385	**16.** 546, 882, 924
2. 24, 32	**7.** 12, 30, 40	**12.** 756, 2205	**17.** 440, 715, 935
3. 25, 45	**8.** 14, 35, 56	**13.** 24, 42, 78	**18.** 784, 1232, 1904
4. 24, 60	**9.** 60, 126	**14.** 65, 78, 104	**19.** 189, 882, 1071
5. 27, 72	**10.** 168, 189	**15.** 108, 162, 270	**20.** 756, 1764, 2268

Finding the HCF by *Elimination and retention*

This is similar to using prime factors but uses any factors common to the numbers.

Find the HCF of 168 and 432.

Having spotted that 168 and 432 are divisible by 2, *elimination* leaves 84 and 216. Both of these are divisible by 4, leaving 21 and 54. On dividing by 3, we are left with 7 and 18. This last pair of numbers are coprime and so the HCF is $2 \times 4 \times 3 = 24$.

$$
\begin{array}{r|rr}
2 & 168 & 432 \\
4 & 84 & 216 \\
3 & 21 & 54 \\
  & 7 & 18 \\
\end{array}
\quad \text{HCF} = 24
$$

This method is faster than the one using prime factors because any common factors are used. The dividing through by factors continues until the remaining numbers are coprime.

Exercise 13e Find the HCF by *Elimination and retention.*

1. 24, 36	**9.** 84, 124	**17.** 84, 132	**25.** 630, 360
2. 48, 56	**10.** 96, 36	**18.** 112, 84	**26.** 868, 372
3. 32, 48	**11.** 117, 81	**19.** 98, 105	**27.** 288, 768
4. 45, 75	**12.** 126, 90	**20.** 112, 176	**28.** 360, 504
5. 36, 54	**13.** 72, 100	**21.** 72, 120	**29.** 704, 320
6. 60, 90	**14.** 150, 225	**22.** 96, 160	**30.** 336, 576
7. 64, 124	**15.** 88, 1000	**23.** 37, 43	**31.** 1428, 2856
8. 72, 28	**16.** 90, 162	**24.** 175, 245	**32.** 272, 1156

Finding the LCM by *Vertically and crosswise*

Finding the lowest common multiple of two numbers is almost the same as finding the highest common factor but includes the two primes factors in the product. The following examples illustrate the method.

Find the LCM of 12 and 30.

Extract common factors until the two numbers remaining are coprime. Since 6 is a factor of both 12 and 30, we divide 6 into 12 and 30, leaving 2 and 5. These are coprime. The LCM is found by cross-multiplying 12×5 or $30 \times 2 = 60$.

$$6 | 12 \quad 30$$
$$| \ 2 \quad 5$$

$$LCM = 30 \times 2$$
$$= 60$$

Find the LCM of 96 and 72.

In this case 8 is a common factor and, upon dividing 96 and 72, leaves 12 and 9. These can further be divided by 3, leaving 4 and 3 which are coprime. The LCM is then the corss-product, .96×3 or $72 \times 4 = 288$.

$$8 | 96 \quad 72$$
$$3 | 12 \quad 9$$
$$| \ 4 \quad 3$$

$$LCM = 72 \times 4$$
$$= 288$$

It should also be noted that the LCM can be found by multiplying all the common factors and all the individual factors together. In the last example, the LCM $= 8 \times 3 \times 4 \times 3 = 288$.

When dividing a pair of numbers by their common factors continually we end up with two numbers which cannot be divided any further. These last two numbers are particular and individual to the original two numbers. Again, in the last example, 4 is particular to 94 and 3 is particular to 72.

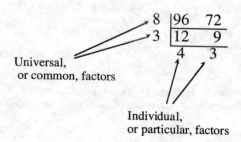

Universal,
or common, factors

Individual,
or particular, factors

This is an application of the sutra which simply states, *Individual and universal.*

The highest common factor is the found by multiplying the universal, or common, factors whilst the lowest common multiple is found by multiplying all the universal factors and the individual factors together. This is summarised in the following two formulae.

Highest common factor = The product of universal factors

Lowest common multiple = The product of universal factors × The product of Individual factors

In algebraic terms, if *abc* and *bcd* are two numbers, then the HCF is $b \times c = bc$ and the LCM is $b \times c \times a \times d = abcd$.

Exercise 13f Find the LCM by the method described above.

1. 8, 12	**9.** 32, 24	**17.** 72, 84	**25.** 72, 162
2. 14, 21	**10.** 24, 40	**18.** 12, 22	**26.** 91, 280
3. 12, 15	**11.** 35, 42	**19.** 55, 40	**27.** 180, 125
4. 18, 12	**12.** 36, 48	**20.** 39, 63	**28.** 75, 165
5. 10, 12	**13.** 54, 72	**21.** 35, 105	**29.** 72, 225
6. 11, 13	**14.** 30, 75	**22.** 112, 60	**30.** 67, 29
7. 15, 20	**15.** 49, 70	**23.** 210, 750	**31.** 303, 309
8. 24, 30	**16.** 105, 84	**24.** 68, 92	**32.** 528, 888

Exercise 13g

1. Find the largest number which is a factor of 504 and 792.

2. Find the smallest number which is a multiple of 63 and 105.

3. What is the least sum of money which is a multiple of both 25p and 35p?

4. What is the least length of rope which can be cut into pieces which are 1 ft 6 in long and into pieces which are 1 ft 3 in long?

5. Either by walking with strides of 96 cm or with strides of 90 cm, I take an exact number of steps to cross a road. What is the least possible width of the road?

6. Three chimes on a clock strike at intervals of 0.4, 0.6 and 0.9 seconds respectively. If they start together, how long will it be before they strike together again?

7. Alice, Amy and Anna run up a flight of stairs, all starting from the bottom. Alice takes two steps at a time, Amy runs three and Anna takes five. After how many stairs will they all land on the same one?

8. Find a pair of numbers between 100 and 130 which have 14 as their HCF.

9. A hearth measuring 5 ft 3 in by 11 ft 3 in is to be covered with square tiles. What is the largest size of tile, if only whole tiles are to be used, and find the number of tiles required.

10. A rectangular block, measuring 6 cm by 12 cm by 15 cm is to be cut up into cubes. Find the smallest possible number of cubes.

Investigation into primes

Exercise 13h Copy the following table and extend it up to twenty rows.

Number, n	$6 \times n$	$6n + 1$	Prime?	$6n - 1$	Prime?
1	6	7	√	5	√
2	12	13	√	11	√
3	18	19	√	17	√

Now copy and complete the following table up to 121. Using the $6n + 1$ or $6n - 1$ lists in the previous table, draw a circle around all the prime numbers in this table.

1	2	3	4	5	6
7	8	9	10	11	12
13	14	15	16	17	18
19	20				

Answer the following questions:

1. Write down all the numbers in the $6n + 1$ and $6n - 1$ lists which are not prime.

2. Are there any prime numbers in any other columns?

3. Why could there not be a prime number in the 2nd, 4th or 6th columns?

4. Why are there no primes in the third column?

Chapter 14 Triangles

Construction 4 To copy a line

Let AB be a given line. It is required to make a line
which has the same length as AB.

Draw a long line, mark a point close to one end
and label it P. With centre A open the
compasses to a measure equal to AB.
With centre P draw an arc cutting the line at Q. PQ is equal in length to AB.

Construction 5 To copy an angle

Let ∠BAC be the given
angle. The aim is to draw
an angle at P equal to
∠BAC.

Let PQ be a straight line.

With centre A and any
suitable radius draw an
arc cutting AB in D and
AC in E. With the same
radius and centre P,
draw an arc.

With centre D adjust the
compasses to the
measure of DE.
Transpose the compass
point to R and draw an
arc cutting the first arc
at S. RS has the same
measure as DE.

Draw the line PS and
produce to T. ∠QPT is
equal to ∠BAC.

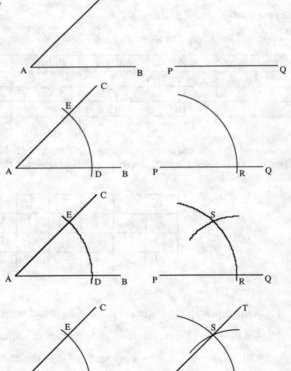

Construction of triangles

Construction 6 To draw a triangle given the lengths of three sides.

Let a, b and c be the three given lengths.
It is required to draw a triangle with sides equal to a, b and c.

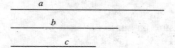

Draw a line, mark and label a point P
close to one end. With compasses set at
a, mark off one side of the triangle as
PQ. Set the compasses to a measure b
and with centre P make an arc. Set the
compasses to measure c and with centre
Q make an arc cutting the first arc at R.
Join QR and PR. The required triangle
is $\triangle$PQR.

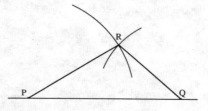

When the sides of the triangle are given lengths in centimetres then the measures
for the compasses can be taken from a ruler.

Construction 7 To draw a triangle given two sides and the included angle.
Let m and n be the given sides and let a be the included angle.

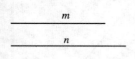

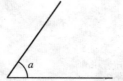

Draw a line AQ and, using Construction 5,
copy the angle a at the point A. Let AP be
the other line of the angle. With centre A
and radius m mark off an arc on AQ and
label the point as B. Similarly, with centre
A and radius n mark off the line AC equal
to n.. Join C to B.

ABC is the required triangle.

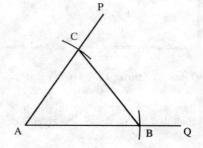

Construction 8 To draw a triangle given two sides and the included angle with a protractor.

Draw △ABC in which AB = 7.5 cm, AC = 6.2 cm and ∠BAC = 63°

Draw a line AB, 7.5 cm long. Use a protractor to measure an angle of 63° from AB at A. Draw a line at this angle. Measure off AC at 6.2 cm. Join C to B.

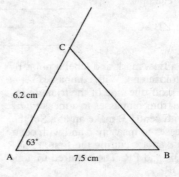

Construction 9 To draw a triangle given two angles and the included side.

Construct △ABC in which AB= 3.6 in, ∠A = 27° and ∠C = 51°

AB is drawn first at 3.6 in. Using a protractor, ∠A is measured at 27° and ∠C is measured at 51°. Lines are drawn at these angles. The point C lies at the intersection of the two lines.

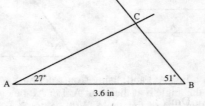

Construction 10 To construct a triangle given two angles and a side not included between them.

The easiest way to do this is to calculate the third angle which is the angle included between the two given sides. The problem then becomes the same as in Construction 8.

Draw △ABC in which ∠ABC = 35°, ∠BCA = 63° and AB = 7.2 cm.

Using the fact that angles in a
triangle add up to 180°, we can
calculate ∠BAC as

∠BAC = 180° − 63° − 35°
       = 180° − 98° = 82°.

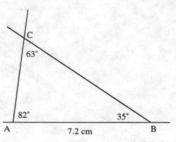

Draw the given side AB, and draw
a line from B at 35° to AB. Draw a
line from A at an angle of 82°
from AB. The two lines intersect at
C.

Construction 11 To draw a triangle given two sides and an angle not included
between them.

Construct △ABC with AB = 7.8 cm, AC = 4.6 cm and ∠ABC = 29°.

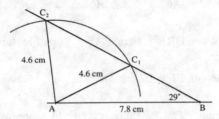

Draw a straight line and mark off from it AB = 7.8 cm.
Measure the ∠ABC at B and draw a line at 29° to AB.
With radius at 4.6 cm draw an arc centred at A. The arc cuts the
straight line at two points. Let these points be C_1 and C_2.
Both the triangles, ABC_1 and ABC_2, satisfy the requirements. Since
there are two possible triangles this is called the *ambiguous case*.

Construct △ABC with AB = 6 cm, BC = 8.8 cm and ∠BAC = 30°.

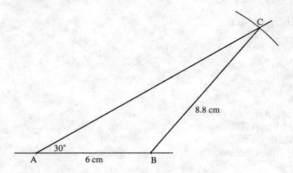

Proceeding as before, having drawn a line from A at 30° to AB, the arc with centre B cuts this line at C. In this case there is only one possible triangle.

Exercise 14a Construct the following triangles using the given information, and give the measurements required:

1. △ABC: AB = 9.6 cm, AC = 7.5 cm, BC = 5.2 cm, Measure (a) ∠A, (b) ∠B.

2. △PQR: PQ = 8.4 cm, QR = 6.4 cm, PR = 8.5 cm, Measure (a) ∠PQR, (b) ∠PRQ.

3. △DEF: DE = 8.6 cm, EF = 7.3 cm, DF = 6.5 cm, Measure (a) ∠EDF, (b) ∠DFE.

4. △ABC: AB = 9 cm, AC = 7.5 cm, ∠A = 54°, Measure (a) BC, (b) ∠B.

5. △PQR: PQ = 7.4 cm, QR = 7.2 cm, ∠Q = 96°, Measure (a) PR, (b) ∠R.

6. △XYZ: XY = 8.6 cm, XZ = 8.9 cm, ∠YXZ = 62°, Measure (a) YZ, (b) ∠XYZ.

7. △ABC: AB = 6.8 cm, ∠BAC = 42°, ∠ABC = 64°, Measure (a) AC, (b) BC.

8. △PQR: PQ = 3.5 cm, ∠PQR = 82°, ∠QPR = 48°, Measure (a) PR, (b) QR.

9. $\triangle$LMN: LM = 4.5 cm, $\angle$M= 32°, $\angle$L = 43°. Measure (a) LN, (b) MN.

10. $\triangle$ABC: AB = 3 in, $\angle$C = 46°, $\angle$A = 30°. Measure (a) AC, (b) BC.

11. $\triangle$XYZ: YZ = 6 cm, $\angle$X = 115°, $\angle$Y = 35°. Measure (a) XZ, (b) XY.

12. $\triangle$ABC: BC = 7 cm, AC = 5.7 cm, $\angle$B = 42°. Measure (a) AB (b) $\angle$C.

13. Draw a triangle ABC in which AB = 6.5 cm, BC = 7 cm and CA = 5.5 cm. Construct the perpendicular from A to BC, meeting BC at D. Measure AD.

14. Draw a triangle PQR in which PQ = 2.5 in, $\angle$P = 40°, and $\angle$Q = 64 °. Construct the perpendicular bisector of PQ, and the bisector of $\angle$R, and let these straight lines cut at S. Measure RS.

15. Draw a triangle DEF in which DE = DF = 6.5 cm and $\angle$D = 36°. Find by construction a point P in DF such that $\angle$PEF = $\angle$EDF, and measure EP.

16. Draw a triangle LMN in which LM = 6.5 cm, $\angle$L = 43°, $\angle$M = 59°. Construct, through N, a parallel to ML, and through L, a parallel to MN. Let these straight lines meet at P. Measure LP.

Definition 12 A **median** of a triangle is a line drawn from one vertex of the triangle to the mid-point of the opposite side.

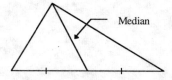

Median

Exercise 14b Further constructions

1. Draw a triangle DEF in which EF = 5.5 cm, $\angle$E = 58°, $\angle$F = 50°. Find, by construction, the mid-point of DE and label it T. Through T construct a line parallel to EF. Measure the lengths into which this parallel divides DF.

2. Construct an equilateral triangle with side 2 in.

3. Construct a right-angled isosceles triangle with the sides containing the right angle equal to 6 cm.

4. Without using a protractor construct angles of 30°, 120°, 45° and 15°.

5. Construct an isosceles triangle with a base of 5 cm and in which the perpendicular from the vertex is 6 cm.

6. Construct an isosceles triangle which has two equal sides of 3 in and the perpendicular from the vertex is 2 in. Measure the base.

7. Construct an isosceles triangle which has base angles equal to 50° and equal sides of 7 cm. Measure the base.

8. Construct ABC in which AB = 7 cm, AC = 6 cm and the median from B = 5.5 cm. Measure BC.

9. Draw a triangle XYZ in which AB = 6.7 cm, AC = 4.5 cm and $\angle$A = 76°. Construct the bisectors of the three angles of the triangle.

10. Repeat the previous question but, instead of the angle bisectors, construct the perpendiculars from the three vertices to the opposite sides.

11. PQR is a triangle, S is the mid-point of QR, and T is the point where the bisector of $\angle$PQR meets PR. Construct the triangle given that QT is 2.5 cm, ST = 3 cm, and $\angle$PQR = 110°. Measure PQ.

12. Two sides of a triangle, IJ and IK, are 4 in and 3 in, respectively, and $\angle$J = 30°. Construct two triangles which satisfy these conditions. Measure the side KJ of each one.

Chapter 15   Vulgar fractions: addition and subtraction

Naming terms

A **vulgar** or **common** fraction consists of two numbers separated by a horizontal line standing for division, such as $\frac{1}{2}$. The other type of fraction is the decimal fraction.

This name is used to indicate that the division of one number by the other has not taken place and is therefore *rough, common, unrefined* or *vulgar*. For example, $\frac{3}{5}$ indicates the division of 3 by 5 without actually performing the division. The line in the fraction is contained within the ÷ symbol and the numbers are indicated by the two dots.

The fraction $\frac{3}{5}$ is considered to be the fifth part of a unit taken three times. 5 is called the **denominator** because it denotes the number of parts into which the unit is divided. 3 is called the **numerator** because it numerates the number of fifth parts. Thus the number on top is called the numerator and the number underneath is called the denominator.

A fraction is in **lowest terms** when the highest common factor of the numerator and denominator is 1. In other words, a fraction is in lowest terms when the two numbers are coprime.

For example, $\frac{3}{5}$ is in lowest terms because the HCF of 3 and 5 is 1, whereas $\frac{6}{9}$ is not in lowest terms because the HCF of 6 and 9 is 3.

When the numerator is greater than the denominator the fraction is called **improper**. All improper fractions are greater than 1.

For example, $\frac{13}{4}$ is an improper fraction.

When an improper fraction is expressed as part whole number and part fraction then it is called a **mixed number**.

For example, $4\frac{2}{5}$ is a mixed number.

Equivalent fractions

Two fractions are **equivalent** if their numerators and denominators are in the same ratio. For example, $\frac{3}{5}$ is equivalent to $\frac{6}{10}$ because 3 : 5 as 6 : 10. It also follows that the two numerators are in the same ratio as the two denominators. In this example, 3 : 6 as 5 : 10. The following rule also follows:-

The value of a fraction is not altered by multiplying or dividing the numerator and denominator by the same number.

To express a fraction in its lowest terms divide both the numerator and denominator by their HCF. If the HCF is not known, continue dividing both the numbers until the numerator and denominator are coprime.

Express $\frac{45}{105}$ in its lowest terms.

We can see that 5 goes into both 45 and 105.
5 into 45 = 9 and 5 into 105 = 21.
9 and 21 are themselves divisible by 3 which leaves 3 and 7. Since 3 and 7 are coprime the answer is $\frac{3}{7}$.

$$\frac{\cancel{45}}{\cancel{105}} = \frac{3}{7}$$

Exercise 15a Bring to lowest terms:

1. $\frac{12}{18}$ 6. $\frac{36}{48}$ 11. $\frac{16}{72}$ 16. $\frac{24}{144}$ 21. $\frac{56}{132}$

2. $\frac{15}{45}$ 7. $\frac{24}{60}$ 12. $\frac{27}{63}$ 17. $\frac{35}{150}$ 22. $\frac{64}{128}$

3. $\frac{15}{20}$ 8. $\frac{25}{125}$ 13. $\frac{18}{72}$ 18. $\frac{90}{150}$ 23. $\frac{72}{120}$

4. $\frac{8}{64}$ 9. $\frac{28}{84}$ 14. $\frac{20}{56}$ 19. $\frac{32}{180}$ 24. $\frac{17}{51}$

5. $\frac{22}{30}$ 10. $\frac{64}{80}$ 15. $\frac{30}{55}$ 20. $\frac{250}{750}$ 25. $\frac{19}{61}$

Find the missing number in $\frac{5}{12} = \frac{15}{?}$

This can be done by the *Proportionately* sutra, 5 : 15 as 12 : 36.
This is equivalent to finding the multiplying factor, $5 \times 3 = 15$, therefore $12 \times 3 = 36$.

$$\frac{5}{12} = \frac{15}{36}$$

$$\frac{5}{12} \overset{\times 3}{\underset{\times 3}{=}} \frac{15}{36}$$

Exercise 15b Write down the missing number: (sutra – *Proportionately*)

1. $\frac{2}{3} = \frac{}{12}$ 7. $\frac{3}{8} = \frac{12}{}$ 13. $\frac{5}{6} = \frac{35}{}$ 19. $\frac{2}{9} = \frac{}{45}$

2. $\frac{3}{5} = \frac{6}{}$ 8. $\frac{4}{5} = \frac{}{25}$ 14. $\frac{2}{3} = \frac{}{33}$ 20. $\frac{6}{7} = \frac{24}{}$

3. $\frac{2}{5} = \frac{}{25}$ 9. $\frac{2}{7} = \frac{22}{}$ 15. $\frac{5}{9} = \frac{}{36}$ 21. $\frac{28}{} = \frac{56}{90}$

4. $\frac{5}{6} = \frac{10}{}$ 10. $\frac{7}{12} = \frac{}{60}$ 16. $\frac{3}{4} = \frac{}{72}$ 22. $\frac{}{45} = \frac{4}{9}$

5. $\frac{3}{4} = \frac{}{16}$ 11. $\frac{2}{3} = \frac{12}{}$ 17. $\frac{4}{5} = \frac{28}{}$ 23. $\frac{}{64} = \frac{3}{8}$

6. $\frac{2}{3} = \frac{}{24}$ 12. $\frac{3}{7} = \frac{}{35}$ 18. $\frac{7}{12} = \frac{56}{}$ 24. $\frac{24}{} = \frac{3}{8}$

Improper fractions and mixed numbers

Express $\frac{13}{5}$ as a mixed number.

Divide the denominator into the numerator, that is, 5 into 13 is 2 remainder 3.

$$\frac{13}{5} = 2\frac{3}{5}$$

Express $4\frac{3}{7}$ as an improper fraction.
Multiply the whole number by the denominator and add the numerator. That is, $4 \times 7 + 3 = 31$.

$$4\frac{3}{7} = \frac{31}{7}$$

Exercise 15c Change to mixed numbers or whole numbers:

1. $\frac{5}{4}$ 4. $\frac{9}{2}$ 7. $\frac{10}{7}$ 10. $\frac{29}{7}$ 13. $\frac{100}{3}$

2. $\frac{8}{3}$ 5. $\frac{13}{3}$ 8. $\frac{19}{6}$ 11. $\frac{45}{7}$ 14. $\frac{50}{6}$

3. $\frac{18}{5}$ 6. $\frac{20}{3}$ 9. $\frac{17}{4}$ 12. $\frac{38}{9}$ 15. $\frac{73}{5}$

Convert to improper fractions:

16. $2\frac{3}{4}$ 19. $6\frac{1}{5}$ 22. $5\frac{5}{12}$ 25. $2\frac{3}{19}$ 28. $3\frac{12}{23}$

17. $3\frac{1}{4}$ 20. $5\frac{3}{8}$ 23. $6\frac{7}{8}$ 26. $1\frac{37}{43}$ 29. $5\frac{7}{20}$

18. $4\frac{2}{5}$ 21. $7\frac{2}{3}$ 24. $4\frac{6}{17}$ 27. $6\frac{9}{11}$ 30. $8\frac{9}{25}$

Any improper fraction arising as an answer should be converted into mixed numbers. Fractions should also be reduced to lowest terms.

Addition and subtraction

Where the denominators of two fractions are the same they can be added or subtracted without any alteration. For example, $\frac{4}{15} + \frac{7}{15} = \frac{11}{15}$. But where the denominators are different then we apply the principles of LCM and HCF dealt with in Chapter 13.

There is a general method for adding or subtracting two fractions by *Elimination and retention* and *Vertically and crosswise* and there are special cases where the general method becomes simplified. We first take up the special cases since they are the easiest.

Where one denominator is a factor of the other then the fraction with that factor is *multiplied up* until the two denominators are the same. This is a case of understanding equivalent fractions and the sutra used is *Proportionately.*

$$\frac{2}{5} + \frac{4}{15}$$

$$= \frac{6}{15} + \frac{4}{15}$$

$$= \frac{10}{15} = \frac{2}{3}$$

By inspecting the denominators we can see that 5 is a factor of 15 and 5 into 15 goes 3 times. We therefore multiply top and bottom of $\frac{2}{5}$ by 3 to give $\frac{6}{15}$.

The two fractions can now be added to give $\frac{10}{15}$ which is then reduced to lowest terms as $\frac{2}{3}$ .With simple fractions this can all be done mentally.

Exercise 15d

1. $\frac{1}{5} + \frac{3}{10}$ **5.** $\frac{5}{6} - \frac{1}{3}$ **9.** $\frac{1}{4} + \frac{5}{16}$ **13.** $\frac{11}{15} - \frac{7}{30}$ **17.** $\frac{7}{9} - \frac{23}{36}$

2. $\frac{2}{3} + \frac{1}{9}$ **6.** $\frac{7}{8} - \frac{5}{24}$ **10.** $\frac{11}{20} + \frac{1}{4}$ **14.** $\frac{13}{16} + \frac{3}{4}$ **18.** $\frac{4}{5} - \frac{31}{40}$

3. $\frac{3}{4} - \frac{3}{8}$ **7.** $\frac{11}{16} + \frac{5}{32}$ **11.** $\frac{11}{12} - \frac{2}{3}$ **15.** $\frac{3}{15} - \frac{1}{45}$ **19.** $\frac{7}{8} - \frac{55}{64}$

4. $\frac{4}{15} + \frac{3}{5}$ **8.** $\frac{7}{8} - \frac{9}{16}$ **12.** $\frac{5}{12} + \frac{5}{24}$ **16.** $\frac{3}{7} + \frac{19}{35}$ **20.** $\frac{1}{12} + \frac{1}{84}$

Where the denominators are coprime then we use *Vertically and crosswise* to obtain the answer. All the working is done mentally.

$$\frac{2}{5} + \frac{3}{7}$$
$$= \frac{29}{35}$$

Are the denominators coprime? Yes!
The numerator is the sum of the cross-product, $2 \times 7 + 3 \times 5 = 14 + 15 = 29$
The denominator is $5 \times 7 = 35$

How does it work? With the example above, the lowest common denominator, that is the LCM of the denominators is 35. By the *Proportionately* sutra both fractions may be expressed as,

$$\frac{2}{5} + \frac{3}{7} = \frac{2 \times 7}{5 \times 7} + \frac{3 \times 5}{7 \times 5} = \frac{14}{35} + \frac{15}{35} = \frac{29}{35}$$

The numerator is then $2 \times 7 + 3 \times 5 = 29$ and the denominator is $5 \times 7 = 35$.

For subtraction a similar process is involved but instead of taking the sum of the cross-product for the numerator we take the difference of the cross-product *starting from the top left-hand number.*

$$\frac{5}{6} - \frac{2}{5}$$
$$= \frac{29}{35}$$

The numerator is the difference of the cross-product, $5 \times 5 - 2 \times 6 = 25 - 12 = 13$
The denominator is $6 \times 5 = 30$. Answer, $\frac{13}{30}$.

Exercise 15e

1. $\frac{1}{5} + \frac{3}{4}$ 6. $\frac{3}{4} - \frac{1}{3}$ 11. $\frac{5}{8} - \frac{5}{11}$ 16. $\frac{6}{11} - \frac{3}{7}$ 21. $\frac{7}{9} - \frac{3}{8}$

2. $\frac{2}{3} + \frac{1}{4}$ 7. $\frac{1}{2} - \frac{1}{3}$ 12. $\frac{4}{5} + \frac{1}{6}$ 17. $\frac{8}{9} + \frac{3}{8}$ 22. $\frac{4}{5} - \frac{2}{21}$

3. $\frac{1}{3} - \frac{1}{5}$ 8. $\frac{1}{16} + \frac{1}{5}$ 13. $\frac{2}{3} - \frac{5}{8}$ 18. $\frac{2}{3} - \frac{3}{10}$ 23. $\frac{5}{6} - \frac{12}{25}$

4. $\frac{1}{5} + \frac{1}{9}$ 9. $\frac{1}{3} + \frac{3}{8}$ 14. $\frac{5}{12} + \frac{1}{5}$ 19. $\frac{15}{16} + \frac{2}{3}$ 24. $\frac{1}{17} + \frac{1}{20}$

5. $\frac{5}{6} - \frac{2}{5}$ 10. $\frac{5}{7} - \frac{1}{3}$ 15. $\frac{3}{5} - \frac{5}{12}$ 20. $\frac{7}{8} - \frac{9}{11}$ 25. $\frac{31}{50} - \frac{1}{3}$

Where the denominators are not coprime we divide through by the HCF of those denominators and then proceed as before with the new denominators. For the denominator of the answer we use the product of the HCF and the new denominators.

$\frac{3}{8} + \frac{5}{12}$

$\underset{4}{\frac{3}{8}} + \underset{2\quad 3}{\frac{5}{12}} = \frac{19}{24}$ —— $3 \times 3 + 5 \times 2$

Are the denominators coprime? No!

$4 \times 2 \times 3$

Write down the HCF of the denominators, 4, on the left and below the two fractions.

Divide the HCF, 4, into each of the denominators and write down the answers below. 4 into 8 = 2 and 4 into 12 = 3.

2 and 3 are now the new denominators and these are used in the sum of the cross-product, $(3 \times 3) + (5 \times 2) = 19$

The denominator is the product of the HCF and the two new denominators, $4 \times 2 \times 3 = 24$.

The answer is $\frac{19}{24}$.

Exercise 15f

1. $\frac{2}{9} + \frac{1}{6}$	6. $\frac{3}{4} - \frac{1}{6}$	11. $\frac{5}{8} - \frac{3}{20}$	16. $\frac{7}{24} - \frac{3}{32}$	21. $\frac{7}{50} - \frac{3}{75}$
2. $\frac{1}{8} + \frac{5}{6}$	7. $\frac{4}{9} - \frac{1}{6}$	12. $\frac{4}{25} + \frac{1}{10}$	17. $\frac{11}{20} + \frac{3}{24}$	22. $\frac{7}{18} - \frac{2}{21}$
3. $\frac{5}{6} - \frac{3}{4}$	8. $\frac{7}{10} + \frac{1}{12}$	13. $\frac{11}{12} - \frac{4}{15}$	18. $\frac{22}{36} - \frac{5}{24}$	23. $\frac{5}{6} - \frac{11}{21}$
4. $\frac{3}{15} + \frac{3}{10}$	9. $\frac{5}{12} + \frac{7}{18}$	14. $\frac{5}{12} + \frac{7}{18}$	19. $\frac{15}{16} + \frac{7}{20}$	24. $\frac{16}{27} + \frac{5}{18}$
5. $\frac{5}{8} - \frac{5}{12}$	10. $\frac{11}{15} - \frac{3}{20}$	15. $\frac{9}{14} - \frac{3}{10}$	20. $\frac{19}{21} - \frac{9}{14}$	25. $\frac{21}{250} - \frac{7}{100}$

When there are mixed numbers involved then the whole numbers may be dealt with before the fractional parts.

$7\frac{5}{9} - 4\frac{7}{15}$

Subtracting the whole numbers, $7 - 4 = 3$.

$$7\frac{5}{\cancel{9}} - 4\frac{7}{\cancel{15}} = 3\frac{4}{45}$$

$$3 \quad 3 \quad \quad 5$$

$$5 \times 5 - 7 \times 3$$

$$3 \times 3 \times 5$$

Write down the HCF of the denominators, 3, and divide through, leaving 3 and 5 as the new denominators.
The difference in the cross-product is $5 \times 5 - 7 \times 3 = 25 - 21 = 4$.
The product of the HCF and the new denominators is $3 \times 3 \times 5 = 45$.
The answer is therefore $3\frac{4}{45}$.

When adding mixed numbers, if the resulting fraction is improper (greater than one) then the whole number and fraction should be adjusted. For example, with $2\frac{7}{8} + 3\frac{5}{6} = 5\frac{41}{24}$, you can see that the fractional part is improper. It should be adjusted by dividing the denominator into the numerator, that is 24 into $41 = 1$ remainder 17, giving the answer $6\frac{17}{24}$.

Exercise 15g Set out clearly:

1. $2\frac{1}{4} + 3\frac{1}{6}$
6. $3\frac{1}{10} + 8\frac{7}{12}$
11. $11\frac{11}{16} + 2\frac{3}{8}$
16. $13\frac{7}{24} + 52\frac{23}{30}$

2. $4\frac{1}{6} + 1\frac{3}{8}$
7. $12\frac{5}{8} + 7\frac{5}{6}$
12. $8\frac{75}{15} - 2\frac{3}{20}$
17. $9\frac{9}{16} - 1\frac{1}{28}$

3. $3\frac{1}{6} + 5\frac{3}{10}$
8. $4\frac{11}{15} + 9\frac{7}{10}$
13. $20\frac{5}{8} + 14\frac{13}{20}$
18. $6\frac{12}{25} - 3\frac{3}{40}$

4. $2\frac{3}{4} - 1\frac{1}{6}$
9. $10\frac{11}{16} - 3\frac{1}{6}$
14. $6\frac{1}{18} + 4\frac{1}{16}$
19. $6\frac{9}{50} - 6\frac{4}{75}$

5. $5\frac{5}{12} + 3\frac{5}{8}$
10. $3\frac{7}{12} + 7\frac{13}{18}$
15. $6\frac{3}{4} - 1\frac{3}{14}$
20. $2\frac{7}{36} + 94\frac{5}{48}$

Exercise 15h Mixed practice:

1. $3\frac{1}{4} + 4\frac{1}{3}$ 6. $5\frac{1}{2} + 6\frac{7}{12}$ 11. $3\frac{7}{12} + 7\frac{3}{5}$ 16. $7\frac{3}{7} + 2\frac{2}{11}$

2. $5\frac{1}{6} + 3\frac{1}{5}$ 7. $17\frac{2}{3} + 24\frac{5}{6}$ 12. $8\frac{9}{10} - 2\frac{7}{15}$ 17. $6\frac{13}{22} - 4\frac{3}{44}$

3. $4\frac{3}{4} + 2\frac{1}{2}$ 8. $2\frac{14}{15} + 8\frac{1}{5}$ 13. $6\frac{1}{21} + 4\frac{3}{20}$ 18. $29\frac{14}{15} - 12\frac{7}{45}$

4. $6\frac{3}{14} - 1\frac{1}{7}$ 9. $13\frac{5}{11} - 5\frac{2}{15}$ 14. $1\frac{4}{5} + \frac{9}{20}$ 19. $21\frac{13}{54} - 16\frac{1}{6}$

5. $3\frac{5}{6} + 2\frac{1}{3}$ 10. $8\frac{11}{12} + 3\frac{5}{24}$ 15. $3\frac{3}{4} - 2\frac{5}{12}$ 20. $5\frac{17}{25} + 24\frac{11}{20}$

When subtracting fractions, if the difference of the cross-product is negative we can use a vinculum in the numerator and then adjust the fraction accordingly using T*ranspose and adjust*.

$$5\frac{2}{5} - 2\frac{3}{4} \qquad\qquad 5\frac{2}{5} - 2\frac{3}{4} = 3\frac{\overline{7}}{20} = 2\frac{13}{20}$$

The difference of the cross-product is $2 \times 4 - 3 \times 5 = \overline{7}$. We are then left with a negative fraction. To *devinculate*, take 1 away from 3 and subtract 7 from the denominator 20. The answer is then $2\frac{13}{20}$

Exercise 15i

1. $3 - \frac{1}{3}$ 6. $5 - 2\frac{5}{12}$ 11. $13\frac{1}{9} - 7\frac{2}{3}$ 16. $17\frac{5}{18} - 12\frac{11}{12}$

2. $5 - \frac{2}{5}$ 7. $10 - 8\frac{5}{7}$ 12. $8\frac{1}{10} - 3\frac{7}{15}$ 17. $26\frac{11}{50} - 14\frac{9}{25}$

3. $4 - \frac{3}{4}$ 8. $12 - 5\frac{14}{19}$ 13. $9\frac{3}{20} - 7\frac{11}{15}$ 18. $24\frac{4}{15} - 11\frac{9}{35}$

4. $6 - \frac{11}{17}$ 9. $15 - 5\frac{7}{15}$ 14. $1\frac{2}{9} - \frac{17}{18}$ 19. $19\frac{3}{28} - 6\frac{3}{14}$

5. $3 - \frac{12}{13}$ 10. $28 - 3\frac{19}{24}$ 15. $7\frac{3}{4} - 4\frac{9}{16}$ 20. $35\frac{3}{20} - 27\frac{6}{25}$

Exercise 15j Problems

1. Janice buys a cake and eats $\frac{9}{16}$ of it; what fraction of the cake remains?

2. The weights of three parcels are $2\frac{3}{4}$ lb., $1\frac{5}{16}$ lb., and $\frac{7}{8}$ lb. respectively; find their total weight.

3. From a stick $12\frac{1}{4}$ in. long, a piece $6\frac{5}{8}$ in. long is cut off; what length remains?

4. A shirt sleeve $24\frac{3}{10}$ in. shrinks in the wash to a length of $22\frac{9}{16}$ in.; how much shorter is it?

5. The perimeter of a rectangle is 15 cm; it is $4\frac{3}{4}$ cm long; how wide is it?

6. If I increase my stride from $\frac{3}{4}$ m. to $\frac{5}{6}$ m. What is the increase as a fraction of a metre?

7. Add $\frac{2}{3}$ to the difference of $3\frac{1}{2}$ and $1\frac{1}{6}$.

8. Subtract $1\frac{3}{4}$ from the sum of $2\frac{1}{6}$ and $3\frac{5}{8}$.

9. A man bequeaths his estate of 6000 acres to his four children. The first receives $\frac{1}{3}$ of it, the second and third each receive $\frac{4}{15}$ of it. How many acres is left to the fourth?

10. A tank is one-third full. After drawing off 22 litres it is just one quarter full. How much will the tank hold?

11. One tap can fill a bath in 6 min. What fraction of the bath can it fill in 1 min? Another tap can fill the bath in 3 min. What fraction of the bath is filled in 1 min. when both taps are running? How long will it take to fill the bath if both taps are running?

12. One tap can fill a bath in 10 min., and another tap in 15 min. How long does it take to fill the bath if both taps are running?

13. Two men can paint an apartment in 8 days; one of them could paint it in 12 days; how long would the other man take by himself?

14. Add together $\frac{1}{2}$, $\frac{1}{3}$, $\frac{1}{4}$, $\frac{1}{5}$ and $\frac{1}{6}$.

Comparing fractions

The sizes of fractions can be compared using the *Vertically and crosswise* sutra. By taking the difference of the cross-product, as for subtraction, if the first product is larger than the second product then the first fraction is larger than the second, and vice versa. In other words, if the difference of the cross-product is positive then the first fraction is larger and if it is negative the second fraction is larger.

Which is larger, $\frac{2}{5}$ or $\frac{3}{7}$?　The difference of the cross-product is $14 - 15 = \bar{1}$. The second fraction is therefore larger.

Which is larger, $\frac{5}{6}$ or $\frac{7}{9}$?　On dividing the denominators by their HCF 3, the difference of the cross-product becomes $5 \times 3 - 7 \times 2 = 15 - 14$. The first fraction is therefore larger.

Exercise 15k　Write down the largest fraction:

1. $\frac{2}{5}$, $\frac{1}{4}$ 5. $\frac{5}{6}$, $\frac{4}{5}$ 9. $\frac{1}{4}$, $\frac{5}{16}$ 13. $\frac{11}{15}$, $\frac{7}{30}$ 17. $\frac{7}{9}$, $\frac{23}{36}$

2. $\frac{2}{3}$, $\frac{3}{5}$ 6. $\frac{7}{8}$, $\frac{8}{9}$ 10. $\frac{11}{20}$, $\frac{1}{4}$ 14. $\frac{13}{16}$, $\frac{3}{4}$ 18. $\frac{4}{5}$, $\frac{31}{40}$

3. $\frac{3}{4}$, $\frac{7}{9}$ 7. $\frac{11}{16}$, $\frac{22}{32}$ 11. $\frac{11}{12}$, $\frac{2}{3}$ 15. $\frac{3}{15}$, $\frac{1}{45}$ 19. $\frac{7}{8}$, $\frac{55}{64}$

4. $\frac{4}{15}$, $\frac{2}{7}$ 8. $\frac{7}{8}$, $\frac{9}{16}$ 12. $\frac{5}{12}$, $\frac{5}{24}$ 16. $\frac{3}{7}$, $\frac{19}{35}$ 20. $\frac{1}{12}$, $\frac{1}{84}$

Write down the smallest fraction:

21. $\frac{5}{6}$, $\frac{7}{8}$ 23. $\frac{8}{9}$, $\frac{9}{10}$ 25. $\frac{14}{15}$, $\frac{4}{5}$ 27. $\frac{7}{10}$, $\frac{11}{15}$ 29. $\frac{5}{9}$, $\frac{7}{18}$

22. $\frac{2}{5}$, $\frac{8}{21}$ 24. $\frac{5}{12}$, $\frac{11}{24}$ 26. $\frac{5}{8}$, $\frac{9}{16}$ 28. $\frac{4}{7}$, $\frac{5}{8}$ 30. $\frac{3}{13}$, $\frac{7}{40}$

Write down the following sets of fractions in order of size, with smallest first:

31. $\frac{2}{3}$, $\frac{5}{8}$, $\frac{4}{7}$ 33. $\frac{3}{8}$, $\frac{5}{12}$, $\frac{4}{9}$

32. $\frac{1}{5}$, $\frac{2}{9}$, $\frac{3}{14}$ 34. $\frac{4}{5}$, $\frac{8}{11}$, $\frac{5}{7}$

Chapter 16 Vulgar fractions: multiplication and division

Multiplying fractions

Exercise 16a Write down the values of:

1. $\frac{3}{4}$ m $\times$ 2	**9.** $\frac{5}{8} \times$ 3 ft	**17.** $\frac{3}{4} \times 12$	**25.** $\frac{2}{3} \times \frac{1}{7}$
2. $\frac{2}{3}$ min $\times$ 6	**10.** $\frac{3}{10} \times 3$	**18.** $\frac{5}{8}$ of 12	**26.** $\frac{1}{2}$ of $\frac{2}{3}$
3. $\frac{3}{4}$ cm $\times$ 3	**11.** $\frac{3}{10} \times 5$	**19.** $\frac{1}{2}$ of 7	**27.** $\frac{1}{4}$ of $\frac{2}{3}$
4. $\frac{3}{4}$ in $\times$ 4	**12.** $\frac{1}{8} \times 8$	**20.** $5 \times \frac{1}{2}$	**28.** $\frac{1}{7}$ of $\frac{2}{3}$
5. $\frac{2}{3}$ km $\times$ 4	**13.** $1\frac{1}{4} \times 3$	**21.** $\frac{1}{4}$ of £5	**29.** $\frac{2}{3} \times \frac{2}{3}$
6. $1\frac{3}{4} \times 6$ sec	**14.** $1\frac{1}{3} \times 4$	**22.** $3 \times \frac{1}{4}$	**30.** $6 \times \frac{1}{6}$
7. $\frac{3}{8} \times 2$ lb	**15.** $1\frac{1}{3} \times$ £3	**23.** $\frac{1}{5} \times 8$	**31.** $2\frac{1}{2} \times \frac{1}{10}$
8. $\frac{3}{8} \times 5$ oz	**16.** $3\frac{2}{3} \times 12$	**24.** $\frac{1}{9} \times 15$	**32.** $2\frac{1}{4} \times \frac{1}{3}$

Fractions are multiplied by multiplying the two numerators together and multiplying the two denominators together.

The order of steps for multiplying fractions together is as follows:

1. Convert any mixed or whole numbers into improper fractions,
2. cancel down any numerator with any denominator,
3. multiply,
4. check to see that the fraction is in lowest terms,
5. convert to a mixed number if the answer is an improper fraction.

$$1\frac{5}{7} \times 1\frac{1}{3} = \frac{\overset{}{12}}{7} \times \frac{\overset{4}{4}}{\underset{1}{3}}$$

The mixed numbers are first expressed as improper fractions.
12 and 3 reduce to 4 and 1.
$4 \times 4 = 16$ and $7 \times 1 = 7$

$$= \frac{16}{7} = 2\frac{2}{7}$$

The answer is $\frac{16}{7}$ which is $2\frac{2}{7}$

$$1\tfrac{1}{5} \times 2\tfrac{1}{3} \times \tfrac{5}{14} = \overset{\overset{1}{2}}{\underset{1}{\cancel{6}}} \times \overset{1}{\underset{1}{\cancel{7}}} \times \overset{1}{\underset{\underset{1}{2}}{\cancel{5}}} = \tfrac{1}{1} = 1$$

Any numerator may cancel with any denominator.

When the word *of* is used it should be replaced with the × symbol.

Exercise 16b $\tfrac{3}{7} \times \tfrac{2}{5}$

1. $\tfrac{3}{7} \times \tfrac{2}{5}$

2. $\tfrac{2}{5} \times \tfrac{3}{4}$

3. $\tfrac{4}{9} \times \tfrac{3}{5}$

4. $\tfrac{4}{7} \times \tfrac{5}{8}$

5. $\tfrac{5}{8} \times 8$

6. $\left(\tfrac{3}{4}\right)^2$

7. $\left(\tfrac{2}{3}\right)^3$

8. $\tfrac{7}{9}$ of $\tfrac{3}{14}$

9. $\tfrac{10}{27}$ of $\tfrac{9}{35}$

10. $\tfrac{14}{21} \times \tfrac{15}{10}$

11. $2\tfrac{1}{4} \times 5\tfrac{1}{3}$

12. $2\tfrac{4}{7} \times 4\tfrac{2}{3}$

13. $\tfrac{3}{10}$ of $\tfrac{5}{12}$

14. $2\tfrac{5}{8}$ of $2\tfrac{2}{7}$

15. $3\tfrac{8}{9} \times 3\tfrac{6}{7}$

16. $\tfrac{4}{63} \times \tfrac{21}{32}$

17. $\tfrac{2}{3} \times \tfrac{6}{7} \times \tfrac{3}{4}$

18. $\tfrac{1}{2}$ of $\tfrac{1}{3} \times \tfrac{1}{4}$

19. $\tfrac{4}{15} \times \tfrac{7}{12} \times \tfrac{25}{21}$

20. $\tfrac{3}{7} \times \tfrac{5}{9} \times \tfrac{21}{5}$

21. $2\tfrac{1}{2} \times 1\tfrac{1}{4} \times \tfrac{8}{75}$

22. $1\tfrac{1}{3} \times 1\tfrac{2}{7} \times 1\tfrac{1}{4}$

23. $3\tfrac{1}{16} \times \tfrac{14}{25}$ of $2\tfrac{1}{7}$

24. $\left(2\tfrac{1}{2}\right)^2 \times 1\tfrac{3}{5}$

25. $\tfrac{2}{5}$ of $\left(1\tfrac{1}{4}\right)^2$

26. $4\tfrac{1}{8} \times \tfrac{14}{17} \times 1\tfrac{13}{21}$

27. $6\tfrac{1}{9} \times \tfrac{8}{13} \times 1\tfrac{17}{22}$

28. $2\tfrac{1}{2} \times \tfrac{18}{35} \times 3\tfrac{1}{3}$

29. $\tfrac{8}{11} \times 16\tfrac{1}{2} \times \tfrac{5}{61}$

30. $\tfrac{3}{11} \times 14\tfrac{2}{3} \times 2\tfrac{5}{8}$

31. $1\tfrac{1}{2} \times 1\tfrac{1}{3} \times 1\tfrac{1}{5}$

32. $\tfrac{1}{4}$ of $\left(2\tfrac{1}{2} \times \tfrac{4}{5}\right)^2$

Dividing by a fraction

The sutra for dividing by a fraction is *Transpose and adjust*. The application of this turns the second fraction up-side-down and changes the ÷ sign to a ×.

$$\tfrac{4}{3} \div \tfrac{5}{7} = \tfrac{4}{3} \times \tfrac{7}{5} = \tfrac{28}{15} = 1\tfrac{13}{15}$$

$$3\tfrac{1}{3} \div 5 = 3\tfrac{1}{3} \div \tfrac{5}{1} = \tfrac{10}{3} \times \tfrac{1}{5} = \tfrac{2}{3}$$

$$3\tfrac{1}{2} \div 2\tfrac{1}{4} = \tfrac{7}{2} \div \tfrac{9}{4} = \tfrac{7}{2} \times \tfrac{4}{9} = \tfrac{14}{9} = 1\tfrac{5}{9}$$

Exercise 16c Write answers only:

1. Divide $\tfrac{1}{2}$ by 3, 4, 5   **4.** Divide $\tfrac{4}{9}$ by 2, 3, 12   **7.** Divide $2\tfrac{1}{4}$ by 3, 6, 9

2. Divide $\tfrac{1}{3}$ by 2, 3, 6   **5.** Divide $\tfrac{12}{25}$ by 4, 5, 8   **8.** Divide $\tfrac{1}{2}$ by $\tfrac{1}{3}$

3. Divide $\tfrac{3}{4}$ by 3, 4, 5   **6.** Divide $1\tfrac{1}{2}$ by 3, 4, 6   **9.** Divide $\tfrac{1}{9}$ by $\tfrac{1}{2}$

10. $3 \div \tfrac{1}{2}$ **14.** $1 \div \tfrac{1}{3}$ **18.** $\tfrac{1}{3} \div \tfrac{1}{2}$ **22.** $\tfrac{2}{3} \div \tfrac{2}{5}$

11. $2 \div \tfrac{1}{3}$ **15.** $1 \div \tfrac{1}{10}$ **19.** $\tfrac{1}{3} \div \tfrac{1}{6}$ **23.** $\tfrac{3}{4} \div \tfrac{4}{5}$

12. $5 \div \tfrac{1}{4}$ **16.** $1 \div \tfrac{2}{3}$ **20.** $\tfrac{1}{12} \div \tfrac{1}{9}$ **24.** $\tfrac{5}{8} \div \tfrac{2}{3}$

13. $7 \div \tfrac{1}{5}$ **17.** $1 \div 1\tfrac{1}{2}$ **21.** $\tfrac{1}{2} \div \tfrac{1}{2}$ **25.** $\tfrac{2}{9} \div \tfrac{4}{3}$

Exercise 16d

1. $1\tfrac{1}{3} \div \tfrac{2}{5}$ **6.** $\tfrac{5}{8} \div \tfrac{5}{8}$ **11.** $\tfrac{28}{48} \div 4\tfrac{5}{18}$ **16.** $1 \div \tfrac{5}{7}$

2. $\tfrac{2}{3} \div 1\tfrac{1}{6}$ **7.** $3\tfrac{3}{14} \div 1\tfrac{4}{21}$ **12.** $2\tfrac{1}{3} \div 1\tfrac{3}{4}$ **17.** $\tfrac{1}{5} \div 7$

3. $1\tfrac{1}{9} \div 2\tfrac{1}{12}$ **8.** $1\tfrac{11}{15} \div 7\tfrac{4}{5}$ **13.** $1\tfrac{5}{7} \div 1\tfrac{1}{7}$ **18.** $5 \div 3\tfrac{1}{3}$

4. $\tfrac{5}{16} \div 2\tfrac{1}{12}$ **9.** $1\tfrac{11}{45} \div 10\tfrac{1}{9}$ **14.** $\tfrac{14}{27} \div \tfrac{35}{36}$ **19.** $3\tfrac{1}{7} \div 11$

5. $1 \div 2\tfrac{3}{4}$ **10.** $\tfrac{25}{15} \div 1\tfrac{2}{3}$ **15.** $\tfrac{1}{12} \div \tfrac{1}{18}$ **20.** $4\tfrac{1}{3} \div 3\tfrac{1}{4}$

Mixed practice

For mixed signs the order of operations should be followed as

> 1 **Brackets**
> 2 **Multiplication and division**
> 3 **Addition and subtraction**

Expressions such as $36 \div 6 \times 2$ should not be used because they are ambiguous. $36 \div 6 \times 2$ could either be $36 \div 12 = 3$ or $6 \times 2 = 12$. To avoid confusion brackets must be inserted. With mixed operations the word "of" should also not be used. For example, $\frac{2}{3} \div \frac{4}{5}$ of $\frac{6}{7}$ means $\frac{2}{3} \div \left(\frac{4}{5} \times \frac{6}{7} \right)$ and so brackets should be used instead.

$$\frac{2}{3} \times \left(\frac{4}{5} + \frac{1}{7} \right) \times \frac{1}{2} = \frac{2}{3} \times \frac{33}{35} \times \frac{1}{2} = \frac{11}{35}$$

Exercise 16e

1. $\frac{1}{2} + \frac{1}{3} \times \frac{1}{4}$

2. $\left(\frac{1}{2} + \frac{1}{3} \right) \times \frac{1}{4}$

3. $\left(\frac{1}{2} + \frac{1}{4} \right) \times \frac{1}{3}$

4. $\left(\frac{2}{3} - \frac{1}{2} \right) \times \frac{2}{3}$

5. $\frac{2}{3} - \frac{1}{2} \times \frac{2}{3}$

6. $\frac{1}{3} + \frac{1}{6} \times \frac{1}{2}$

7. $1\frac{3}{4} - \frac{1}{2} \div \frac{1}{3}$

8. $\left(\frac{3}{5} + \frac{1}{3} \right) \div \frac{2}{3}$

9. $\frac{3}{5} + \frac{2}{5} \div \frac{4}{5}$

10. $\frac{1}{3} \times \frac{1}{2} + \frac{1}{4} \times \frac{1}{5}$

11. $\frac{1}{3} \times \left(\frac{1}{2} + \frac{1}{4} \right) \times \frac{1}{5}$

12. $\frac{1}{3} \times \left(\frac{1}{2} + \frac{1}{4} \times \frac{1}{5} \right)$

13. $\left(\frac{1}{3} \times \frac{1}{2} + \frac{1}{4} \right) \times \frac{1}{5}$

14. $\frac{2}{3} \times \frac{1}{4} - \frac{1}{12} \div \frac{1}{2}$

15. $\frac{2}{3} \times \left(\frac{1}{4} - \frac{1}{12} \div \frac{1}{2} \right)$

16. $\frac{2}{3} \times \left(\frac{1}{4} - \frac{1}{12} \right) \div \frac{1}{2}$

17. $\left(\frac{2}{3} \times \frac{1}{4} - \frac{1}{12} \right) \div \frac{1}{2}$

18. $3\frac{1}{2} - \frac{1}{3} \div \left(\frac{1}{4} \times \frac{5}{12} \right)$

19. $\left(\frac{1}{2} + \frac{1}{3} \right) \times \frac{1}{5} - \frac{1}{6}$

20. $3\frac{3}{4} \div \left(2\frac{1}{2} + 3\frac{1}{4} \right)$

21. $1\frac{5}{6} + \frac{1}{3} \times \left(3\frac{1}{2} - 2\frac{1}{4} \right)$

22. $\left(\frac{2}{5} + \frac{1}{7} \right) \div \left(\frac{1}{5} - \frac{1}{8} \right)$

23. $\left(3\frac{1}{4} - 1\frac{1}{2} \right) \div \left(2\frac{5}{6} - \frac{1}{2} \right)$

24. $\left(1\frac{2}{3} - 1\frac{1}{2} \right) \div \left(3\frac{1}{2} - 2\frac{3}{8} \right)$

25. $8\frac{1}{2} - 4\frac{2}{3} - 1\frac{1}{6} \times \frac{2}{5} + \frac{3}{5}$

Exercise 16f Problems

1. A girl's stride is 72 cm; what fraction of a metre is this?

2. Express £1.25 as a fraction of £5.

3. 1 pint of water weighs $1\frac{1}{4}$ lb; find the weight of $\frac{3}{4}$ of a gallon.

4. Find the area of a mat $3\frac{1}{2}$ ft long and $2\frac{3}{4}$ ft wide.

5. A piece of timber is 4 ft 4 in long. How many pieces, each $6\frac{1}{2}$ in long can be cut from it?

6. In a school there are 36 members of staff and 450 pupils. What fraction of the entire school are staff?

7. A man sleeps for $6\frac{1}{4}$ hrs every day; for what fraction of a day is he awake?

8. On one particular day the sun rose at 5 30 am and set at 7 00 pm. On that day there were 10 hrs of sunshine. Find the fraction of daylight hours which were overcast.

9. Find the volume of a rectangular block $5\frac{1}{4}$ in long, $3\frac{1}{2}$ in wide and $2\frac{3}{4}$ in high.

10. The area of a floor of a hall, $4\frac{2}{3}$ ft wide, is 140 sq.ft. Find the length of the hall.

11. A boy can run $\frac{1}{4}$ of a lap in 16 seconds; at this rate how long will it take him to run 2 laps?

12. How many times does $\frac{2}{3}$ go into 6?

13. A man can paint $\frac{5}{8}$ of a room in 6 days. How long will it take him to paint the whole room?

14. $\frac{2}{3}$ of a tank can be filled in $14\frac{1}{4}$ minutes. How long will it take to fill the whole tank?

15. A man buys an antique chair for £95 and sells it for £120. What fraction of the cost price is his profit?

16. A girl spends $\frac{2}{5}$ of her money and now has £5.40 left. How much did she have originally?

17. A diesel locomotive weighing 240 tons can pull a train $3\frac{1}{6}$ times its own weight. Find the combined weight of the locomotive and train.

18. A girl collects a basketful of apples from under an apple tree. $\frac{1}{6}$ are rotten and she throws them away. There are then 25 apples left. How many were there originally?

19. A man buys 1500 shares at £3.50 each and sells them when they have increased by $\frac{1}{5}$ of their value. How much profit does he make?

20. If $\frac{2}{5}$ of a journey takes 36 minutes, how long will the rest of it take at the same rate?

21. If I take $1\frac{1}{4}$ more minutes to walk $\frac{3}{4}$ of a mile than I take to walk $\frac{2}{3}$ of a mile, how long do I take to walk a mile?

22. A man spends $\frac{3}{5}$ of his monthly income in the first week and $\frac{1}{4}$ of the remainder in the second week. What fraction of his income does he have left for the remaining period?

23. $\frac{7}{15}$ of the water in a full reservoir is used in one month and $\frac{5}{6}$ of the remainder is used in the following month. If 20,000 gallons of water are then left how much does the reservoir hold, assuming that no water has entered the reservoir during those two months?

24. A car loses $\frac{1}{5}$ of its value in the first year and $\frac{2}{11}$ of its subsequent value in the second year. If it is then worth £18,000, find its original value.

25. A cash prize is divided between A, B and C. A receives $\frac{2}{5}$ of the prize, B receives $\frac{5}{9}$ of the remainder. If C's share is £900, find the value of the prize.

26. A man aged 28 marries a woman aged 21; he dies at the age of 84 and she dies at the age of 91.
  (a) For how many years is the man married?
  (b) For what fraction of his life is he married?
  (c) For how many years is the woman a widow?
  (d) For what fraction of her life is she a widow?

Chapter 17 Discrimination in division

So far we have learnt several different methods of division. The aim of this chapter is to give some practice in choosing the most appropriate method for any particular sum. This choice is called discrimination. It is similar to having a Swiss-Army penknife with several different blades and tools. To open a bottle of wine one of the blades could be used but it is far easier to use the corkscrew! In the same way the easiest method of division depends on the task in hand.

The different methods are called:

> Simple
> All from 9 and the last from 10
> Transpose and Adjust
> Proportional
> Straight

The special case methods by *All from 9 and the last from 10* and *Transpose and adjust* are really different forms of Straight division but for the present we will treat them as separate.

We will begin with some revision of each method.

Extending simple division

Simple division is used for single digit divisors. It can also be used for larger divisors which can be treated as single digits. Whether or not this can be done easily depends on the particular sum and so by *Mere Inspection* is the key.

$5642 \div 8$

This is simple division with a single-digit divisor.
8 into 56 = 7, 8 into 4 = 0 rem. 4, 8 into 42 = 5 rem. 2.
The answer is 705/2.

$$8 | 5\,6\,4\,2$$
$$\underline{\quad\quad 4\quad}$$
$$7\,0\,5\,/\,2$$

$357 \div 16$

By looking at the divisor and dividend it becomes clear that straight division, or any other method, is unnecessary. 16 into 35 = 2 rem. 3, 16 into 37 = 2 rem. 5 and so the answer is 22/5.

$$16 | 3\,5\,7$$
$$\underline{\quad\quad 3\quad}$$
$$2\,2\,/\,5$$

Exercise 17a Use simple division:

1. $534 \div 6$	**6.** $1210 \div 4$	**11.** $65707 \div 10$	**16.** $564754 \div 11$
2. $364 \div 3$	**7.** $8765 \div 8$	**12.** $65777 \div 11$	**17.** $657022 \div 3$
3. $6786 \div 4$	**8.** $2432 \div 2$	**13.** $80654 \div 12$	**18.** $567000 \div 12$
4. $1242 \div 5$	**9.** $8769 \div 9$	**14.** $64563 \div 4$	**19.** $219943 \div 8$
5. $6475 \div 7$	**10.** $43455 \div 4$	**15.** $873211 \div 9$	**20.** $300000 \div 11$

21. $1600 \div 13$	**26.** $509 \div 23$	**31.** $1648 \div 53$	**36.** $6000 \div 25$
22. $3168 \div 15$	**27.** $7428 \div 35$	**32.** $8800 \div 44$	**37.** $6616 \div 32$
23. $4242 \div 21$	**28.** $5098 \div 24$	**33.** $3798 \div 18$	**38.** $7575 \div 15$
24. $301 \div 14$	**29.** $4058 \div 13$	**34.** $4420 \div 221$	**39.** $4200 \div 14$
25. $191 \div 17$	**30.** $390 \div 38$	**35.** $589 \div 28$	**40.** $4976 \div 16$

Division by nine

There is a very quick and easy way to divide numbers by 9. It is a special case of division by All from 9 and the last from 10 dealt with in the next section.

When dividing a two digit number by 9 we simply give the first digit as the quotient and the sum of the two digits as the remainder. The following examples demonstrate this:

> 9 into 12 = 1 remainder 3 (1 is the quotient digit and 3 = 1 + 2)
> 9 .. .. 14 = 1 5
> 9 .. .. 21 = 2 3
> 9 .... 52 = 5 7

When dividing a number with three or more digits we add the digits and set down the sum at each stage. For example, 9 into 1231 = 136/7. Where the remainder is larger than 9 it should be redivided. For example, 9 into 78 = 7/15 = 8/6

Exercise 17b Divide each of the following numbers by 9: (answers only)

1. 25	**9.** 53	**17.** 38	**25.** 122	**33.** 343
2. 31	**10.** 25	**18.** 86	**26.** 125	**34.** 156
3. 421	**11.** 81	**19.** 78	**27.** 134	**35.** 270
4. 51	**12.** 27	**20.** 99	**28.** 222	**36.** 190
5. 71	**13.** 18	**21.** 104	**29.** 331	**37.** 283
6. 43	**14.** 45	**22.** 112	**30.** 414	**38.** 471
7. 12	**15.** 63	**23.** 124	**31.** 800	**39.** 1121
8. 35	**16.** 75	**24.** 142	**32.** 702	**40.** 1234

Division by *All from nine and the last from ten*

This is used where the divisor is a little less than a power of 10, such as 100, 1000, etc. This was dealt with in Chapter 3 and the next exercise provides further practice.

1792 ÷ 98

The base of the divisor is 100 which has two zeros. This gives the number of digits required after the remainder stroke. The number of digits in the dividend to the left of the remainder stroke gives the number of lines required before the answer line can be drawn.

```
9 8 | 1 7 / 6 2
0 2 |   0 2
     |     1 4
     | 1 7 / 9 6
```

The complement of 98 is 02.
The first digit is brought down, 1. 1 × 02 = 02, and this is placed below the next two digits of the dividend.
Add up the next column, 7 + 0 = 7, and this gives the next answer digit.
7 × 02 = 14, which is written in the next two columns.
Add up for the remainder, 96

Exercise 17c Use *All from 9* division:

1. 1123 ÷ 97	**6.** 152 ÷ 97	**11.** 11112 ÷ 89	**16.** 12342 ÷ 998
2. 2103 ÷ 96	**7.** 285 ÷ 98	**12.** 21045 ÷ 97	**17.** 11321 ÷ 987
3. 1321 ÷ 89	**8.** 163 ÷ 88	**13.** 12323 ÷ 98	**18.** 3645 ÷ 999
4. 2145 ÷ 95	**9.** 167 ÷ 96	**14.** 23143 ÷ 99	**19.** 11032 ÷ 988
5. 3124 ÷ 99	**10.** 213 ÷ 89	**15.** 20203 ÷ 89	**20.** 1122 ÷ 977

This method of division does have its limitations because where the divisor is not close to a base or where the dividend digits are large it can become difficult to use. The example on the right shows the sort of difficulty which can arise. 4578 ÷ 78.

```
7 8 | 4 5 / 7 8
2 2 |   8  8
     | 4 13 /
```

The sum in the second column gives 13 as the second quotient digit and the next step is to multiply this by 22!

Division by eleven

Just as there is a very quick and easy way to divide numbers by 9 so there is a similar method for dividing numbers by 11. The reason for this is that 9 and 11 are deficient from 10 by 1.

$$11 \text{ into } 259 = 23/6$$

This method is a special case of *Transpose and adjust*. The first digit of the dividend is the first quotient digit, 2. This 2 is subtracted from the second digit, $5 - 2 = 3$, to give the second quotient digit. This in turn is subtracted from the last digit to give the remainder, $9 - 3 = 6$. The answer is 23 remainder 6.

Exercise 17d Mentally divide each of the following by 11:

1. 27	**9.** 58	**17.** 42	**25.** 783	**33.** 692
2. 36	**10.** 28	**18.** 61	**26.** 469	**34.** 251
3. 48	**11.** 99	**19.** 72	**27.** 128	**35.** 680
4. 55	**12.** 12	**20.** 91	**28.** 336	**36.** 392
5. 69	**13.** 25	**21.** 111	**29.** 286	**37.** 471
6. 23	**14.** 34	**22.** 134	**30.** 347	**38.** 1234
7. 38	**15.** 70	**23.** 254	**31.** 230	**39.** 13579
8. 49	**16.** 32	**24.** 341	**32.** 451	**40.** 100

Division by *Transpose and adjust*

Division by *Transpose and adjust* may be used where the divisor has small digits and which is a little more than a base of 10, 100, 1000, etc.

124868 ÷ 1113

The base of the divisor is 1000 which has three zeros. This gives the number of digits required after the remainder stroke. As previously, the number of digits to the left of the remainder stroke gives the number of lines required before the answer line can be drawn.

$$\begin{array}{r|l} 1113 & 1\,2\,4/8\,6\,9 \\ \bar{1}\bar{1}3 & \bar{1}\ \bar{1}\ \bar{3} \\ & \ \ \bar{1}\ \bar{1}\ \bar{3} \\ & \ \ \ \ \bar{2}\ \bar{2}\ \bar{6} \\ \hline & 1\,2\,2/2\,1\,3 \end{array}$$

The digits in excess of the base are transposed to vinculum digits and written below the divisor. The process is then the same as for *All from 9* division.

Exercise 17e Use *Transpose and adjust*:

1. 1448 ÷ 11	**10.** 1366 ÷ 132	**19.** 2577 ÷ 111	**28.** 13445 ÷ 121
2. 12378 ÷ 11	**11.** 1473 ÷ 121	**20.** 3791 ÷ 121	**29.** 24789 ÷ 1121
3. 23469 ÷ 11	**12.** 1496 ÷ 112	**21.** 3786 ÷ 111	**30.** 137987 ÷ 1121
4. 1588 ÷ 12	**13.** 2573 ÷ 121	**22.** 1781 ÷ 161	**31.** 243813 ÷ 1212
5. 1579 ÷ 102	**14.** 2388 ÷ 113	**23.** 13696 ÷ 113	**32.** 13545 ÷ 1212
6. 1435 ÷ 101	**15.** 2584 ÷ 123	**24.** 23766 ÷ 112	**33.** 2578787 ÷ 11202
7. 1233 ÷ 112	**16.** 2653 ÷ 131	**25.** 13565 ÷ 112	**34.** 13888 ÷ 1122
8. 1377 ÷ 123	**17.** 2683 ÷ 121	**26.** 36951 ÷ 123	**35.** 321987 ÷ 1003
9. 1481 ÷ 131	**18.** 2684 ÷ 122	**27.** 1258 ÷ 104	**36.** 79999 ÷ 111

Dividing by 5

A quick and easy way to divide any number by 5 is to divide it by 10 and then multiply the answer by 2. Alternatively one can multiply by 2 and then divide by 10. For example, $23 \div 5 = 2.3 \times 2 = 4.6$. This is a special case of proportionate division.

Exercise 17f Mentally divide each number by 5, leaving answers in decimal form where appropriate:

1. 23	**5.** 231	**9.** 109	**13.** 8325	**17.** 3.23
2. 42	**6.** 437	**10.** 439	**14.** 6032	**18.** 6.211
3. 64	**7.** 621	**11.** 1034	**15.** 43245	**19.** 56.213
4. 38	**8.** 738	**12.** 2133	**16.** 12.4	**20.** 0.024321

Proportional division

Proportional division is similar to cancelling down with fractions. The Vedic sutra is *Proportionately*. This can be used whenever the divisor and dividend can be divided through by a common factor.

(i) 124 ÷ 16 $\qquad \frac{124}{16} = \frac{62}{8} = \frac{31}{4} = 7\frac{3}{4}$

(ii) 3.14 ÷ 1.25 $\qquad \frac{3.14}{1.25} = \frac{6.28}{2.5} = \frac{12.56}{5} = 1.256 \times 2 = 2.512$

Exercise 17g Leave remainders as either vulgar or decimal fractions:

1. 250 ÷ 25	**9.** 3600 ÷ 72	**17.** 3.15 ÷ 4200	**25.** 39 ÷ 1.3
2. 96 ÷ 16	**10.** 1250 ÷ 25	**18.** 38388 ÷ 84	**26.** 5.6 ÷ 0.7
3. 450 ÷ 75	**11.** 10,000 ÷ 16	**19.** 372 ÷ 0.75	**27.** 0.46 ÷ 0.23
4. 23 ÷ 0.2	**12.** 2000 ÷ 24	**20.** 5184 ÷ 144	**28.** 12.1 ÷ 0.11
5. 64 ÷ 0.32	**13.** 0.108 ÷ 15	**21.** 3.5 ÷ 0.5	**29.** 0.48 ÷ 1.6
6. 560 ÷ 20	**14.** 43.2 ÷ 160	**22.** 8.4 ÷ 1.2	**30.** 17 ÷ 0.25
7. 312 ÷ 50	**15.** 0.252 ÷ 210	**23.** 1.75 ÷ 0.25	**31.** 0.225 ÷ 15
8. 0.08 ÷ 2.5	**16.** 213 ÷ 0.25	**24.** 2.56 ÷ 12.8	**32.** 12.25 ÷ 0.35

Straight division with altered remainders

We now take up the case of general straight division with altered remainders by the Vedic sutra *On top of the flag*. An altered remainder may be used to avoid negative dividends. The following example shows the method.

3425 ÷ 34

The sum is set out as shown on the right with the final digit of the divisor hoisted into the flag position. The remainder stroke is placed so that the number of digits after it is the same as the number of digits in the flag.

$$3 \,^6|8\,1\,6\,4/3$$
$$\underline{\quad|2\quad\quad}$$
$$2$$

3 into 3 = 2 rem. 2.

$$3 \,^6|8\,1\,6\,4/3$$
$$\underline{\quad|2\,3\quad\quad}$$
$$2\,2$$

21 − 2 × 6 = 9, 3 into 9 = 3. But this would not give us a large enough number for the following subtraction and so we say that 3 into 9 = 2 rem. 3. This is an altered remainder.

$$3 \,^6|8\,1\,6\,4/3$$
$$\underline{\quad|2\,3\,6\quad}$$
$$2\,2\,6$$

36 − 2 × 6 = 24, 3 into 24 = 8. Again, the remainder is not large enough and so we try 3 into 24 = 7 rem. 3. This is also not large enough but 6 rem. 6 does meet the requirement.

$$3 \,^6|8\,1\,6\,4/3$$
$$\underline{\quad|2\,3\,6\,7\quad}$$
$$2\,2\,6\,7/$$

64 − 6 × 6 = 28, 3 into 28 = 9 rem. 1. Again, this is not large enough. Try 3 into 28 = 8 rem. 4. No! 3 into 28 = 7 rem. 7. Yes!

$$3 \,^6|8\,1\,6\,4/3$$
$$\underline{\quad|2\,3\,6\,7\quad}$$
$$2\,2\,6\,7/31$$

For the final remainder 73 − 7 × 6 = 31.

Exercise 17h Leave whole number remainders:

1. 345 ÷ 26	**9.** 5613 ÷ 54	**17.** 23435 ÷ 66	**25.** 765843 ÷ 37
2. 540 ÷ 37	**10.** 8170 ÷ 36	**18.** 60067 ÷ 35	**26.** 325465 ÷ 26
3. 914 ÷ 56	**11.** 6509 ÷ 27	**19.** 65741 ÷ 28	**27.** 700000 ÷ 47
4. 578 ÷ 29	**12.** 4406 ÷ 58	**20.** 76801 ÷ 47	**28.** 456992 ÷87
5. 471 ÷ 68	**13.** 1285 ÷ 86	**21.** 98862 ÷ 56	**29.** 213077 ÷ 46
6. 725 ÷ 57	**14.** 3247 ÷ 17	**22.** 11215 ÷ 75	**30.** 680432 ÷ 55
7. 945 ÷ 48	**15.** 7848 ÷ 77	**23.** 43005 ÷ 68	**31.** 219000 ÷ 38
8. 863 ÷ 18	**16.** 6700 ÷ 46	**24.** 32146 ÷ 18	**32.** 342876 ÷ 19

Using a vinculum in the flag

The previous exercise gives practice in altered remainders but there is an easier technique where the flag digit is a large number, such as 6, 7, 8 or 9. This is to replace the flag digit with a vinculum number. This changes the process because instead of subtracting we add the product of the previous quotient digit and the flag digit. This is due to the rule of signs when subtracting negative quantities. The following example demonstrates the technique.

63542 ÷ 38

Since 8 of 38 is a large digit we can change it into a 2 by writing 38 as 4$\bar{2}$.

$$4^{\bar{2}}|6\ 3\ 2\ 4\ /\ 2$$
$$2$$
$$1$$

Proceeding as before, 4 into 6 = 1 rem. 2.
From 23 we then *add* the product of 1 and 2. This is because the result of subtracting a negative quantity or number is to add it. In particular, 23 − 1 × (−2) = 23 − (−2) = 23 + 2 = 25.

$$4^{\bar{2}}|6\ 3\ 2\ 4\ /\ 2$$
$$2\ 1$$
$$1\ 6\ 6$$

4 into 25 = 6 rem. 1.
12 + 6 × 2 = 24, 4 into 24 = 6
4 + 6 × 2 = 16, 4 into 16 = 4
2 + 4 × 2 = 10, which is the final remainder.

$$4^{\bar{2}}|6\ 3\ 2\ 4\ /\ 2$$
$$2\ 1$$
$$1\ 6\ 6\ 4\ /\ 10$$

It is possible for the addition part of this method to give a quotient which is too big. In this case another type of altered remainder might have to be used.

Exercise 17i Use a vinculum for each flag digit:

1. 3246 ÷ 38	**9.** 10245 ÷ 58	**17.** 765465 ÷ 29	**25.** 50067 ÷ 89
2. 7760 ÷ 49	**10.** 98768 ÷ 37	**18.** 300000 ÷ 18	**26.** 23053 ÷ 28
3. 1232 ÷ 78	**11.** 27615 ÷ 79	**19.** 546732 ÷ 89	**27.** 42604 ÷ 27
4. 4028 ÷ 89	**12.** 30098 ÷ 68	**20.** 546322 ÷ 46	**28.** 629874 ÷ 58
5. 2431 ÷ 19	**13.** 43232 ÷ 69	**21.** 321021 ÷ 26	**29.** 200000 ÷ 79
6. 3724 ÷ 27	**14.** 70205 ÷ 48	**22.** 364732 ÷ 57	**30.** 641034 ÷ 67
7. 7026 ÷ 48	**15.** 11011 ÷ 37	**23.** 747438 ÷ 78	**31.** 716000 ÷ 19
8. 5699 ÷ 69	**16.** 54364 ÷ 88	**24.** 438085 ÷ 28	**32.** 10000000 ÷ 19

Choosing which method to use.

The key to choosing the easiest division method is to look at the numbers involved. A few pointers may help with the decision, and these are listed below.

1. Begin by inspecting the numbers to see if either simple division or proportionate division can be used.

2. If the divisor is close to a power of ten and less than that base then try *All from nine and the last from ten*. It is easiest when the first digit of the dividend is small.

3. If the divisor is close to a power of ten but more than that base then try *Transpose and adjust*. Again it is often easiest when the first digit of the dividend is small.

4. If all else fails then use straight division for this is the general method applicable in all cases. Altered remainders or vinculum digits can often make the working easier.

149284 ÷ 113

At first sight it looks as if *Transpose and adjust* can be used.

On adding the digits in the third column we
find 2 + $\bar{2}$ + $\bar{5}$ = $\bar{5}$, and this is set down in the
answer line. The next step is to multiply $\bar{5}$ by
$\bar{1}\bar{3}$, and following the rules for signs, that
− × − = +, we have 65.
The remainder is then 129 which is too large.
On redividing the remainder by 113 we have 1/16.

```
1 1 3 | 4 9 2 / 8 4
  1 3 |   5 2
      |   5   2
      |     6 5
      -------------
      4 4 5/12 9
              1 / 1 6
      -------------
      4 3 6 / 1 6
```

By *devinculating* the 44$\bar{5}$ to 435 and adding the 1 which has been
carried the answer is 436/16.

This whole process is a little cumbersome and so we should try
straight division with 3 as the flag digit and 11 as the working divisor.

```
      3
  11  | 4 9 2 8 / 4
      |   5 7   3
      -------------
      4 3 6 / 16
```

Using straight division in this way is evidently easier.

Exercise 17j Mixed practice:

1. 1463 ÷ 19	**6.** 11866 ÷ 34	**11.** 17366 ÷ 15	**16.** 112233 ÷ 89
2. 3055 ÷ 13	**7.** 15283 ÷ 29	**12.** 21004 ÷ 97	**17.** 16497 ÷ 47
3. 947250 ÷ 90	**8.** 1224 ÷ 98	**13.** 10245 ÷ 102	**18.** 156541 ÷ 11
4. 2444 ÷ 26	**9.** 56062 ÷ 16	**14.** 62935 ÷ 14	**19.** 765860 ÷ 24
5. 1953 ÷ 31	**10.** 3689 ÷ 17	**15.** 249071 ÷ 18	**20.** 24687 ÷ 111

21. 809712 ÷ 21	**26.** 12873 ÷ 82	**31.** 45764 ÷ 998	**35.** 44730 ÷ 105
22. 33072 ÷ 53	**27.** 485073 ÷ 35	**32.** 41753 ÷ 43	**36.** 185452 ÷ 71
23. 27458 ÷ 104	**28.** 65084 ÷ 106	**33.** 49928 ÷ 79	**37.** 597035 ÷ 97
24. 24057 ÷ 99	**29.** 46200 ÷ 78	**32.** 9027 ÷ 17	**38.** 809908 ÷ 113
25. 18428 ÷ 68	**30.** 953682 ÷ 36	**34.** 3876 ÷ 19	**39.** 151782 ÷ 123

Chapter 18 Further algebra

Simplifying in addition and subtraction

Terms which are *like* can be collected together. **Like terms** are those which are exactly the same except for the number or sign at the beginning.

Simplify $5a + 9b - 2a + a - 4b - 2b$

Collect like terms together and then sum them up.

$$5a + 9b - 2a + a - 4b - 2b = 5a - 2a + a + 9b - 4b - 2b$$
$$= 4a + 3b$$

Exercise 18a Simplify:

1. $a + a + a + a$

2. $b + b + b + b + b$

3. $d + d - d$

4. $y + y - y - y$

5. $e + e - e + e + e$

6. $2x + 3x$

7. $5y + y$

8. $8p - 3p$

9. $5r - 4r$

10. $7f + f$

11. $w + w + 3w$

12. $3c + 2c + c$

13. $6b + b + 6b$

14. $a + 5a - 3a$

15. $4b + 2b - 5b$

16. $7k + 7k - 5k$

17. $10n - 4n - 4n$

18. $5d - 4d - d$

19. $9a - 6a - 2a$

20. $5t + t - 3t + t - 2t$

21. $x + y + y + x$

22. $f + g + f + f$

23. $6a + 4b - 2a - b$

24. $7c + 4d + c - 3d$

25. $8m - 6n - 2m - 2n$

26. $4x - 2y - 2y - y$

27. $8p - 4q + 4$

28. $8k + 6 - 4k - 3$

29. $12v + 8w - 4v - v + 2w$

30. $i + j + k - i + j - k$

31. $3x - 5y - 4z - 2x - y - z$

32. $5r + s - 6 + 7t$

33. $3a + 6b - 3b + 2a - 5$

34. $1 + 4x + 2y - 3x + y$

35. $2x + y - z - x + 3y + z$

36. $4g - 2 + 3h + 9 - h + 3g$

Simplifying in multiplication and division

Simplify, (i) $3x \times 4xy$; (ii) $6a \div 4b$; (iii) $1\frac{1}{5}x \times 4$; (iv) $\dfrac{2p^2}{3} \div \dfrac{1}{6}pq$

(i) $3x \times 4xy = 3 \times 4 \times x \times x \times y = 12x^2 y$

(ii) $6a \div 4b = \dfrac{6a}{4b} = \dfrac{3a}{2b}$

(iii) $1\frac{1}{5}x \times 4 = \dfrac{6x}{5} \times 4 = \dfrac{24x}{5}$

(iv) $\dfrac{2p^2}{3} \div \dfrac{pq}{6} = \dfrac{2p^2}{3} \times \dfrac{6}{pq} = \dfrac{2 \times p \times p}{3} \times \dfrac{6}{p \times q} = \dfrac{4p}{q}$

Exercise 18b Simplify:

1. $5d \times 4$
2. $7 \times 7b$
3. $9f \times 1$
4. $4w \times 0$
5. $5x \times 5x$
6. $6 \times r \times 4s$
7. $gh \times h$
8. $pq \times 2t$
9. $5mn \times 5mn$
10. $7yz \times 7z$
11. $3bc \times 4bd$
12. $2u^2 \times 2v^2$
13. $6xyz \times 6xz$
14. $6x \div 3$
15. $8m \div 1$
16. $3n \div 3$

17. $\dfrac{12p}{4}$
18. $\dfrac{4}{8x}$
19. $\dfrac{7h}{7}$
20. $\dfrac{2w}{2w}$
21. $\dfrac{16y}{12}$
22. $\dfrac{h}{4} \times 6$
23. $2 \times \dfrac{3a}{4}$
24. $\dfrac{a}{8} \times 5a$
25. $\dfrac{b}{2} \times 7b$
26. $2\frac{1}{2}k \times 4$
27. $1\frac{1}{4}z \times 8$
28. $1\frac{3}{4}v \times 2v$
29. $1\frac{1}{3}n \times \frac{3}{4}n$
30. $d \div 1$
31. $7h \div \frac{1}{2}$
32. $\dfrac{bc}{bd}$
33. $\dfrac{f}{fg}$
34. $\dfrac{k}{k^2}$
35. $\dfrac{xy^2}{xy}$
36. $\dfrac{pq}{p}$
37. $\dfrac{d^2}{de}$
38. $\dfrac{r^2 s^2}{rs}$
39. $\dfrac{6ab}{5} \div \dfrac{9ac}{10}$
40. $\dfrac{2a^2}{3} \div \dfrac{ab}{6}$

137

Using brackets

Brackets are used to indicate that the contents may be regarded as a single number.

Exercise 18c Evaluate the following, if $x = 3$, $y = 5$, $b = 8$:

1. $2(b - x)$

2. $b(y - x)$

3. $3(b - y)$

4. $y(b + x)$

5. $(x - 2)y$

6. $\dfrac{x + y}{b}$

7. $(2y - b)x$

8. $\dfrac{b - x}{y}$

9. $4(x + y) - (4x + 4y)$

10. $(x + y)(b - y)$

11. $5(x + y) - (5x + y)$

12. $(3y - 5x)(2b - x)$

Remove the brackets and simplify where possible:

13. $5(2a + 3)$

14. $4(3c - 2d)$

15. $5(3a - b)$

16. $17(p - 3q)$

17. $d(e - f)$

18. $ab(c - d)$

19. $3g(4h - 1)$

20. $7(2d - 3e + 1)$

21. $8(3a - 5b - 1)$

22. $a(b + c - 2d)$

23. $2(4x - 3) + 3(x - 1)$

24. $3p(2x + y) + 2p(2a + b)$

25. $5(k + 4) + 2(3k - 8)$

26. $x(a - 2b) + 3y(3a + b)$

27. $a(2b + 3c) + b(3a - c)$

Evaluate the following, if $a = 3$, $b = 2$, $c = 6$, $d = 4$:

28. $a + b(c + d)$

29. $(a + b)(c + d)$

30. $(a + b)c + d$

31. $a + (b + c)d$

32. $a + bc + d$

33. $b + c \div a + d$

34. $b + c \div (a + d)$

35. $(a + b + c)^2$

36. $a^2 + b^2 + c^2$

By using brackets express the result of subtracting three times the sum of a and b from two times the sum of x and y.

Three times the sum of a and b is represented by $3(a + b)$, two times the sum of x and y is represented by $2(x + y)$
$\therefore$ required result is $2(x + y) - 3(a + b)$

An empty jar weighs x g and contains 200 g of jam. 40 such jars are packed into a box which weighs w g. Find the total weight.

One jar of jam weighs $(200 + x)$ g
$\therefore$ 40 jars weigh $40(200 + x)$ g
$\therefore$ the box, when packed weighs $[w + 40(200 + x)]$ g

Exercise 18d Express the answers by using brackets: (Do not expand the brackets.)

1. Add $2a$ to b and multiply the result by 3.

2. Subtract e from $3f$ and multiply the result by 4.

3. Multiply $3x - y$ by z.

4. Divide $a + b + c$ by 2.

5. Find the product of $2x$ and $y - 3z$.

6. Divide $2a + 3b - 5$ by 7.

7. Half the sum of $3m$ and $7n$.

8. Subtract $a - 2b$ from $2c - d$.

9. Find the product of $r - s$ and $r + s$.

10. Find the number by which b exceeds $d - c$.

11. Find one fifth of the sum of $3f$ and $5g$.

12. Subtract five times the sum of $2b$ and 3 from two times the sum of $2c$ and d.

13. Subtract the square of the sum of x and y from the sum of the squares of y and z.

14. Find the product of two consecutive whole numbers the smallest of which is n.

15. Find the product of three consecutive whole numbers the smallest of which is $m - 1$.

16. A box of chocolate weighs x grams and when empty weighs y grams. What is the weight of the chocolate in the box? What is the weight of the chocolate in p boxes of the same kind?

17. I have 10 coins; n of them are 20p pieces and the rest of them are 10p pieces. What is the number of 10p pieces? What is the total value of the coins?

18. In the figure, the line PQ is 10 cm long and PA is x cm long. AQ is divided into three equal parts at B and C. Find the lengths of (i) AB, (ii) AC, (iii) PC.

19. A barrel of port weighs x kg when empty and y kg when full. (i) Find the weight of the port in the full barrel. (ii) Find the weight of the barrel and the port when it is one third full.

Factorising expressions

The process opposite to expanding brackets is called factorisation. To factorise a number simply means to express it as the product of two numbers. For example, $45 = 5 \times 9$. Similarly with algebraic expressions to factorise means to express it as the product of two factors. This is usually done by using brackets. For example,
$4a + 2b$ may be expressed as $2(2a + b)$.

To factorise expressions like this we have to take outside the brackets the HCF of all the terms in the expression.

Factorise, (a) $2y - 2z$, (b) $ab + ac$, (c) $6xy - 9xz$, (d) $a^2 + a$

$2y - 2z = 2(y - z)$	The HCF of $2y$ and $2z$ is 2 and so this is placed outside the brackets. By division, $2y \div 2 = y$ and $-2z \div 2 = -z$ gives the inside of the brackets.
$ab + ac = a(b + c)$	a is the HCF
$6xy - 9xz = 3x(2y - 3z)$	Here the HCF of the coefficients, 6 and 9 is 3, and the HCF of the other parts is x. The HCF is then $3x$.
$a^2 + a = a(a + 1)$	The HCF is a, $a^2 \div a = a$ and $a \div a = 1$

If the highest common factor is not used then the expression is said not to be factorised completely. For example, $4a + 4b = 2(2a + 2b)$ but 2 is not the HCF. The correct factorised form is $4(a + b)$.

Exercise 18e Factorise:

1. $3x - 3y$

2. $6a + 9b$

3. $4r - 8s$

4. $16a - 24b$

5. $3a + 3b + 3c$

6. $6x - 9y - 12z$

7. $ab + ad$

8. $bx - by$

9. $ac + bc$

10. $pq + pr - ps$

11. $tu - uv - uw$

12. $3ab + 3ac$

13. $2xy - 4xz$

14. $4bc - 4cd$

15. $4mn + 6mp$

16. $8xy - 12y + 14yz$

17. $x^2 + x$

18. $a^2 - 3a$

19. $3b + 2b^2$

20. $4y^3 - 6y$

21. $10a^3 + 15a^2 - 5a$

Multiplying binomials using *Vertically and crosswise*

A binomial is an algebraic expression consisting of two terms. $a + b$, $3x^2 - 2x$, $6y - 8$ are examples of binomials. You can multiply two binomials together using *Vertically and crosswise*.

Expand (i) $(x + 3)(x + 2)$ (ii) $(x - 1)(x - 7)$ (iii) $(2x + 5)(3x - 1)$

$$\begin{array}{r} x + 3 \\ \times\, x + 2 \\ \hline x^2 + 5x + 6 \end{array}$$

Using the *Vertically and crosswise* sutra as for multiplying two-digit numbers, from the left,
$x \times x = x^2$
$x \times 2 + 3 \times x = 2x + 3x = 5x$
$3 \times 2 = 6$

$$\begin{array}{r} x - 1 \\ \times\, x - 7 \\ \hline x^2 - 8x + 7 \end{array}$$

$x \times x = x^2$
$x \times (-7) + (-1) \times x = -8x$
$(-7) \times (-1) = 7$

$$\begin{array}{r} 2x + 5 \\ \times\, 3x - 1 \\ \hline 6x^2 + 13x - 5 \end{array}$$

$2x \times 3x = 6x^2$
$2x \times (-1) + 5 \times 3x = 13x$
$5 \times (-1) = -5$

The following step-by-step procedure may explain how the *Vertically and crosswise* method works.

$$(x + 3)(x + 2) = (x + 3) \times x + (x + 3) \times 2 = x^2 + 3x + 2x + 6 = x^2 + 5x + 6$$

Another explanation considers $(x + 3)$ and $(x + 2)$ as two sides of a rectangle. The area of the rectangle is the product of these two binomials.

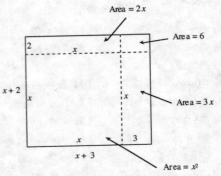

The total area of the four sections is $x^2 + 3x + 2x + 6 = x^2 + 5x + 6$

Exercise 18f

1. Multiply together $(x + 3)$ and $(x + 1)$. Now multiply 13 and 11 using *Vertically and crosswise* from the left.

2. Multiply $(x + 2)$ and $(x + 4)$. Now multiply 12 and 14.

3. Multiply $(x + 3)$ and $(x + 4)$ and then multiply 13 and 14.

Expand:

4. $(x + 1)(x + 1)$
5. $(x + 2)(x + 1)$
6. $(x + 3)(x + 6)$
7. $(x + 1)(x + 7)$
8. $(x + 8)(x + 9)$
9. $(x + 3)(x + 7)$
10. $(x + 2)(x + 2)$
11. $(x + 3)(x + 3)$
12. $(x - 2)(x - 4)$
13. $(x - 4)(x - 5)$
14. $(x - 1)(x - 9)$

15. $(x - 7)(x - 8)$
16. $(x - 5)(x - 9)$
17. $(x - 1)(x - 1)$
18. $(x - 2)(x - 2)$
19. $(x - 3)(x - 3)$
20. $(x + 2)(x - 4)$
21. $(x + 1)(x - 3)$
22. $(x + 3)(x - 5)$
23. $(x - 2)(x + 2)$
24. $(x - 6)(x + 6)$
25. $(x + 7)(x - 1)$

26. $(x - 8)(x + 9)$
27. $(x - 1)(x + 1)$
28. $(x + 3)(x + 8)$
29. $(x - 7)(x - 7)$
30. $(x + 6)(x - 7)$
31. $(x - 8)(x + 4)$
32. $(x + 6)(x + 1)$
33. $(x - 6)(x - 1)$
34. $(x + 6)(x - 1)$
35. $(x - 6)(x + 1)$
36. $(x - 12)(x + 11)$

Exercise 18g Expand:

1. $(x + 5)(x + 5)$
2. $(x + 6)(x + 6)$
3. $(x + 10)(x + 10)$
4. $(x - 8)(x - 8)$
5. $(x - 4)(x - 4)$
6. $(x - 9)(x - 9)$
7. $(2x + 1)(x + 2)$
8. $(x + 1)(2x + 1)$
9. $(2x + 3)(x + 1)$
10. $(x + 3)(2x + 1)$
11. $(2x + 1)(x + 7)$
12. $(3x + 8)(x + 2)$
13. $(4x + 3)(x + 7)$

14. $(2x - 7)(x - 1)$
15. $(x - 5)(2x - 3)$
16. $(2x - 1)(x - 8)$
17. $(x - 3)(5x - 2)$
18. $(2x - 3)(x - 3)$
19. $(x + 5)(3x - 4)$
20. $(2x + 1)(3x - 1)$
21. $(3x + 1)(3x + 1)$
22. $(4x + 2)(4x + 1)$
23. $(5x + 3)(2x + 6)$
24. $(3x + 1)(2x + 7)$
25. $(x + 8)(9x + 8)$
26. $(2x + 3)(2x + 7)$

27. $(3x - 8)(x + 9)$
28. $(x - 1)(7x + 1)$
29. $(2x + 3)(5x + 8)$
30. $(3x - 7)(2x - 7)$
31. $(7x + 6)(x - 2)$
32. $(5x - 8)(3x + 4)$
33. $(7x + 6)(x + 1)$
34. $(x + 4)(2x + 1)$
35. $(5x + 2)(9x + 1)$
36. $(3x + 7)(x + 6)$
37. $(5x + 1)(2x + 7)$
38. $(2x + 1)(3x + 11)$
39. $(7x + 3)(3x + 7)$

Construction of formulae

A formula is an equation in which the terms have a practical meaning. For example, the area, A, of a rectangle is related to the base, b, and its height, h, by the formula, $A = bh$.

Exercise 18h If brackets occur in the answer they should not be removed.

1. What is the perimeter of a rectangle 12 cm long and 4 cm wide?

2. If the rectangle in the figure is l cm long and w cm wide, find a formula for the perimeter, p in terms of l and w.

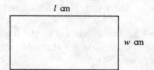

3. The perimeter of an isosceles triangle is 14 cm and the two equal sides each have lengths of 5 cm. Find the length of the third side.

4. The perimeter of the isosceles triangle in the figure is p. Find a formula for p in terms of a and b.

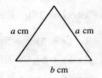

5. A car travelling at a constant speed covers a distance of 106 miles in 2 hours. Find its speed on this journey.

6. Find a formula for the speed of a car v in terms of the distance, s, and the time taken, t.

7. The formula for the volume of a rectangular block with width w, length l and height h, is $V = blw$. Write down the formula for the volume of a similar block with width 4 cm, length x cm, and height y cm.

8. Find the volume of a rectangular block 6 cm high, 7 cm long and 7 cm wide.

9. A rectangular block, of volume V cm^3, is h cm high, b cm long and b cm wide. Find a formula for V in terms of h and b.

10. Find the total area of the six faces of the block in question 8,

11. Find a formula for the total area, A, of the six faces of the rectangular block in question 9 in terms of h and b.

12. A lady has £500 in the bank. Each month she deposits £50 and does not take any out. How much will she have in the bank after 24 months?

13. If she has £D in the bank and deposits £C every month for n months, find a formula for the total amount, £T, in the bank.

14. To convert a temperature of $F°$ Fahrenheit into $C°$ Centigrade, 32 is subtracted from F and then the result is multiplied by 5 and divided by 9. Express this as a formula with C as the subject.

15. The formula for the volume of a pyramid is one third times the base area times the vertical height. Write down the formula for the volume V of a square based pyramid whose square has edge length l and whose vertical height is h.

Substitution

Substitution is the name given to the process of replacing letters by specific numbers. Since this is a move from the general to the specific the sutra is *Individuality - Totality*.

If $x = 2$ and $y = 3$ find the value of (i) $5x^2$, (ii) $3xy^2$, (iii) $\frac{1}{2}xy - 1$

(i) $5x^2 = 5 \times 2 \times 2 = 20$

(ii) $3xy^2 = 3 \times 2 \times 3 \times 3 = 54$

(iii) $\frac{1}{2}xy - 1 = \frac{1}{2} \times 2 \times 3 - 1 = 1 \times 3 - 1 = 2$

Exercise 18i

If $x = 3$ and $y = 4$, evaluate:

1. $4x + 7$ 4. $7y - 7$ 7. $2y^2$ 10. $x(x + y)$
2. $5x - 2y$ 5. $3x + 9y$ 8. $x^3 + 3$ 11. $\frac{2}{3}xy$
3. $\frac{1}{3}x + \frac{1}{4}y$ 6. $4x^2$ 9. $x + xy$ 12. $y^2 - x^2$

If $x = 5$, $y = 0$, $z = 3$, evaluate:

13. xyz 16. $3y + xz^2$ 19. $\frac{5z}{x}$ 22. $\frac{1}{x} + \frac{1}{z}$
14. $2xy + yz$ 17. $x(z - 2y)$ 20. $\frac{x - 1}{x + 3}$ 23. $\frac{2y + x}{2z}$
15. $x(x - 2z)$ 18. $\frac{x}{2z}$ 21. $\frac{1}{z} - \frac{1}{x}$ 24. $\frac{x + y}{x - y}$

If $a = \frac{2}{5}$ and $b = 1\frac{1}{4}$, evaluate:

25. $a + 2b$ 28. ab 31. $b - 2\frac{1}{2}a$ 34. $\frac{2a}{b}$
26. $b - a$ 29. b^2 32. a^2b 35. $4ab^2$
27. $3a$ 30. $5b$ 33. $b \div a$ 36. $4b^2 - 5a^2$

Using formulae

If a speed of x feet per second is the same as a speed of v miles per hour, v is given by the formula, $v = \dfrac{15x}{22}$.

Find, in miles per hour, a speed of 66 ft per second.

Putting $x = 66$ into the formula,

$$v = \frac{15 \times 66}{22} = \frac{15 \times 3}{1} = \underline{45 \text{ mph}}$$

Exercise 18j

1. The cost of hiring a yacht for n days is £C. C is given by the formula, £$C = 400 + 40n$. Find the cost of hiring the yacht for 14 days.

2. When a stone is dropped from the top of a building, the distance s meters, it falls in t seconds is given by the formula, $s = 4.9t^2$. Find how far it falls in 4 seconds.

3. If K is a distance in kilometres and M is the same distance in miles, then K is approximately given by the formula, $K = \dfrac{8M}{5}$. Find the number of kilometres in 25 miles.

4. A climbing rope of diameter d mm can support a load of w kg. w is given by the formula $w = 120d^2$. Find the safe load for a rope of diameter 1.5 cm.

5. If the circumference of a circle of radius r cm is C cm, C is given by the formula $C = 2\pi r$, where $\pi = \frac{22}{7}$ approximately. Find the circumference of a circle of radius 12 cm.

6. If the area of a circle of radius r cm is A cm^2, then A is given by the formula, $A = \pi r^2$, where $\pi = \frac{22}{7}$ approximately. Find the area of a circle of radius 7 cm.

7. The rise PQ of a stairway is a inches and the tread PR is b inches. a and b are related by the formula, $a = \frac{1}{2}(24 - b)$
Find the rise if the tread is (i) 12 inches and (ii) 9 inches.

8. If a temperature F° Fahrenheit is equal to C° Centigrade, F is given by the formula, $F = 32 + \frac{9C}{5}$.
Express in degrees Fahrenheit the following temperatures,
(i) 100° Centigrade, (ii) 0° Centigrade, (iii) 15° Centigrade.

Chapter 19 Ratio and proportion

Ratio

The sutra governing all aspects of ratio and proportion is *Proportionately*.

A **ratio** is a relation of quantity in respect of multiple size within a given unity.

Consider a book-shelf with 50 hardback and 120 paperback books. The unity in which these two quantities are related is *books*. Whenever two things or quantities are related there is always a unity.

On comparing 50 hardbacks with 120 paperbacks we may say that there are 70 more paperbacks than hardbacks. However, this does relate the two quantities in terms of multiple size. For a ratio we seek to relate the two quantities to provide us with some idea of how many times one quantity is larger than the other.

In this example, the ratio of the number of hardbacks to the number of paperbacks is 50 : 120. This is read as *fifty to one hundred and twenty*.

A ratio may be brought to lowest terms (or simplest form) by dividing the numbers by their HCF. This is the same process as used for reducing fractions. The HCF of 50 and 120 is 10 and so, 50 : 120 : : 5 : 12. This is read as *50 is to 120 as 5 is to 12*.

Exercise 19a Bring the following ratios to their simplest form:

1. 24 : 42	**6.** 72 : 18	**11.** 144 : 256	**16.** 2 : 6 : 26
2. 19 : 38	**7.** 56 : 28	**12.** 312 : 123	**17.** 12 : 54 : 96
3. 36 : 24	**8.** 80 : 16	**13.** 680 : 72	**18.** 75 : 450 : 125
4. 15 : 5	**9.** 125 : 100	**14.** 35 : 105	**19.** 39 : 72 : 120
5. 24 : 96	**10.** 22 : 132	**15.** 420 : 860	**20.** 256 : 512 : 64

Proportion

Proportion is an equality of ratios.

The ratio 12 to 20 is the same as the ratio of 3 to 5 for by dividing both 12 and 20 by 4 we obtain 3 and 5. 12 : 20 and 3 : 5 are in proportion and when written as 12 : 20 :: 3 : 5 is often called a **ratio equation**.

Solving ratio equations

When one of the quantities in a ratio equation is unknown then it may be found by using the Vedic sutra, *The product of the means equals the product of the extremes*. In this sutra, the word *means* refers to the inner two numbers and the word *extremes* refers to the outer two numbers. So in the example, 12 : 20 :: 3 : 5, the inner two numbers are 20 and 3 and the outer two numbers are 12 and 5. The sutra tells us that the product of these is the same, 60 in both cases.

Find the value of x in, 14 : 4 :: x : 22

Using, The product of the means equals the product of the extremes,

$$4x = 14 \times 22$$

On transposing the 4 to the other side,

$$x = \frac{14 \times 22}{4}$$

On cancelling the 4 with a factor of 2 in 14 and a factor of 2 in 22 we have,

$$x = \frac{7 \times 11}{1}$$

[After some practice it will be more convenient to go straight to the second stage.]

$$\therefore \underline{x = 77}$$

Exercise 19b Solve the following: (Set them out as shown in the example.)

1. $x : 12 :: 7 : 4$

2. $2 : 3 :: 40 : x$

3. $5 : 25 :: x : 1$

4. $6 : 15 :: x : 1$

5. $1 : \frac{5}{8} :: 1 : x$

6. $0.6 : 0.2 :: x : 1$

7. $5 : x :: 35 : 6$

8. $x : 25 :: 30 : 150$

9. $56 : 80 :: 7 : x$

10. $7 : 21 :: x : 1$

11. $x : 1 :: 11 : 15$

12. $x : 4 :: 3 : 8$

13. $4 : x :: 6 : 5$

14. $x : 35 :: 10 : 7$

15. $9 : 16 :: x : 64$

16. $x : 1 :: 3 : 5$

17. $120 : 45 :: x : 72$

18. $600 : 325 :: x : 195$

19. $2 : \frac{3}{4} :: 1 : x$

20. $28 : x :: 84 : 14$

21. $x : 20 :: 3 : 7$

22. $12.4 : x :: 16.8 : 2$

23. $x : 1.21 :: 3 : 6.6$

24. $48 : x :: \frac{1}{3} : 14$

Problems in direct proportion

The following problems involve what is called *direct proportion*. This is where when one quantity is increased the other quantity is increased in the same ratio. For example, if three atlases cost £30 then we would expect six atlases to cost

£60. As the number of atlases increases the cost increases in the same ratio. The simplest way to solve such problems is to begin by writing down a ratio equation with the given quantities.

If five bags of coffee cost £7.20, how much do two bags cost?

Let x be the cost of 2 bags of coffee. Then $5 : 720 :: 2 : x$

Always begin with a statement of letting x be the unknown quantity which is to be found.

$$5x = 720 \times 2$$

$$x = \frac{720 \times 2}{5}$$

Costs in pounds are converted to pence for ease of calculation.

$$= \frac{144 \times 2}{1}$$

Having established the ratio equation from the problem, then use *The product of the means equals the product of the extremes* and solve for x.

$$\therefore x = 288$$

Two bags cost £2.88

Exercise 19c

1. Thomas cycles 24 km in 3 hours. How far would he cycle in 5 hours at the same rate?

2. A litre of water has a mass of 1000 grams. Find the mass of 4 litres of water.

3. 2 people can stay in a hotel for a week for £560. Find how much it will cost them to stay for 10 days.

4. If 150 units of gas cost £6.30, find the cost of 250 units.

5. My car uses 8 gallons of petrol on a journey of 252 miles. How many gallons shall I use on a journey of 630 miles?

6. If 10 pens cost £17.80, how much would 7 pens cost?

7. To insure a house valued at £160,000 costs £90. What will it cost to insure a house valued at £100,000?

8. A train travels at 60 km/h. Find the number of metres it travels per second.

9. £300 invested brings £12 interest per year. Find the interest on £800 in a year.

10. If 6 litres of liquid have a mass of 30 kg, find the mass of 16 litres of the liquid.

11. If 12 electric bulbs cost £7.56, how many can be bought for £9.45?

12. A salesman's commission on sales of £448 is £27.20. How much had he sold when his commission was £20.40?

13. If cherries cost £0.70 per half-pound, find the cost of $2\frac{1}{4}$ pounds.

14. If 5 planes can land at Heathrow airport every 6 minutes, find how many planes can land in half an hour.

15. In a sponsored swim a girl calculated that she would receive £56.14 for 35 lengths. How much should she receive if, in the event, she actually swam 45 lengths?

16. A shire horse weighing 2800 lbs can pull a carriage weighing 11,200 lbs. If a man weighing 150 lbs has the same weight-to-strength ratio, what weight of carriage should he be able to pull?

17. The population of Great Britain is about 56 million and the area is about 100,000 square miles. If the USA, with an area of about 3,700,000 square miles had the same number of people per square mile, what would be its population?

18. The total loss of allied shipping during the second world war was 21,000,000 tons of which 54 tons out of every 100 was British. Find the number of tons of British ships sunk.

Problems in inverse proportion

Where one quantity increases in the same ratio as another quantity decreases then the proportion is inverse. For example, if it takes four men three days to build a wall, how long will it take six men working at the same rate? Clearly if the number of men working increases then the time it takes must decrease.

Such problems come under the heading of *inverse proportion.* and are solved using the sutra, *The first by the first and the last by the last.*

In the example above, there are two situations, as it were. One where there are four men working for three days and the other in which six men work for an unknown, or x number of days. The *first by the first* is 4×3 and *the last by the last* is $6 \times x$. With inverse proportion, the product is constant and so $4 \times 3 = 6x$, which gives $x = 2$ days as the answer.

If 15 men can build a brick wall in 14 hours, how long will it take 21 men?

Let x be the number of hours taken by 21 men.

$15 \times 14 = 21x$

$\dfrac{15 \times 14}{21} = x$

$\dfrac{5 \times 2}{1} = x$

$\therefore x = 10$

It will take 10 hrs.

By *The first by the first and the last by the last* sutra, the number of men times the number of hours is the same in both situations.

It is usually easier to cancel down to lowest terms before multiplying or dividing.

Exercise 19d

1. A 3 ton lorry removes a mound of earth in 15 journeys. How many journeys would a 5 ton lorry have to make?

2. A certain ditch can be dug by 8 men in 3 days. How long would it take 6 men?

3. At 90 km/h a train takes 5 hours to make a certain journey. How long would it take at 150 km/h?

4. From a bottle of wine I can pour 5 glasses each with a capacity of 15 cl. How many glasses can I pour if each has a capacity of 12.5 cl?

5. A book has 150 pages each of which are 0.1 mm thick. How many pages would there be if the thickness of each page was 0.075 mm and the total thickness of the book is the same?

6. If I bake 24 loaves of bread in $1\frac{1}{2}$ lb tins how many loaves could I bake using 2 lb tins?

7. A certain sum of money is sufficient to pay the wages of 12 men for 30 days. For how many days is it sufficient for 10 men, if all receive the same amount?

8. The oats in a bin will feed 18 horses for 20 days; how long will they feed 15 horses?

9. A man packs 40 boxes of apples with 36 in each box. How many boxes are needed if only 30 are put in each box?

10. 30 men can mend a section of railway track in 24 days. How long will it take 18 men to mend it?

11. A nursery gardener ties up 108 bunches of flowers with 10 in each bunch. How many bunches would there be if he put 12 in each bunch?

12. A ship's sump **can be** emptied by 5 pumps working together in 40 minutes. How long would it take 8 pumps?

13. Three decorators can paint an apartment in 10 days, working 8 hours a day. How long would it take five decorators working at 6 hours a day? [Consider the number of man-hours in each situation.]

14. If the sun can dry 12 shirts on a washing line in one and a half hours, how long will it take to dry fifteen shirts?

15. A section of wall can be covered with 72 tiles each 4 in by 4 in. How many tiles are needed if the tiles used are 6 in by 6 in?

Dividing a quantity in a given ratio

Dividing a quantity in a given ratio is invariably done by relating the ratio to the *whole*. For example, if £60 is to be divided in the ratio 5 : 7, we first relate the ratio to the *whole* number of parts, that is, 5 + 7 = 12. This whole of 12 parts is equivalent to the £60. We then have to find 5 parts and 7 parts and to do this we can again use ratio equations.

Divide £60 in the ratio 5 : 7

Total number of parts is 5 + 7 = 12

Let x and y be the amounts required.

$$12 : 60 :: 5 : x \text{ gives } x = \frac{60 \times 5}{12} = 25$$

$$\text{and } 12 : 60 :: 7 : y \text{ gives } y = \frac{60 \times 7}{12} = 35$$

Dividing a quantity in a given ratio may also be done by what is called the unitary method. In the example above, having found that the total number of parts is 12, you then find 1 part by dividing £60 by 12. You can then find 5 parts and 7 parts as required. This is shown below.

Divide £60 in the ratio 5 : 7

Total number of parts is 5 + 7 = 12 $\qquad$ 1 part $= \dfrac{£60}{12}$

$$5 \text{ parts} = \frac{5 \times £60}{12} = £25$$

$$7 \text{ parts} = \frac{7 \times £60}{12} = £35$$

Note that a ratio does not have any units of measurement and so in the previous example it would not be correct to give the answer as £25 : £35.

Exercise 19e

1. Divide 56 in the ratio 3 : 5.

2. Divide £350 in the ratio 4 : 3.

3. Divide £60 in the ratio (i) 2 : 3, (ii) 5 : 7, (iii) 4 : 1

4. Divide 20 kg in the ratio 21 : 19.

5. Divide 360° in the ratio 4 : 5. What is the difference between the two angles?

6. Divide 80 cm in the ratios 2 : 3 : 5. What fraction of the whole is the first part?

7. Divide 1280 in the ratios 3 : 5 : 8.

8. The profits, £7500, of a business are divided among three men so that their shares are in the ratios 3 : 4 : 8. Find each share.

9. Three sisters, Amy, Eva and Ida are 7, 9 and 12 years old, respectively. They are each bought a dress the costs of which are in the ratios of their ages. If the total cost is £112, find the cost of each girl's dress.

10. The sides of a triangle are in the ratio 4 : 5 : 7 and its perimeter is 64 cm. Find the lengths of the sides.

11. Divide a line of length 1 m into three parts whose ratios are 2 : 3 : 5.

12. Divide £20 into two parts so that one part is three times the other.

13. Divide $11200 between Ricardo Ruby , Fingers Malloy and Al Afsome in the ratio 3 : 5 : 6.

14. A lady receives a quote of £1397 to have her front and back gardens redeveloped. The cost is proportional to the areas which are in the ratio 5 : 6. Find the cost of just having the back garden redeveloped.

15. A farmer wishes to fence off a rectangular field so that the length is twice as long as the breadth. If he has 1200 m of fencing, find the length, breadth and area of the field.

16. Divide £98 into two parts so that one is $\frac{3}{4}$ of the other.

17. Helen scores $\frac{1}{2}$ as many marks as Rebecca and Rebecca scores $\frac{1}{2}$ as many marks as Kirsty. If the sum of their marks is 224, how many did each score?

18. A grandfather leaves £750,000 to be divided between his three grandsons in the ratios 3 : 5 : 7. How much does each receive?

Percentages

A **percentage** is a ratio of one quantity to 100. We can use ratio equations to solve problems in percentages.

Express Lydia's exam mark of 28 out of 40 as a percentage.

Let x be her percentage,

$$28 : 40 :: x : 100$$

$$x = \frac{28 \times 100}{40}$$

$$x = \frac{7 \times 10}{1} = 70\%$$

The conventional way of expressing one quantity as a percentage of another is to express the two quantities as a fraction and then multiply by 100.

That is, $x = \frac{28}{40} \times 100$

By using a ratio equation we can see why the usual method works.

Find 3% of £5500

Let x be the required amount.

$3 : 100 :: x : 5500$

$x = \dfrac{3 \times 5500}{100}$

$x = \dfrac{3 \times 55}{1} = £165$

Again the conventional method is to consider 3% as the fraction $\dfrac{3}{100}$ and then to multiply the given quantity by this.

That is, $x = \dfrac{3}{100} \times 5500$

Exercise 19f In numbers 1 - 12 express the first quantity as a percentage of the second:

1. 12, 48   **4.** $3\frac{1}{2}$, $17\frac{1}{2}$ **7.** 3 in, 10 ft   **10.** 6 yds, 9 ft

2. 900 g, 1000 g   **5.** 160 m, 400 m   **8.** 56p, £3.50   **11.** 133, 200

3. 12, 480   **6.** 60 cm, 4 m   **9.** £120, £80   **12.** 2.25, 0.75

Find:

13. 15% of 300   **16.** 18% of 6 kg   **19.** 78% of 800   **22.** 124% of 1.2 km

14. 25% of £1.40   **17.** 30% of 2.4 m   **20.** 200% of £19   **23.** 3.5% of £2000

15. 7% of 56 m   **18.** 46% of 230   **21.** 112% of 60 m   **24.** 4.5% of £56000

25. Clare obtained 26 out of 40 for a biology test. What percentage is this?

26. If the pass mark for an exam is 56 out of 70, what is the pass mark as a percentage?

27. Express as a percentage the fact that in a certain school three out of every four children have a bicycle.

28. If 6% of pupils in a school are absent, what percentage is present?

29. In a railway accident 88% of passengers were unhurt. What percentage were injured?

30. A man whose income is £22,400 spends £10,080 on rent. What percentage of his income is spent on rent?

31. If the population of New York City is 12,000,000 and that of the USA is 250,000,000, what percentage is the population of New York City of the whole of the USA?

32. A man invests £3,650,000 at 6% p.a. for a period of 4 days. How much interest should he receive?

33. A secretary earning £24,000 p.a. has to pay income tax of 35%. Find, (i) how much tax she has to pay, (ii) what her take-home salary is per year and (iii) what her take-home pay is per month.

34. A bottle of whisky costs £1.60 to produce and sell. Tax is charged at 900% of the cost price and then 17.5% VAT is added. Find the final selling price.

35. If 65% of the British working population of 23,500,000 are happy with their jobs, how many might be looking for a different job?

36. 26,000 children sat a GCSE examination. 12% obtained a grade A and 24% a grade B. How many children did not get either an A or a B?

Percentage increase and decrease

Problems in percentage increase and decrease can be solved using ratio equations.

Increase 60 kg by 16%

An increase of 16% means a ratio of 100 : 116. Therefore the ratio of 60 kg to the new quantity is 100 : 116. This forms the basis of the ratio equation which is then solved in the usual manner.

Let x be the required quantity.

$$60 : x :: 100 : 116$$

$$x = \frac{60 \times 116}{100}$$

$$x = \frac{6960}{100} = 69.6 \text{ kg}$$

When considering problems in percentages it is important to understand that a percentage is always a percentage *of* something. For example, if a tea dealer buys a quantity of tea for £500 and sells it for £800 his profit is £300. His percentage profit is 60% because £300 is 60% *of* the cost price, £500.

The key is to ask the question, *of what is this a percentage?*

With this understanding coupled with the simplicity of using ratio equations, quite difficult problems become easy.

Find the percentage loss when an unwise householder buys a house for £112,000 and sells it for £84,000.

The loss is £112,000 − £84,000 = £28,000

Let x be the percentage loss.

$$28,000 : 112,000 :: x : 100$$

$$x = \frac{28,000 \times 100}{112,000} = \frac{28 \times 100}{112}$$

$$= \frac{7 \times 100}{28} = \frac{1 \times 100}{4} = 25\%$$

Exercise 19g Use a ratio equation to solve each problem.

1. Increase £350 by 25%.

2. Decrease 400 by 20%.

3. Increase 60 by 30%.

4. Decrease 80 by 10%.

5. A man, whose salary is £18,000 p.a. receives an 8% pay rise. Find his new salary.

6. A retailer bought some silk scarves for £18.00 each and sold them at 30% profit. What was the selling price?

7. Amit bought a cricket ball for £4.50 and sold it to Prakesh at 20% profit. What did Prakesh pay?

8. A housekeeper has a weekly allowance of £460. If the cost of living rises by 8%, what should her allowance become?

9. If the temperature in London is 18°C and the temperature in Athens is 80% higher, what is the temperature in Athens?

10. A water company produces 48 million litres of water per day. If 18 million litres are lost through leakage, find the percentage of the original amount which is then left for consumption.

11. A eucalyptus tree is planted when it is 2.7 m tall and after one year it is 3.2 m tall. Find, to the nearest whole number, the percentage increase in height during that year.

12. If 68% of the population of 53,000,000 have full-time jobs, how many do not have full-time jobs?

Pie Charts

A pie chart is a circular representation of a set of information. It looks rather like a cake cut into different sized slices. The angle of each slice represents the size of a quantity.

In a certain orchestra there are 60 musicians. Of these 28 play stringed instruments, 24 play wind instruments and 8 play timpani.

To represent this information on a pie chart we need to calculate the angles for each type of wine. Since 60 musicians are represented by 360°, 1 musician is represented by 6°.

This is calculated from the ratio equation, 60 : 360° :: 1 : 6°.
6° then becomes the *multiplying factor* and the following chart is set ou

Strings $28 \times 6° = 168°$
Wind $24 \times 6° = 144°$
Timpani $8 \times 6° = 48°$

The pie chart is then drawn with these angles.

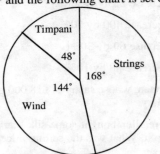

Exercise 19h

1. The pie chart below shows the origin of 3,000,000 cars sold one year in one country. Use the pie chart to find the number of each type.

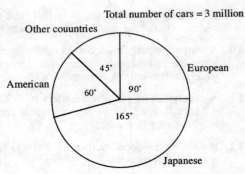

Total number of cars = 3 million

158

2. In a certain shoe manufacturing company there is a total work-force of 120 made up of directors, managers, secretaries and manual workers. Use the pie chart to find how many of each there are.

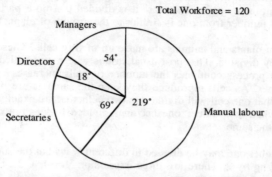

Total Workforce = 120

3. A garden designer sets out a plan for a new garden. Of the total area of 400m², the lawn is 250m², the patio is 50m², the path is 35m² and the flower-beds are 65m². Construct a pie chart to show this.

4. Just over half the world production of greenhouse gases comes from six nations: USA 17%, Russia 13%, Brazil 9%, China 8%, India 5% and Japan 4%. Make a pie chart with seven sections (one for the rest of the world) showing this information.

5. On entering the war in December 1941 Japan had 10 battleships, 11 aircraft-carriers, 41 cruisers, 129 destroyers, 67 submarines and 12 gunboats. Represent this information in a pie chart.

6. The following pie chart shows the distribution of 32 natural satellites (moons) throughout the solar system. Find the number of satellites orbiting each planet.

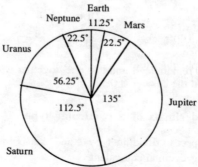

Chapter 20 Fractions to decimals

Our consideration of fractions and decimals begins with the possibility of dividing 1 into many parts. The more it is divided the more parts there are. This expansion of number from one is similar to the growth of plants and animals.

The bodies of plants and animals are made up of tiny cells. These cells reproduce themselves by division. The most usual case is where one cell divides itself into two. As this process continues the number of cells increases and so the living creature grows. As cells reproduce they keep the same nature or characteristics. This means that one cell will divide into two cells that are exactly like first. In the same way, when the number one becomes divided it does not change its nature but remains the same.

Now the number one may be divided in different ways but the simplest division is that of dividing by 2. There are three expressions for $1 \div 2$ or 2 into 1, as we say. These three expressions are

$$2 \text{ into } 1 = 0 \text{ remainder } 1$$
$$2 \text{ into } 1 = \tfrac{1}{2}$$
$$\text{and } 2 \text{ into } 1 = 0.5$$

With 0 remainder 1, the answer is zero or nought because, in truth, one cannot be divided. The 1 which is at the beginning remains at the end undivided. In the second expression, no division has taken place because $\tfrac{1}{2}$ is just another way of writing the question! The line in the fraction indicates division and is the same as the line in the division symbol, $\div$. We ordinarily think that the 1 has been divided by supplying the name *half*. The name gives us the idea.
In the final expression we have arrived at division, but only by first turning the 1 into 10.

$$2 \overline{)1.0}$$
$$\underline{1}$$
$$0.5$$

We say 2 into 1 is 0 remainder 1 and this one, together with the 0 of 1.0 becomes 10. 2 into 10 = 5 and the answer is 0.5.

Large recurring decimals of a particular type

There is another aspect to dividing 1 by 2 and this is in the magical process of converting $\tfrac{1}{19}$ into its decimal equivalent.

The conventional method is very long and cumbrous and part of it is shown below.

$$
\begin{array}{r}
0.05263157 \\
19\overline{)1.000000000000} \\
\underline{95} \\
50 \\
\underline{38} \\
120 \\
\underline{114} \\
60 \\
\underline{57} \\
30 \\
\underline{19} \\
110 \\
\underline{95} \\
150 \\
\underline{133} \quad \text{etc., etc.}
\end{array}
$$

This is a great toil and to be avoided at all costs! The easy Vedic method relies upon the sutra, *By one more than the one before*, and can be used where the denominator ends in 9. Before the 9 in $\frac{1}{19}$ is a 1 and one more than this is 2. The word *by* in the sutra tells us to either multiply or divide by that 2. Starting with division the simple steps of working are set out below.

Write down 0. as a starting point. Divide 2 into the numerator, 1, 0 rem. 1. The 0 is placed after the decimal point and the remainder digit is placed below and to the left of 0. We now have 10 as the next number to be divided.

$0._10$

2 into 10 = 5, 2 into 5 = 2 rem. 1. Again 2 is set down next to the 5 and the remainder digit is placed below and to the left of the 2 giving 12 as the next dividend.

$0._10\,5_12$

2 into 12 = 6 and 2 into 6 = 3.

$0._10\,5_12\,6\,3$

Continuing in this way the pattern begins to repeat after eighteen digits. At this stage the decimal is given its recurring dots to indicate that the pattern repeats.

$0._10\,5_12\,6\,3_11$

$$0.\dot{0}5263157894736842\dot{1}$$

A recurring decimal is one in which a digit, or a pattern of digits repeats. In the case of $\frac{1}{19}$, the pattern has eighteen digits and thereafter repeats forever with these same digits.

We can also arrive at this sequence by multiplying by 2 but this time we start at the right hand end. Of course it is necessary to know that the final digit in the pattern is 1.

	1
$2 \times 1 = 2$	2 1
$2 \times 2 = 4$	4 2 1
$2 \times 4 = 8$	8 4 2 1
$2 \times 8 = 16$, put down 6 and carry 1 to the left.	$_1$6 8 4 2 1
$2 \times 6 = 12$, plus a carry $1 = 13$	$_1$3 $_1$6 8 4 2 1
$2 \times 3 = 6$, plus a carry $1 = 7$, and so on.	7 $_1$3 $_1$6 8 4 2 1

In the final step, once recognising the repeating pattern, place the decimal point in the correct position and the two dots to show that it is recurring.

$$0._10\,5_12\,6\,3_1\,1_1\,5_1\,7_18\,9_14\,7_13_16\,8\,4\,2\,\dot1$$

This is all very good but even these eighteen easy steps for $\frac{1}{19}$ can be reduced by half. Setting the decimal out in two rows there is a pattern to be seen.

$$
\begin{array}{r}
0\,5\,2\,6\,3\,1\,5\,7\,8 \\
+\,9\,4\,7\,3\,6\,8\,4\,2\,1 \\
\hline
9\,9\,9\,9\,9\,9\,9\,9\,9
\end{array}
$$

The digits sum to 9 in every case. If, the half-way stage has been reached then the remaining digits can be written down just by subtraction from 9.

$$0.\dot0\,5\,2\,6\,3\,1\,5\,7\,8\,9\,4\,7\,3\,6\,8\,4\,2\,\dot1$$

When the numerator is not 1 but some other number then the first step is to divide into that numerator. For example, for $\frac{12}{19}$ the division begins with 2 into 12.

$$\frac{12}{19} = 0.0_16\ldots$$

With denominators such as 29, 39, and 49, the *One more than...*, is always one more than the one before the 9. So for $\frac{1}{29}$ the divisor is 3. The start is shown below.

$$\frac{1}{29} = 0 ._10 _13 _14 _24...$$

Exercise 20a Convert to their decimal form:

1. $\frac{1}{19}$ 3. $\frac{17}{19}$ 5. $\frac{1}{39}$ 7. $\frac{11}{19}$

2. $\frac{2}{19}$ 4. $\frac{1}{29}$ 6. $\frac{5}{19}$ 8. $\frac{1}{69}$

Converting fractions to decimals by division

The line drawn between numerator and denominator in a vulgar fraction is a division symbol, $\div$, without the dots. When converting a vulgar fraction into its decimal equivalent we can divide the denominator into the numerator.

Covert $\frac{1}{3}$ into a decimal fraction.

The fraction $\frac{1}{3}$ is really the same as $1 \div 3$, or 3 into 1.

Since the remainder is constant we immediately have the recurring decimal, $0.\dot{3}$

$$\begin{array}{r} 3\,)\,1.0\,0\,0 \\ \underline{1\ 1\ 1} \\ 0.3\ 3\ 3 \end{array}$$

Convert $\frac{5}{7}$ into a decimal.

With this fraction, the decimal digits start to repeat after six places.

The answer is written as, $0.\dot{7}1428\dot{5}$

$$\begin{array}{r} 7\,)\,5.0\,0\,0\,0\,0\,0\,0 \\ \underline{5\ 1\ 3\ 2\ 6\ 4\ 5} \\ 0.7\ 1\ 4\ 2\ 8\ 5 \end{array}$$

Exercise 20b Change to decimals by dividing denominator into numerator:

1. $\frac{2}{3}$ 3. $\frac{2}{5}$ 5. $\frac{3}{7}$ 7. $\frac{4}{9}$ 9. $\frac{6}{11}$

2. $\frac{3}{4}$ 4. $\frac{5}{6}$ 6. $\frac{7}{8}$ 8. $\frac{7}{10}$ 10. $\frac{5}{12}$

How to write recurring decimals

$0.33333... = 0.\dot{3}$	When there is one repeating digit then a single dot is placed above that digit.
$0.467146714671... \; 0.\dot{4}67\dot{1}$	When there is a repeating pattern then dots are placed above the first and last digits of the pattern.
$0.676767... = 0.\dot{6}\dot{7}$	
$0.498222... = 0.498\dot{2}$	Some decimals are partly-recurring, with a non-recurring portion before the recurring part.

Exercise 20c Write the following decimal fractions with the recurring dots placed in the correct position:

1. 0.222222...   **3.** 2.323232...   **5.** 0.47234723...   **7.** 4.32199999...

2. 0.53955555...   **4.** 0.00777777...   **6.** 0.01010101...   **8.** 0.791791791...

Proportionately

There are several uses of the *Proportionately* sutra for converting fractions to decimals and we begin with the case in which the denominator of the fraction ends in zero.

Convert $\frac{23}{30}$ into a decimal.	$\frac{23}{30} = \frac{2.3}{3} = 0.7\dot{6}$	$3)\underline{2 \cdot {}_2 3 \, {}_2 0 \, {}_2 0}$ $0 . \; 7 \; 6 \; 6$

Divide top and bottom by 10, that is, $23 \div 10 = 2.3$ and $30 \div 10 = 3$

$\frac{2.3}{3}$ is called an auxiliary fraction.

Divide 3 into 2.3 in the normal fashion to give $0.7\dot{6}$

Exercise 20d Convert to decimals:

1. $\frac{17}{20}$ 5. $\frac{7}{30}$ 9. $\frac{59}{60}$ 13. $\frac{53}{60}$ 17. $\frac{37}{100}$

2. $\frac{13}{30}$ 6. $\frac{3}{20}$ 10. $\frac{37}{40}$ 14. $\frac{41}{90}$ 18. $\frac{79}{110}$

3. $\frac{19}{40}$ 7. $\frac{9}{40}$ 11. $\frac{67}{80}$ 15. $\frac{33}{70}$ 19. $\frac{7}{80}$

4. $\frac{21}{50}$ 8. $\frac{43}{50}$ 12. $\frac{29}{30}$ 16. $\frac{17}{60}$ 20. $\frac{53}{90}$

Factors of 10, 100, 1000, etc., may also be dealt with using the *Proportionately* sutra.

Convert $\frac{23}{25}$ into a decimal. $\frac{23}{25} = \frac{23 \times 4}{25 \times 4} = \frac{92}{100} = 0.92$

Since 25 is a quarter of 100, multiply numerator and denominator by 4. The new denominator is then 100
$92 \div 100$ becomes 0.92

Exercise 20e Convert to decimals:

1. $\frac{3}{50}$ 5. $\frac{23}{25}$ 9. $\frac{31}{500}$ 13. $\frac{111}{200}$ 17. $\frac{1021}{2000}$

2. $\frac{13}{25}$ 6. $\frac{7}{50}$ 10. $\frac{81}{200}$ 14. $\frac{41}{250}$ 18. $\frac{3219}{5000}$

3. $\frac{4}{5}$ 7. $\frac{11}{20}$ 11. $\frac{112}{500}$ 15. $\frac{213}{500}$ 19. $\frac{1241}{2500}$

4. $\frac{19}{50}$ 8. $\frac{7}{25}$ 12. $\frac{43}{250}$ 16. $\frac{3}{125}$ 20. $\frac{1111}{1250}$

For the case where the denominator ends in 5 but is not a factor of 10, 100, 1000, etc., apply the *Proportionately* sutra by dividing both the numerator and denominator by 5 and then use division on the auxiliary fraction as before. The quick way to divide by five is to multiply by 2 and then divide by 10. This can be done mentally. For example, if the denominator is 45, we divide both the numerator and denominator by 5. The new denominator is then 7 and a simple division will obtain the answer. This is shown in the next example.

Convert $\frac{17}{45}$ into a decimal.

$45 \div 5 = 9$ and $17 \times 2 \div 10 = 3.4$
The auxiliary fraction is then $\frac{3.4}{9}$
which gives the answer $0.3\dot{7}$.

$$\frac{17}{45} = \frac{3.4}{9} = 0.3\dot{7}$$

$$\begin{array}{r} 9 \,) \overline{3.4\ 0\ 0} \\ \underline{3\ 7\ 7} \\ 0.3\dot{7} \end{array}$$

Exercise 20f Convert to decimals:

1. $\frac{7}{15}$	5. $\frac{23}{45}$	9. $\frac{1}{35}$	13. $\frac{14}{15}$	17. $\frac{6}{35}$
2. $\frac{11}{15}$	6. $\frac{3}{45}$	10. $\frac{3}{35}$	14. $\frac{17}{35}$	18. $\frac{32}{45}$
3. $\frac{8}{15}$	7. $\frac{31}{45}$	11. $\frac{1}{55}$	15. $\frac{2}{55}$	19. $\frac{13}{15}$
4. $\frac{1}{15}$	8. $\frac{1}{45}$	12. $\frac{48}{55}$	16. $\frac{2}{35}$	20. $\frac{12}{55}$

The following decimal fractions should be learnt by heart:-

$\frac{1}{2} = 0.5$ $\qquad \frac{3}{4} = 0.75$ $\qquad \frac{4}{5} = 0.8$ $\qquad \frac{1}{8} = 0.125$ $\qquad \frac{1}{9} = 0.\dot{1}$

$\frac{1}{3} = 0.\dot{3}$ $\qquad \frac{1}{5} = 0.2$ $\qquad \frac{1}{6} = 0.1\dot{6}$ $\qquad \frac{3}{8} = 0.375$ $\qquad \frac{1}{10} = 0.1$

$\frac{2}{3} = 0.\dot{6}$ $\qquad \frac{2}{5} = 0.4$ $\qquad \frac{5}{6} = 0.8\dot{3}$ $\qquad \frac{5}{8} = 0.625$ $\qquad \frac{1}{11} = 0.\dot{0}\dot{9}$

$\frac{1}{4} = 0.25$ $\qquad \frac{3}{5} = 0.6$ $\qquad \frac{1}{7} = 0.\dot{1}4285\dot{7}$ $\quad \frac{7}{8}$ 0.875

We can use the known decimal fractions from this table to obtain others. This is done by looking at the factors of the denominator and using one of them as a divisor.

Find the decimal for $\frac{1}{18}$

Since $\frac{1}{18} = \frac{1}{9} \div 2$, we can write down the known decimal for $\frac{1}{9}$ and then divide it by 2.

$$\frac{1}{18} = \frac{1}{9} \div 2$$

$$\begin{array}{r} 2 \,) \overline{0.1\ 1\ 1} \\ \underline{1\ 1} \\ 0.0\ 5\ 5 \end{array}$$

$$\frac{1}{18} = 0.05\dot{5}$$

Whenever a number is divided into 1 in decimals the answer is called the **reciprocal** of that number. For example, the reciprocal of 2 is 0.5, because $1 \div 2 = 0.5$. The word *reciprocal* means something which has been turned back and in this case it is when a number has been turned back and divided into one.

Exercise 20g Find as a decimal the reciprocal of each of the following:

1. $\frac{1}{12}$ 5. $\frac{1}{20}$ 9. $\frac{1}{25}$ 13. $\frac{1}{32}$ 17. $\frac{1}{40}$ ·

2. $\frac{1}{14}$ 6. $\frac{1}{21}$ 10. $\frac{1}{27}$ 14. $\frac{1}{33}$ 18. $\frac{1}{44}$

3. $\frac{1}{15}$ 7. $\frac{1}{22}$ 11. $\frac{1}{28}$ 15. $\frac{1}{35}$ 19. $\frac{1}{45}$

4. $\frac{1}{16}$ 8. $\frac{1}{24}$ 12. $\frac{1}{30}$ 16. $\frac{1}{36}$ 20. $\frac{1}{54}$

One seventh

The division of 7 into 1 gives the decimal form and is set out below.

$$7)1.0000000$$
$$1326451$$
$$0.142857$$

From this we can arrive at the value for $\frac{2}{7}$ simply by doubling the digits for $\frac{1}{7}$.

$$\begin{array}{r} 1\,4\,2\,8\,5\,7 \\ \times 2 \\ \hline \end{array}$$
$$\frac{2}{7} = 2\,8\,5\,7\,1\,4$$

Similarly $\frac{3}{7}$ can be obtained by multiplying 142857 by 3

$$\begin{array}{r} 1\,4\,2\,8\,5\,7 \\ \times 3 \\ \hline \end{array}$$
$$\frac{3}{7} = 4\,2\,8\,5\,7\,1$$

You can see that in every case the same digits are involved but that they begin in a different place. The digits used are 1, 2, 4, 5, 7 and 8. The digits not involved are 3, 6 and 9.

It is possible to arrive at answers for $\frac{4}{7}$, $\frac{5}{7}$ and $\frac{6}{7}$ without any further working and this is by inspection of the original digits, 142857. By looking at $\frac{1}{7}$, $\frac{2}{7}$ and $\frac{3}{7}$ it will be seen that $\frac{1}{7}$ begins with a 1 which is the lowest number in 142857. $\frac{2}{7}$ begins with a 2 which is the second lowest number in 142857 and $\frac{3}{7}$ begins with 4, the third lowest number in 142857. Knowing this we can say that $\frac{4}{7}$ begins with 5, $\frac{5}{7}$ begins with 7 and $\frac{6}{7}$ begins with the 8.

You therefore have $\frac{4}{7}$ = 0.571428 $\frac{5}{7}$ = 0.714285   and $\frac{6}{7}$ = 0.857142

One more aspect of note is that the digits in 142857 have the complement from 9 system found earlier in $\frac{1}{19}$. The decimal fraction for $\frac{1}{19}$ has a recurring pattern of eighteen digits. The first nine digits are complements (from 9) of the second nine digits. With $\frac{1}{7}$, there are two groups of three digits as shown below.

$$
\begin{array}{r}
1\,4\,2 \\
+\,8\,5\,7 \\
\hline
9\,9\,9
\end{array}
$$

To see what the pattern of 142857 looks like pictorially we can plot the digits on the circle of nine points. To do this, draw a circle and mark off a point at the top. Measure round and mark off a point every 40°. Number the points clockwise from 1 to 9.

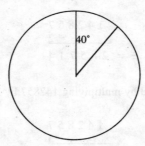

Draw a straight line joining the point 1 to the point 4. Join 4 to 2, 2 to 8 and so on until the pattern repeats itself. This is shown in the diagram in the diagram on the page.

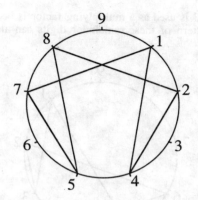

The next aspect of one seventh has to do with the remainder digits, 1326451..., in the original division of 7 into 1. There is an easy way of arriving at the remainder digits and then another quick way of getting from the remainder digits to the answer digits.

The first step of the division is, 7 into 1 goes 0 remainder 1. 1 is then the first remainder digit. To obtain the other remainder digits we use the *Proportionately* sutra because they are all in ratio. The proportion is by 3 but this is disguised because sevens are cast out on the way.

Starting with the first remainder digit, 1, multiply by 3. This gives 3.	$1 \times 3 = 3$
Multiply this 3 by 3 to get 9 and cast out 7. This leaves 2 as the next remainder digit.	$3 \times 3 = 9,\ 9 - 7 = 2$
$2 \times 3 = 6$, the third remainder digit.	$2 \times 3 = 6$
$6 \times 3 = 18$. With 18 we can cast out two sevens (14) leaving 4.	$6 \times 3 = 18,\ 18 - 14 = 4$
$4 \times 3 = 12$, cast out 7 leaving 5.	$4 \times 3 = 12, 12 - 7 = 5$
$5 \times 3 = 15$, cast out 2×7 leaving 1 and this is where the remainder digits begin to repeat.	$5 \times 3 = 15, 15 - 14 = 1$

The remainders are then 132645.

The real reason why 3 is used as a multiplying factor is because 7 is 3 less than 10. The repeating pattern of these remainder digits can also be plotted on the circle of nine points.

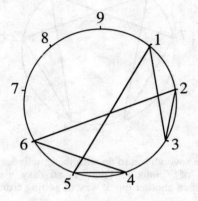

To obtain the answer digits from the remainder digits the sutra employed is *The remainders by the last digit.*

Take each remainder digit in turn, beginning with 3, multiply by 7, and write down only the last digit.

This gives our pattern for $\frac{1}{7}$ as 142857.

$3 \times 7 = 21$, final digit = 1
$2 \times 7 = 14$, final digit = 4
$6 \times 7 = 42$, final digit = 2
$4 \times 7 = 28$, final digit = 8
$5 \times 7 = 35$, final digit = 5
$1 \times 7 = 7$, final digit = 7

Chapter 21 The octahedron

In book 1 we looked at the construction of a Platonic solid called the dodecahedron. Here we will construct another solid - the octahedron. As the name suggests it has eight faces and each face is an equilateral triangle.

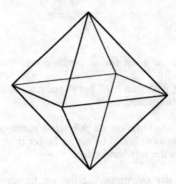

OCTAHEDRON

In ancient Greece Plato indicated that each of the five Platonic solids represented an element. The dodecahedron represented Ether or Space, the octahedron - Air, the tetrahedron - Fire, the icosahedron - Water, and the cube - Earth. The octahedron, in some way, relates to Air. Apart from this, the shape occurs naturally in some crystals. There are many substances which are formed from crystals. Metals, salts and gems are just a few examples.

There is one substance called chrome alum which naturally forms into the shape of an octahedron. Chrome alum is otherwise known as mordant and is used for fixing dyes to cloth. It has been used for many centuries, even in ancient Egypt.

Construction 10 To draw an equilateral triangle from a given base.

Let AB be the given base.

With centre A and radius AB draw a circle.
With centre B and the same radius as before draw another circle. Let C be the point above AB where the circles intersect.
Join AC and BC.
ABC is an equilateral triangle.

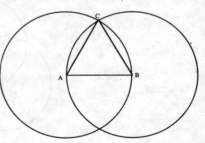

A **net** is a shape which can be folded up to form a solid. The net for the octahedron is shown below.

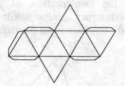

Construction 11 To draw a net for an octahedron.

This model is best made with thin card but paper may also be used if great care is taken with the scoring and gluing.

Begin with a circle. If working on an A4 sized piece of paper or card, placed sideways, then the compasses should be set no larger than 6 cm and the first circle should be drawn close to the left-hand edge.

Once the first circle is drawn, mark a point on the circumference over on the right-hand side of it. This gives the centre for the second circle.

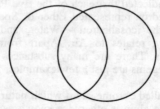

Where these two circles intersect forms the centre for the third circle as shown.

Four more circles are drawn as shown so that there are seven altogether.

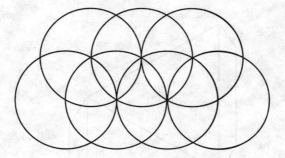

Lines forming the eight equilateral triangles are then drawn.

Tabs for gluing will also need to be drawn (see diagram of completed net on the next page).

Once the net has been drawn then it may be cut out. If a modelling knife is used with a straight edge the cuts will be more accurate than when cutting with scissors. Any lines along which there are to be folds should be scored. Scoring should always be done gently so as not to cut right through the paper or card. The folds will then be precise.

173

NET FOR OCTAHEDRON

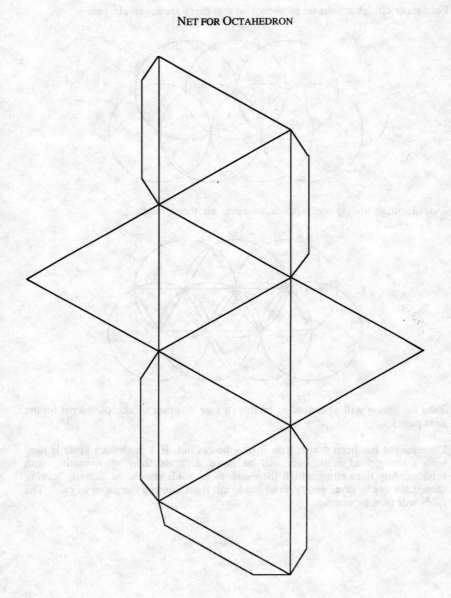

The following net is for the same octahedron but with an equilateral triangle cut from each face.

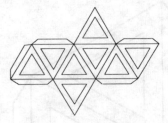

To draw this net begin with the net for the octahedron. Choosing a radius of about one fifth the edge-length of a triangle, draw a circle centred at each corner as shown.

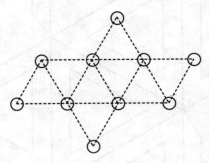

Draw lines from the points where the circles cut the sides of the triangles.

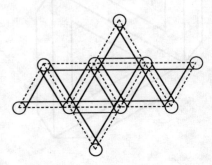

NET FOR OCTAHEDRON WITH FACES CUT

Internal model for octahedron

The internal model is made up from eight identical segments. These are formed from the following net and can easily be constructed.

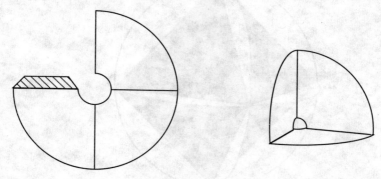

The internal angle for the octahedron is 90° and three such angles form each segment. The small circle at the centre helps with the fixing together.

When cut and scored each segment is folded and glued as shown on the right.

Eight of these are fixed together to form the internal model.

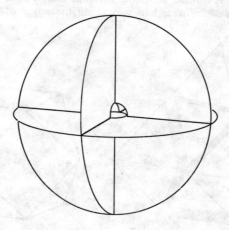

The internal model may be seen in relation to the external model in the next diagram where the triangular faces have been place in the segments.

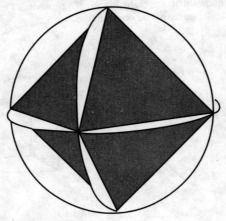

Truncating the octahedron

To truncate means to cut something short. In geometry a new shape can be formed by truncating the original shape. There are two ways of evenly truncating an octahedron. The first gives a shape called a cuboctahedron and the second forms a shape called a truncated octahedron.

The cuboctahedron is formed be slicing pyramid shapes from the corners of the octahedron. The cuts are made half way along the edges of the octahedron as shown below.

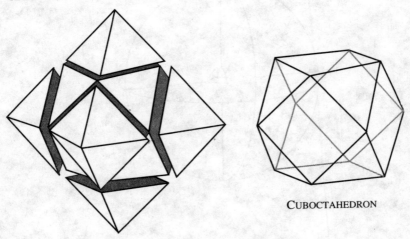

CUBOCTAHEDRON

NET FOR CUBOCTAHEDRON

Net For Cuboctahedron With Faces Cut

The truncated octahedron is also formed by slicing eight pyramid shapes from the corners of the octahedron. The cuts are a third of the way along the edges instead of half way as before.

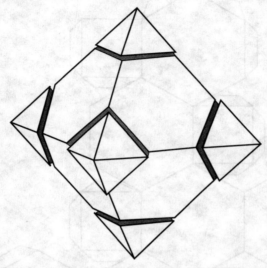

The remaining shape is shown below. It is made up of squares and hexagons. How many of each shape are there?

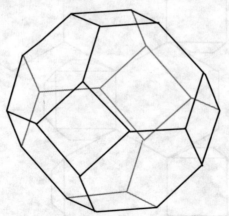

TRUNCATED OCTAHEDRON

Net For Truncated Octahedron

Chapter 22 Practice and revision 2

Consolidation Test 1

1. 326 + 498

2. 4.26 + 0.78

3. (−4) − (−6)

4. 526 − 278

5. 3.14 − 0.79

6. 1466 × 4

7. 23 × 21

8. 98 × 97

9. 35 × 20

10. 2.4 × 7

11. 5)$\underline{1420}$

12. 98)$\underline{10241}$

13. 102)$\underline{1247}$

14. 460 ÷ 20

15. 52174 ÷ 32

16. Find the HCF of 28 and 35.

17. Find the LCM of 10 and 15.

18. Find if 362175 is divisible by 3.

19. Bring $\frac{14}{35}$ to lowest terms.

20. Express $\frac{6}{5}$ as a mixed number.

21. Express $2\frac{2}{3}$ as an improper fraction.

22. $\frac{2}{3} \times \frac{4}{7}$

23. $\frac{2}{3} \div \frac{4}{7}$

24. $\frac{3}{5} + \frac{7}{10}$

25. $\frac{7}{10} - \frac{3}{5}$

26. Find $\frac{3}{4}$ of 12 kg

27. Find the value of $3 \times 2 - 1$

28. If $a = 2$, $b = 3$, find the value of $3a + 5b$

29. Simplify $y \times y \times y \times z \times z$

30. Simplify $4a + a - 2b - P$

31. Express in its simplest form the ratio, 32 : 72

32. Solve the ratio equation, $2 : 3 :: x : 12$

33. Solve $3x - 2 = 19$

34. Find 25% of 12 kg

35. Express 6 m as a percentage of 20 m.

Consolidation Test 2

1. $756 + 528$

2. $3.56 + 4.87$

3. $(+5) + (-2)$

4. $728 - 342$

5. $6.74 - 2.86$

6. 5463×6

7. 32×14

8. 96×93

9. 52×30

10. 7.8×8

11. $4)\underline{6576}$

12. $89)\underline{1021}$

13. $111)\underline{2458}$

14. $1350 \div 150$

15. $46957 \div 23$

16. Find the HCF of 45 and 75.

17. Find the LCM of 12 and 16.

18. Is 2435224 is divisible by 4?

19. Bring $\frac{24}{32}$ to lowest terms.

20. Express $\frac{9}{4}$ as a mixed number.

21. Express $3\frac{1}{3}$ as an improper fraction.

22. $\frac{5}{6} \times \frac{3}{10}$

23. $\frac{5}{6} \div \frac{3}{10}$

24. $\frac{5}{6} + \frac{3}{10}$

25. $\frac{5}{6} - \frac{3}{10}$

26. Find $\frac{5}{6}$ of 84 m

27. Find the value of $4 + 3 \times 4$

28. If $a = 3$, $b = 4$, find the value of $6a - 2b$

29. Simplify $m \times m \times m \times m \times n \times n$

30. Simplify, $4c - 3d + 2c - 6d$

31. Express in its simplest form the ratio, $48 : 12$

32. Solve the ratio equation, $4 : 5 :: x : 25$

33. Solve $4x - 17 = 23$

34. Find 15% of 120 cm

35. Express 8 m as a percentage of 40 m.

Consolidation Test 3

1. $659 + 784$

2. $4.58 + 6.58$

3. $4 + (-7)$

4. $5463 - 7771$

5. $65.7 - 17.9$

6. 1238×3

7. 26×14

8. 95×92

9. 65×30

10. 6.8×6

11. $6)\underline{3198}$

12. $88)\underline{1122}$

13. $112)\underline{1236}$

14. $864 \div 160$

15. $76879 \div 42$

16. Find the HCF of 64 and 96.

17. Find the LCM of 7 and 9.

18. Is 362145 is divisible by 9?

19. Bring $\frac{12}{16}$ to lowest terms.

20. Express $\frac{9}{7}$ as a mixed number.

21. Express $5\frac{2}{5}$ as an improper fraction.

22. $\frac{3}{4} \times \frac{2}{9}$

23. $\frac{3}{4} \div \frac{2}{9}$

24. $\frac{3}{4} + \frac{2}{9}$

25. $\frac{3}{4} - \frac{2}{9}$

26. Find $\frac{3}{4}$ of 56 minutes

27. Find the value of $4 \times 5 - 2 \times 3$

28. If $a = 5$, $b = 2$, find the value of $3a + 5b - 6$

29. Simplify $a \times a \times b \times b \times b$

30. Simplify, $3a - 2b + 8 - 3b + 2$

31. Express in its simplest form the ratio, $24 : 40$

32. Solve the ratio equation, $3 : x :: 2 : 18$

33. Solve $29 = 5x - 1$

34. Find 40% of 20 km

35. Express £12 as a percentage of £15.

Consolidation Test 4

1. $654 + 348$

2. $0.258 + 3.56$

3. $3 - (+5)$

4. $6238 - 2454$

5. $62.1 - 7.4$

6. 567×6

7. 34×14

8. 97×76

9. 340×200

10. 0.68×5

11. $7)\underline{5474}$

12. $86)\underline{1111}$

13. $113)\underline{2384}$

14. $850000 \div 5000$

15. $264768 \div 41$

16. Find the HCF of 64 and 48.

17. Find the LCM of 64 and 48.

18. Is 4532123265863 divisible by 4?

19. Bring $\frac{24}{48}$ to lowest terms.

20. Express $\frac{13}{3}$ as a mixed number.

21. Express $7\frac{5}{8}$ as an improper fraction.

22. $\frac{2}{5} \times \frac{15}{22}$

23. $\frac{3}{4} \div \frac{3}{8}$

24. $1\frac{3}{85} + 2\frac{3}{4}$

25. $5\frac{11}{16} - 3\frac{3}{8}$

26. Find $\frac{2}{5}$ of 120 m

27. Find the value of $5 \times 3 - 2 \times 4$

28. If $a = 4$, $b = 7$, find the value of $8a - 2b - 18$

29. Simplify $p \times q \times q \times p \times p$

30. Simplify, $5c - 2d + c - 8d$

31. Express in its simplest form the ratio, $48 : 16$

32. Solve the ratio equation, $4 : 5 :: x : 60$

33. Solve $47 - 3x = 23$.

34. Find 15% of £2000

35. Express £45 as a percentage of £300.

Consolidation Test 5

1. $1245 + 647$

2. $52.8 + 46.9$

3. $7 - 10$

4. $600 - 278$

5. $6 - 0.4$

6. 9122×5

7. 41×51

8. 992×992

9. 32×4000

10. 0.089×3

11. $8)\underline{6576}$

12. $89)\underline{10021}$

13. $112)\underline{1486}$

14. $55000 \div 1100$

15. $627894 \div 51$

16. Find the HCF of 112 and 48.

17. Find the LCM of 112 and 48.

18. Is 6327459 is divisible by 6?

19. Bring $\frac{22}{36}$ to lowest terms.

20. Express $\frac{36}{11}$ as a mixed number.

21. Express $5\frac{4}{9}$ as an improper fraction.

22. $\frac{5}{6} \times \frac{9}{20}$

23. $\frac{5}{6} \div 4$

24. $6\frac{5}{6} + 7\frac{1}{10}$

25. $2\frac{5}{6} - 1\frac{1}{10}$

26. Find $\frac{5}{6}$ of 144 miles

27. Find the value of $27 \div 9 + 16 \times 2$

28. If $a = 11$, $b = 9$, find the value of $43 - 6a - b$

29. Simplify $a \times b \times a \times b \times a$

30. Simplify $3a - 2b - a + 7b$

31. Express in its simplest form the ratio, $150 : 250$

32. Solve the ratio equation, $3 : x :: 16 : 20$

33. Solve $18 = 5x - 7$

34. Find 5% of 250 litres

35. Express £18 as a percentage of £45.

Exam Paper 1 (1 hour)

1. $1245 + 647$

2. $52.8 + 46.9$

3. $(-3) + 10 =$

4. $600 - 278$

5. $6 - 0.4$

6. 9122×5

7. 41×51

8. 992×992

9. 32×4000

10. 0.089×3

11. $8)\underline{6576}$

12. $89)\underline{10021}$

13. $112)\underline{1486}$

14. $55000 \div 1100$

15. $627894 \div 51$

16. Find the HCF of 112 and 48.

17. Find the LCM of 112 and 48.

20. Express $\frac{36}{11}$ as a mixed number.

21. Express $5\frac{4}{9}$ as an improper fraction.

22. $\frac{5}{6} \times \frac{9}{20}$

23. $\frac{5}{6} \div \frac{9}{20}$

24. $6\frac{5}{6} + 7\frac{1}{10}$

25. $2\frac{5}{6} - 1\frac{1}{10}$

26. Find $\frac{5}{6}$ of 144 miles

27. Find the value of,
$27 \div 9 + 16 \times 2$

18. Is 6327459 is divisible by 6?

19. Bring $\frac{22}{36}$ to lowest terms.

28. If $a = 11$, $b = 9$, find the value of
$43 - 6a - b$

29. Simplify $a \times b \times a \times b \times a$

30. Simplify $3a - 2b - a + 7b$

31. Express in its simplest form the ratio, $150 : 250$

32. Solve the ratio equation, $3 : x :: 16 : 24$

33. Solve $18 = 5x - 7$

34. Find 5% of 250 litres

35. Express £18 as a percentage of £45.

Numbers 36 - 38 are to be done using rulers and compasses, not protractors.

36. Draw a line AB and mark on it a point P. Construct a perpendicular at P.

37. Draw a line PQ and a point M which is not on the line. Construct the perpendicular from M to the line PQ.

38. Draw a triangle ABC in which AB = 6.5 cm, BC= 7 cm and CA = 5.5 cm. Construct the perpendicular from A to BC, meeting BC at D. Measure AD and $\angle$DAC.

Exam Paper 2 ($1\frac{1}{2}$ hours)

1. Calculate $3\frac{1}{2} \times 1\frac{2}{7}$

2. Multiply 7.24 by 0.28

3. Write 19.75,
(i) correct to 2 sig. figures,
(ii) correct to 1 dec. place.

4. Write 65 cm as a fraction of 2m. Answer in lowest terms.

5. Divide 561251 by 23 leaving your answer with a whole number remainder.

6. Express (a) 42 and (b) 63 as the product of prime factors.
(ii) Hence, or otherwise, write down the HCF of 42 and 63.

7. Four members of a boxing team have the following masses: 74 kg, 82 kg, 113 kg, 55 kg. What is the average mass of the four members?

8. Calculate 15% 0f £1600

9. (i) Remove the brackets and simplify:
$$4(2a+b)-3(a-2b)$$

(ii) Simplify $\dfrac{4c^3 \times 12d^2}{8cd^3}$

10. Factorise:
$$3x^2y^2 - 6x^2y^3$$

11. Solve: (i) $3(x-2)=18$

(ii) $\dfrac{5a}{3}-1=6$

12. The cost £C of hiring a pony at the West Riding Pony Club is a payment of £5 for each hour of use plus a fixed charge of £15.

(i) Write down a formula for the cost of hiring a pony for y hours.
(ii) Re-arrange the formula to make y the subject.

13. The perimeter of a triangle is 45 cm. The sides are in the ratio 2 : 3 : 4. Calculate the length of each side of the triangle.

14. On average a certain barber can cut three peoples' hair in 50 minutes. How many hair-cuts can he make in 5 hrs?

189

15. Nigella obtained 28 marks out of 40 in a history test. What percentage did she score?

16. Draw a triangle ABC in which AB = 7.5 cm, ∠CAB= 56° and ∠ABC= 72°. Measure AC and BC. Construct the perpendicular from C to AB, measure its length and use this measurement to calculate the area of the triangle.

17. In the diagram ACF and BCD are straight lines. AB is parallel to EC, AB = A and ∠BAC = 32°. Calculate, showing your working,

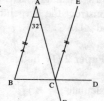

    (i) ∠BAC
    (ii) ∠ECD
    (iii) ∠BCF

18. Mr Townsend went to the builder's merchants and spent £600. He spent £250 on stone paving, £160 on bricks, £100 on fencing and £40 on sand and cement. He spent the remainder on a wheel barrow. Draw a carefully labelled pie chart to show this information.

19. A line has equation, $y = x - 2$. Using 1 cm per unit, draw an x-axis from −2 to 7 and a y-axis from −4 to 5. Using the equation, copy and complete the table of values.

x	0	−1	6
y			

Plot the three points given in the table of values and draw a straight line through them.

20. A cyclist makes a journey starting at 2 00 pm. In the first hour he travels 15 km and from 4 30 pm to 6 pm he travels another 20 km.

(a) What is his speed during the first hour?
(b) Describe what is happening between 3 00 pm and 4 30 pm.
(c) At what speed did he make the second part of his journey?
(d) How far from home was he at 6 00 pm?
(e) At what time was he 25 km from home?

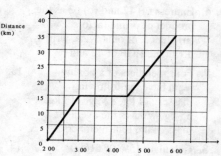

Exam Paper 3 ($1\frac{1}{2}$ hours)

1. Calculate $1\frac{1}{2} \div \frac{3}{4}$

2. Multiply 1.28 by 3.4

3. Write 2.357 correct to 2 decimal places.

4. If $x = 3$ and $y = 4$, find the value of, $x(x + y)$

5. Write 420 g as a fraction of 2 kg. Answer in lowest terms.

6. Divide 152436 by 987 leaving your answer with a whole number remainder.

7. If the average weight of two girls is 6.5 stone and the average weight of these two together with a third is 7 stone, find the weight of the third girl.

8. (i) Express (a) 72 and (b) 64 as the product of prime factors.
   (ii) Hence, or otherwise, write down the HCF of 72 and 64.

9. Calculate 35% of £840

10. 'Danny the Dealer' bought a car for £12,000 and sold it for £14160. Find the percentage profit he made.

11. (i) Remove the brackets and simplify:

    $$3(6a + 5b) - 4(a - 3b)$$

    (ii) Simplify $\dfrac{6c^2 \times 8d}{24cd^2}$

12. Factorise: $8xy - 12y + 14yz$

13. Expand $(x + 8)(x + 9)$

14. Solve: (i) $5y - 3y + 7y + 3 = 30$

    (ii) $(3 - 2y) + 7 = -36$

15. If 12 men can paint a railway bridge in 8 months, how long will it take 16 men at the same rate?

16. When a stone is dropped from the top of a building, the distance s meters, it falls in t seconds is given by the formula, $s = 4.9t^2$. Find how far it falls in 3 seconds.

17. The length of a rectangle is 24 cm and its breadth is 30 cm.
    (i) Write the ratio of its length to its breadth as a ratio in its simplest form.
    (ii) Another rectangle has the length of its sides in the same ratio but the total perimeter is 54 cm. Find its length and breadth.

18. If 26 French francs are worth £5, find, in pounds the value of 208 francs.

19. Construct the triangle JKL in which JK = 8.3 cm, and JL = KL = 6.3 cm. Construct the perpendicular bisectors of JK and JL and let these two bisectors meet at O. With centre O and radius OK draw a circle. Measure the radius of the circle.

20. In the diagram, PQ is parallel to RS, AB = AC, AC bisects ∠BAQ and ∠ABR = 68°

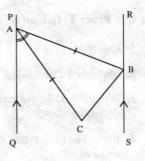

Calculate, showing your working,

   (i) ∠BAC

   (ii) ∠ACB

   (iii) ∠CBS

   (iv) ∠PAC

21. Out of 40 lessons a week one class had 5 lessons in Maths, 5 in English, 7 in Languages, 8 in Sciences, 1 in Scipture, 3 in History, 2 in Art and 9 in Sport. Construct a pie chart to illustrate this information.

22. A line has equation, $y = 2x - 3$. Using 1 cm per unit, draw an x-axis from −2 to 6 and a y-axis from −4 to 8. Using the equation, copy and complete the table of values.

x	0	2	5
y			

Plot the three points given in the table of values and draw a straight line through them. Use your graph to find the value of x when $y = 4$

23. A train leaves station A at 7 00 hr and reaches staion B at 8 30 hr. At 9 00 hr it leaves station B and goes to station C. At 12 30 it leaves station C and goes to station D. On the return journey it goes straight back to station A without stopping. The distance/time graph for this trip is shown below.

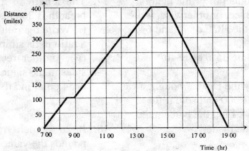

   (a) For how long did it stop at station C?

   (b) For how long did it stop at station D?

   (c) Find the speed of the train for the last part of its journey.

   (d) How far from station A was the train at 16 30 hrs?

Exam Paper 4 ($1\frac{1}{2}$ hours)

1. Calculate $2\frac{2}{5} \times 2\frac{1}{2}$

2. Multiply 3.14 by 5.6

3. Write 17.48571 correct to 3 decimal places

4. If $x = 2$ and $y = 7$, find the value of, $30 - 2x(y - x)$

5. Write 425 cm as a fraction of 5 m. Answer in lowest terms.

6. Divide 134564 by 112, leaving your answer with a whole number remainder.

7. The heights of three boys are 1.45 m, 1.36 cm and 1.72 cm. Find the height of a fourth boy if the average of all four is 1.50 m.

8. If a factory worker can make a certain toy in 6 min 25 sec, how long would it take to make 9?

9. Convert $\frac{9}{25}$ into a decimal fraction.

10. A lady has £p in her purse. She spends £q in one shop and £r in another shop. How much does she have left?

11. Increase £640 by 12%.

12. Express (a) 84 and (b) 24 as the product of prime factors and hence find their LCM.

13. (i) Expand the brackets and simplify:

$$2(5b + 3c) - 3(2b - 5c)$$

(ii) Simplify $\dfrac{3x^2 y^4}{6x^3 y}$

14. Factorise: $8ab^2 - 4a^2b + 12ab$

15. Expand $(2x + 3)(x + 5)$

16. Solve $5(x - 3) + 7 = 42$

17. If it takes eight light bulbs at 60 Watts to light a room, how many bulbs at 40 Watts would it take to light the same room?

18. For every £5 invested in a certain bank a man gets a return of £5.50. How much would he receive on an investment of £3460?

19. A tea and coffee dealer buys x kg of tea at £7 per kg and y kg of coffee at £11 per kg.
(a) What is the cost of x kg of tea?
(b) What is the cost of y kg of coffee?
(c) Write a formula for the total cost, £C, for the tea and coffee.
(d) If $x = 40$ and $y = 35$, find the total cost of the tea and coffee.

20. Construct triangle DEF in which DE = 7.8 cm, $\angle$EDF = 125° and $\angle$DEF = 25°.
Construct the perpendicular bisector of EF and the bisector of $\angle$DFE.
Let these two lines meet at P.
Measure EP.

21. The pie chart below shows the nutritional contents of a 30 g packet of crisps. Measure the angles and calculate the weight of each substance.

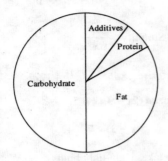

22. A line has equation, $y = \frac{1}{2}x - 1$. Using 1 cm per unit, draw an x-axis from −5 to 9 and a y-axis from −4 to 4. Using the equation, copy and complete the table of values.

x	−4	0	8
y			

Plot the three points given in the table of values and draw a straight line through them. Use your graph to find the value of x when $y = -1\frac{1}{2}$.

23. In the diagram, OP is parallel to QR, RS = RT and $\angle QTS = 112°$

Find, (i) $\angle STR$

    (ii) $\angle TRS$

    (iii) $\angle POS$

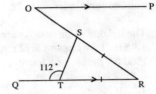

24. A cyclist makes a journey starting at 2 00 pm. In the first hour he travels 15 km and from 4 30 pm to 6 pm he travels another 20 km.

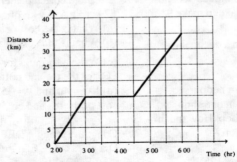

(a) What is his speed during the first hour?
(b) At what speed did he make the second part of his journey?
(c) How far from home was he at 5 15 pm?
(d) At what time was he 20 km from home?

194

Exam Paper 5 ($1\frac{1}{2}$ hours)

1. Calculate $3\frac{3}{5} \div 1\frac{11}{25}$

2. Multiply 0.35 by 7.1

3. Write 8.09513 correct to 2 decimal places

4. If $x = 4$ and $y = 3$, find the value of, $18 - x(x - 2y)$

5. Write 625 m as a fraction of 3 km. Answer in lowest terms.

6. Use straight division to find $1685328 \div 72$, leaving your answer with a whole number remainder.

7. After three 100 m races a runner's average time is 12.6 secs. After a fourth race her average is 12.4 secs. Find her time for the last race.

8. A bricklayer took 4 hrs 35 mins to lay five courses of bricks. Find how long, on average, it took for each course.

9. Convert $\frac{9}{40}$ into a decimal fraction.

10. A lady bought 12 oranges at x pence each and 15 apples at y pence each. Find, in terms of x and y, expression for the amount spent.

11. Express £3.30 as a percentage of £55.

12. Find the LCM of 64 and 96.

13. (i) Expand the brackets and simplify:

$$6(3m + 2n) - 2(9m - 4n)$$

(ii) Simplify $\dfrac{3abc \times 8a^2}{12a^2c}$

14. Factorise: $12x^2y + 16xy^2 - 4xy$

15. Expand $(2x - 3)(x + 7)$

16. Solve $3(x - 1) - 4 = 23$

17. If it takes 6 hours to fill a pool with a tap running at 9 gallons per minute, how long will it take to fill the pool with the tap running at 12 gals. per min?

18. A cricketer scores 32 runs in 48 mins. How many runs will he score in an hour and a half batting at the same rate?

19. The population of Ingham increased by 20% between 1980 and 1990. In 1990 the population was 2868.
(a) Find what the population was in 1980.
(b) By how many did the population increase during this time?

20. (a) Construct triangle PQR in which PQ = 12.5 cm, QR = 8.6 cm and $\angle PQR = 51°$.
(b) Construct the bisectors of $\angle RPQ$ and $\angle PQR$.
(c) Label the point S where these two lines meet.
(d) Construct the perpendicular from S which cuts PQ at T.
(e) with centre S and radius ST draw a circle.

195

21. If the rectangle in the figure is l cm long and w cm wide, find a formula for the perimeter, p in terms of l and w.

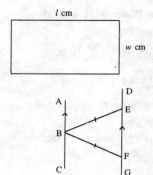

22. In the diagram, AC is parallel to DG, BE = BF and $\angle BFG = 105°$

Find, (a) $\angle BEF$, (b) $\angle ABE$, (c) $\angle EBC$

23. A farm has an area of 7200 acres of which 3500 is used for cattle, 1200 for cerials, 500 for other crops and 2000 for forest. Draw a pie chart to display this information.

24. A line has equation, $y = \frac{1}{3}x + 2$. Using $\frac{1}{2}$ cm per unit, draw an x-axis from −7 to 10 and a y-axis from −1 to 6. Using the equation, copy and complete the table of values.

x	−3	0	9
y			

Plot the three points given in the table of values and draw a straight line through them. Use your graph to find the value of x when $y = 0$.

25. A cyclist makes a journey starting at 10 00 am. The graph shows his journey from home. Use the graph to answer the questions below.

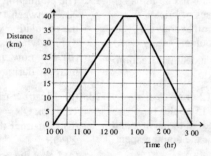

(a) What was his speed during the first two and a half hours?
(b) At what speed did he travel between 1 and 3 o'clock?
(c)
(c) How far from home was he at 2 15 pm?
(d) At what times was he 35 km from home?

196

Answers

Chapter 1 Simple arithmetic

Exercise 1a Page 1

1. 369	6. 12670	11. 5164	16. 76	21. 197
2. 466	7. 11961	12. 23473	17. 107	22. 164
3. 1062	8. 21898	13. 25	18. 113	23. 878
4. 1351	9. 12400	14. 32	19. 186	24. 1613
5. 9894	10. 9979	15. 31	20. 180	

Exercise 1b Page 2

1. 235	10. 287	19. 39999	28. 33	37. 45
2. 621	11. 187	20. 39999	29. 19	38. 137
3. 212	12. 171	21. 56166	30. 23	39. 237
4. 422	13. 1233	22. 39691	31. 77	40. 379
5. 623	14. 3446	23. 24783	32. 125	41. 453
6. 334	15. 1878	24. 227807	33. 34	42. 523
7. 288	16. 2603	25. 588888	34. 34	43. 72
8. 375	17. 3524	26. 33	35. 57	44. 299
9. 355	18. 5695	27. 13	36. 99	45. 263

Exercise 1c Page 3

1. 390	11. 2580	21. 768336	31. 246	41. 84
2. 96	12. 4698	22. 147290	32. 56	42. 60
3. 378	13. 3736	23. 262287	33. 78	43. 800
4. 99	14. 1944	24. 591687	34. 64	44. 1800
5. 696	15. 1984	25. 688569	35. 42	45. 693
6. 228	16. 12972	26. 46	36. 369	46. 30,000
7. 747	17. 10335	27. 162	37. 170	47. 150
8. 532	18. 9438	28. 408	38. 147	48. 2000
9. 253	19. 32004	29. 255	39. 333	49. 2000
10. 1359	20. 9104	30. 99	40. 1869	

Exercise 1d Page 4

1. 18	7. 19	13. 89	19. 979	25. 27097
2. 13	8. 24	14. 151	20. 794	26. 8
3. 13	9. 16	15. 157	21. 1858	27. 34
4. 24	10. 33	16. 815	22. 2487	28. 22
5. 18	11. 22	17. 2932	23. 4585	29. 15
6. 14	12. 64	18. 514	24. 5443	30. 33

31. 27	**35.** 17	**39.** 40	**43.** 206	**47.** 302
32. 15	**36.** 25	**40.** 62	**44.** 3	**48.** 303
33. 17	**37.** 16	**41.** 115	**45.** 10	**49.** 503
34. 13	**38.** 61	**42.** 321	**46.** 125	**50.** 30

Exercise 1e Page 4

1. 56	**6.** 4608	**11.** 9	**16.** 35	**21.** 12
2. 165	**7.** 41	**12.** 21	**17.** 63	**22.** 5
3. 207	**8.** 136	**13.** 25	**18.** 43	**23.** 26
4. 166	**9.** 28	**14.** 28	**19.** 57	**24.** 1
5. 81	**10.** 36	**15.** 32	**20.** 25	**25.** 76

Exercise 1f Page 5

1. 23	**6.** 3600	**11.** 5000 tons	**16.** 90	**21.** 3
2. 21 hrs	**7.** 91	**12.** 1.92 m	**17.** 20	**22.** 56
3. 66	**8.** 80	**13.** £34.45	**18.** 67	**23.** 39
4. 640	**9.** 8:16	**14.** 323 hrs	**19.** 1195	**24.** 40,000 km
5. 56	**10.** 2240	**15.** £22.75	**20.** £23	**25.** 1840

Exercise 1g Page 7

1. 2	**9.** -1	**17.** 1	**25.** 1	**33.** 0	**41.** 1
2. 1	**10.** 14	**18.** 0	**26.** -6	**34.** -5	**42.** -1
3. 4	**11.** 7	**19.** 0	**27.** -2	**35.** -4	**43.** -16
4. 7	**12.** 7	**20.** 10	**28.** -5	**36.** 2	**44.** 1
5. 6	**13.** 0	**21.** 9	**29.** -9	**37.** -12	**45.** 13
6. 2	**14.** 16	**22.** 1	**30.** -10	**38.** -3	
7. 1	**15.** 3	**23.** 13	**31.** 1	**39.** -6	
8. 9	**16.** 6	**24.** 2	**32.** -10	**40.** 0	

Exercise 1h Page 8

1. -8	**7.** -3	**13.** $-\dfrac{a}{b}$	**19.** $-x^2$	**25.** -90	**31.** $-5ab$
2. -9	**8.** -4	**14.** $3x$	**20.** $\dfrac{5}{a}$	**26.** -16	**32.** abc
3. 10	**9.** -12	**15.** $-\dfrac{c}{d}$	**21.** 48	**27.** -30	**33.** -2
4. -48	**10.** 1	**16.** $6y$	**22.** -8	**28.** 35	**34.** z
5. -63	**11.** $-ad$	**17.** -1	**23.** -1	**29.** 28	**35.** $-3x^2$
6. 2	**12.** $-mn$	**18.** $\dfrac{ab}{c}$	**24.** -24	**30.** -6	

Exercise 1i Page 9

1. 39	11. 0.8	21. 100	31. 32	41. 396	51. 286
2. 24	12. 2.9	22. 77	32. 20	42. 2001	52. 1100
3. 184	13. 35	23. 40	33. 34	43. 500	53. 462
4. 200	14. 443	24. 3600	34. 7.2	44. 20	54. 7.6
5. 140	15. 250	25. 98	35. 0.45	45. 8.5	55. 17
6. 15	16. 134	26. 7	36. 9.9	46. 57	56. 844
7. 72	17. 56	27. 0	37. 80	47. 85	57. 4
8. 25	18. 90	28. 30	38. 0.6	48. 25	58. 147
9. 24	19. 144	29. 995	39. 0.35	49. 972	59. 120
10. 46	20. 288	30. 645	40. 656	50. 214	60. 40

Chapter 2 Multiplication by *All from 9 and the last from 10*

Exercise 2a Page 11

1. 87/22	7. 86/40	13. 67/68	19. 862/405	25. 8673/2650
2. 75/24	8. 62/98	14. 59/80	20. 451/641	26. 3424/6575
3. 88/32	9. 35/28	15. 992/015	21. 518/916	27. 99934/00605
4. 77/08	10. 45/59	16. 981/078	22. 9998/0001	28. 95320/18704
5. 80/51	11. 27/72	17. 894/505	23. 9784/0639	
6. 73/71	12. 55/51	18. 877/242	24. 9461/2140	

Exercise 2b Page 12

1. 105/06	7. 131/25	13. 160/68	19. 1023/132	25. 10015/0056
2. 116/63	8. 18/2	14. 202/74	20. 1127/492	26. 11140/6804
3. 117/60	9. 25/5	15. 1009/018	21. 1020/075	27. 13254/9187
4. 134/64	10. 25/6	16. 1003/002	22. 1655/654	28. 12351/1725
5. 190/89	11. 184/62	17. 1014/048	23. 1194/945	
6. 173/34	12. 184/08	18. 1012/020	24. 1661/450	

Exercise 2c Page 12

1. 9792	7. 10573	13. 12502	19. 1,107,552	25. 100,039,988
2. 10260	8. 9828	14. 13050	20. 1,222,620	26. 112,286,304
3. 112	9. 9360	15. 999,996	21. 1,784,214	27. 106,674,592
4. 144	10. 6767	16. 1,000,988	22. 1,034,550	28. 98,349,496
5. 91	11. 11074	17. 1,004,916	23. 1,098,779	
6. 10080	12. 13632	18. 982,890	24. 1,230,815	

Exercise 2d Page 13

1. 9409	7. 8100	13. 992,016	19. 99,920,016	25. 9,998,600,049
2. 9604	8. 8281	14. 986,049	20. 99,880,036	26. 9,999,400,009
3. 9025	9. 7921	15. 994,009	21. 99,820,081	27. 9,998,000,100
4. 8464	10. 7744	16. 998,001	22. 99,960,004	28. 9,998,800,036
5. 8649	11. 81	17. 982,081	23. 99,900,025	29. 999,986,000,049
6. 8836	12. 64	18. 980,100	24. 99,840,064	30. 999,996,000,004

Exercise 2e Page 14

1. 10816	7. 12544	13. 1010025	19. 1014049	25. 121
2. 10404	8. 11449	14. 1016064	20. 1006009	26. 144
3. 11236	9. 12100	15. 1008016	21. 1024144	27. 169
4. 10201	10. 11664	16. 1002001	22. 1020100	28. 196
5. 11881	11. 12321	17. 1012036	23. 1018081	29. 225
6. 11025	12. 10000	18. 1004004	24. 1022121	30. 256

Exercise 2f Page 14

1. 2025	7. 7225	13. 422500	19. 42.25	25. 0.0625
2. 3025	8. 625	14. 902500	20. 2.25	26. 0.0225
3. 5625	9. 13225	15. 22500	21. 56.25	27. 0.4225
4. 225	10. 202500	16. 302500	22. 90.25	28. 0.1225
5. 9025	11. 62500	17. 562500	23. 132.25	29. 0.2025
6. 11025	12. 122500	18. 6.25	24. 30.25	30. 0.9025

Exercise 2g Page 15

1. 624	7. 209	13. 3024	19. 4224	25. 0.2009
2. 1221	8. 224	14. 5624	20. 5621	26. 0.4216
3. 5616	9. 216	15. 2016	21. 30.21	27. 0.5609
4. 3009	10. 609	16. 9009	22. 42.09	28. 0.3016
5. 4221	11. 621	17. 7221	23. 72.24	29. 0.9021
6. 221	12. 616	18. 1209	24. 90.16	30. 0.007216

Exercise 2h Page 16

1. 7546	6. 12305	11. 102468482	16. 99760144	21. 12321
2. 8075	7. 105493794	12. 116659888	17. 1024144	22. 902500
3. 883666	8. 123585795	13. 7569	18. 1030225	23. 0.5625
4. 9995400385	9. 9328	14. 982081	19. 2021	24. 42.16
5. 11024	10. 10695	15. 99940009	20. 289	

Exercise 2i Page 16

1. 9702	**7**. 9021	**13**. 11024	**19**. 11881	**25**. 998001
2. 9312	**8**. 9016	**14**. 10404	**20**. 12100	**26**. 1005006
3. 8832	**9**. 9216	**15**. 10201	**21**. 996003	**27**. 1009020
4. 9801	**10**. 9604	**16**. 11556	**22**. 994008	**28**. 1015056
5. 8463	**11**. 10403	**17**. 11772	**23**. 990024	**29**. 1010025
6. 8930	**12**. 10608	**18**. 11128	**24**. 985056	**30**. 1020100

Chapter 3 Division

Exercise 3a Page 17

1. 151 r 1	**8**. 260 r 1	**15**. 1099 r 5	**22**. 1094 r 6	**29**. 203	**36**. 10587 r 2
2. 155 r 4	**9**. 149 r 5	**16**. 1097 r 2	**23**. 1939 r 4	**30**. 2114	**37**. 26001 r 2
3. 163	**10**. 130	**17**. 550 r 2	**24**. 1055 r 2	**31**. 2205 r 6	**38**. 16009 r 4
4. 69 r 4	**11**. 1412	**18**. 2314 r 2	**25**. 714 r 6	**32**. 3323 r 6	**39**. 6096 r 7
5. 251	**12**. 1370 r 2	**19**. 1327 r 3	**26**. 2004 r 1	**33**. 19607	**40**. 2956 r 6
6. 45 r 5	**13**. 2294 r 1	**20**. 2167	**27**. 701 r 1	**34**. 5077 r 5	
7. 12 r 6	**14**. 375 r 2	**21**. 156 r 6	**28**. 1242 r 3	**35**. 1028 r 3	

Exercise 3b Page 18

1. 542 r 1	**4**. £0.80	**7**. 98 g	**10**. 3421656,	**11**. 559
2. 2157, 7	**5**. 47	**8**. 738	488808,	
3. 34	**6**. 10800	**9**. 111111 r 1	61101,	
			6789	

Exercise 3c Page 19

1. 2/3	**5**. 5/7	**9**. 566/7	**13**. 237/8	**17**. 13447/8
2. 3/5	**6**. 25/6	**10**. 111/1	**14**. 348/8	**18**. 13467/8
3. 4/7	**7**. 12/4	**11**. 135/6	**15**. 4678/8	**19**. 12345/5
4. 7/8	**8**. 46/7	**12**. 113/5	**16**. 13455/6	**20**. 55556/7

Exercise 3d Page 20

1. 128/3	**5**. 158/4	**9**. 380/1	**13**. 25901/2	**17**. 136711/3
2. 147/4	**6**. 589/0	**10**. 680/8	**14**. 17792/4	**18**. 356790/8
3. 148/6	**7**. 240/0	**11**. 23693/7	**15**. 46701/8	**19**. 360012/7
4. 268/6	**8**. 179/7	**12**. 26010/1	**16**. 666794/6	**20**. 246913/5

Exercise 3e Page 21

1. 1/24	**5.** 1/60	**9.** 1/3197	**13.** 4/303	**17.** 21/640
2. 1/55	**6.** 1/55	**10.** 1/4286	**14.** 6/760	**18.** 20/611
3. 1/19	**7.** 1/342	**11.** 2/646	**15.** 2/568	**19.** 13/563
4. 1/26	**8.** 1/388	**12.** 2/398	**16.** 23/865	**20.** 24/610

Exercise 3f Page 22

1. 11/1	**8.** 21/15	**15.** 34/12	**22.** 111/14	**29.** 321/024
2. 11/24	**9.** 21/01	**16.** 11/10	**23.** 22/127	**30.** 720/79
3. 11/40	**10.** 20/33	**17.** 121/23	**24.** 123/104	**31.** 311/52
4. 10/46	**11.** 22/21	**18.** 212/22	**25.** 201/201	**32.** 22/000
5. 12/21	**12.** 22/00	**19.** 121/13	**26.** 11/213	
6. 13/40	**13.** 23/24	**20.** 300/51	**27.** 230/2327	
7. 21/32	**14.** 31/40	**21.** 12/10	**28.** 12/424	

Exercise 3g Page 22

1. 1452/0	**6.** 72/6	**11.** 748/0	**16.** 1/4397	**21.** 855843/0
2. 10/22	**7.** 298/0	**12.** 12/457	**17.** 12/495	**22.** 2/6545
3. 821/6	**8.** 20/094	**13.** 34/46	**18.** 8/5	**23.** 913/89
4. 5477/0	**9.** 409/4	**14.** 107/61	**19.** 344/0	**24.** 2406/7
5. 132/05	**10.** 101/41	**15.** 7662/2	**20.** 28/0	

Chapter 4   Algebra

Exercise 4a Page 23

1. 9	**6.** 5	**11.** 18	**16.** 7	**21.** 108	**26.** 2
2. 15	**7.** 10	**12.** 6	**17.** 18	**22.** $1\frac{1}{3}$	**27.** $\frac{1}{2}$
3. 4	**8.** 16	**13.** 0	**18.** 0	**23.** $\frac{3}{4}$	**28.** $\frac{11}{12}$
4. 7	**9.** 3	**14.** 6	**19.** 11	**24.** 6	
5. 6	**10.** 5	**15.** 2	**20.** 17	**25.** 2	

Exercise 4b Page 24

1. 3	**6.** 8	**11.** 16	**16.** 27	**21.** 83	**26.** 8
2. 9	**7.** 4	**12.** 7	**17.** $\frac{1}{4}$	**22.** 38	**27.** 50
3. 51	**8.** 4	**13.** 12	**18.** 3	**23.** 4	**28.** 18
4. 12	**9.** 6	**14.** 8	**19.** 36	**24.** 30	
5. 21	**10.** 10	**15.** 42	**20.** 230	**25.** 6	

Exercise 4c Page 25

1. 8	**4.** 6	**7.** $\frac{1}{2}$	**10.** 2	**13.** -2
2. 11	**5.** 0	**8.** 4	**11.** 11	**14.** -3
3. 7	**6.** 1	**9.** 4	**12.** -2	**15.** -4

Exercise 4d Page 25

1. 3	**6.** 5	**11.** 12	**16.** 3	**21.** -2	**26.** 0
2. 2	**7.** 5	**12.** 0.1	**17.** 4	**22.** 1	**27.** 1
3. 17	**8.** 2	**13.** 1	**18.** 8	**23.** 0	
4. 4	**9.** 7	**14.** 0	**19.** 5	**24.** 0.6	
5. 3	**10.** 6	**15.** 5	**20.** 1	**25.** 3	

Exercise 4e Page 26

1. $6a - 8b$	**6.** $6n - 21$	**11.** $2a + ab$	**16.** $a^2 + 2a$
2. $20h + 5$	**7.** $5a + 5b + 5c$	**12.** $2ab - 4bc$	**17.** $a^2b - 8ab$
3. $3x + 3y$	**8.** $4a + 6b - 2c$	**13.** $3bc + 15bd$	**18.** $x^2y - 3xy^2$
4. $8a - 68$	**9.** $72a - 30 + 6b$	**14.** $6u + 10uv$	**19.** $x^2y - 3xy$
5. $18 + 48k$	**10.** $-12a + 4b - 4c$	**15.** $9pq + 12pr$	**20.** $15xy + 15xy^2$

Exercise 4f Page 27

1. $5x + 25$	**3.** $8 + 3x$	**5.** $8a - 12b$	**7.** $18a + 46b$	**9.** $5a + 15b$
2. $-x - 29$	**4.** $13a + 18b$	**6.** $14m - 20n$	**8.** $16p - 8q$	**10.** $14x + 18y - 32z$

Exercise 4g Page 27

1. 7	**6.** 2	**11.** $2\frac{1}{2}$	**16.** 0	**21.** 5	**26.** 2
2. 5	**7.** 7	**12.** $4\frac{1}{2}$	**17.** 3	**22.** 3	**27.** 3
3. 6	**8.** 6	**13.** 2	**18.** 2	**23.** 5	**28.** 1
4. 3	**9.** 7	**14.** $1\frac{3}{8}$	**19.** 10	**24.** 4	**29.** 2
5. $5\frac{1}{2}$	**10.** 1	**15.** $\frac{1}{2}$	**20.** 2	**25.** $-3\frac{1}{2}$	**30.** 15

Exercise 4h Page 28

1. $x + 5$	**6.** $2x - 1$	**11.** $\dfrac{a+b}{2}$	**16.** £$\dfrac{15x}{100}$	**21.** $45d$
2. $8 - y$ ft	**7.** $\dfrac{n}{3}$	**12.** a) $n - 1$, b) $n + 1$	**17.** $24y$ pence	**22.** $3t + 5$
3. $42x$ cm^2	**8.** $4p$	**13.** $\dfrac{a+b+c}{3}$	**18.** £$\dfrac{12.68}{h}$	**23.** £$(x + y + z)$
4. $84 + 2x$ cm	**9.** $x - 5$ min	**14.** a) $2x + 2 = 14$ b) $x = 6$	**19.** $235 - 2x$	**24.** $4a$ kilos
5. $180 - x°$	**10.** $y - 46$	**15.** $15x$ pence	**20.** $y/4$	**25.** £$(p - q - r)$

Exercise 4i Page 30

1. $-4a + 2b - 3c$
2. $5x - y + 2z$
3. $-6m + 3n - 14$

4. $-7 - 3i + 2j - k$
5. $9 + 2p + 3p^2$
6. $-2 + 3x + 6x^2$

7. $11 - 3y + x + z$
8. $2a + b - b^2$.
9. $-a + b - c + d + e$

10. 1
11. 25
12. 12
13. 27
14. 10
15. 9
16. 10

17. $11a - 1$
18. $15b - c - d$
19. $3c - 2a - b$
20. $12g - 3h$
21. $14a - 3b$
22. $14m - 3n$
23. $5x - 3y$

24. $21s - 4t$
25. $a - c + b$
26. $-c - b + a$
27. $a - b - c$
28. $2a^3$
29. $7a$
30. $ab + 56$

Exercise 4j Page 31

1. 2
2. 1
3. 4
4. 6

5. 3
6. -1
7. 3
8. 4

9. -4
10. 8
11. 1
12. $\frac{2}{3}$

13. $1\frac{1}{4}$
14. -5
15. 2
16. $\frac{1}{2}$

17. 4
18. -12
19. 8
20. -2

21. -11
22. 23
23. $8\frac{1}{2}$
24. 3

Exercise 4k Page 32

1. a) 5
   b) 49
2. a) 3
   b) 8
   c) 3
   d) 13

3. a) $6a - 12b$
   b) $5x^2y - 20x^2$
4. a) $7m - 9n$
   b) $6a + 16b$

5. a) -3
   b) 16
   c) $3\frac{5}{9}$
6. $3y + 2$
7. $\dfrac{a + b + c + d}{4}$

8. $6m$
9. $23x$ pence
10. 29
11. $-\frac{1}{2}$
12. $-4\frac{2}{3}$

Chapter 5   Coordinate Geometry

Exercise 5a Page 34

1. A (1,1)
2. B (2,1)
3. C (2,3)

4. D (5,2)
5. E (8,0)
6. F (8,4)

7. G (9,6)
8. H (5,7)
9. I (4,9)

10. K (0,6)
11. L (1,8)
12. M (6,10)

13. N (10,10)

Exercise 5b Page 34

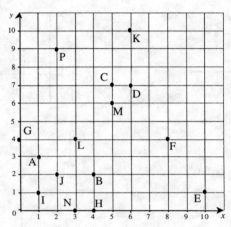

Exercise 5c Page 35

1. A (3,0)	**5.** E (-1,5)	**9.** I (-5,2)	**13.** M (-2,-2)	**17.** R (1,-2)
2. B (5,1)	**6.** F (-2,2)	**10.** J (-3,1)	**14.** N (-4,-4)	**18.** S (2,-4)
3. C (3,3)	**7.** G (-4,4)	**11.** K (-3,-1)	**15.** P (-2,-5)	**19.** T (4,-3)
4. D (2,5)	**8.** H (-5,3)	**12.** L (-5,-2)	**16.** Q (0,-3)	**20.** U (4,-1)

Exercise 5d Page 35

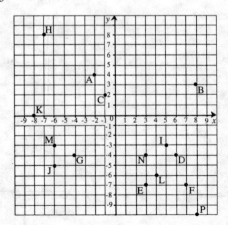

205

Exercise 5e Page 35

1.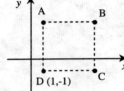

2.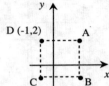

3.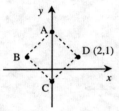

4.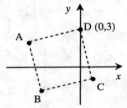

5.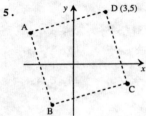

6.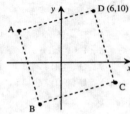

7.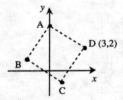

8.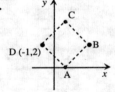

9.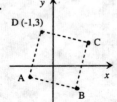

10.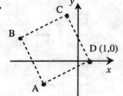

Exercise 5f Page 37

1.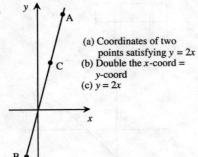

   (a) Coordinates of two
      points satisfying $y = 2x$
   (b) Double the x-coord =
      y-coord
   (c) $y = 2x$

2.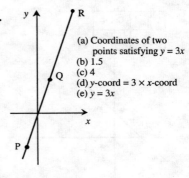

   (a) Coordinates of two
      points satisfying $y = 3x$
   (b) 1.5
   (c) 4
   (d) y-coord = $3 \times x$-coord
   (e) $y = 3x$

3. (a) Three points satisfying $y = \frac{1}{2}x$, (b) x-coord is double the y-coord, (c) $y = \frac{1}{2}x$

4.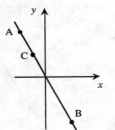

   (a) -4
   (b) $y = -2x$

Exercise 5g Page 38

1. Yes	3. No	5. Yes	7. Yes	9. Yes
2. Yes	4. No	6. No	8. No	10. Yes

Exercise 5h Page 39

1. 15	3. 19	5. 4	7. 13	9. 4
2. 13	4. -1	6. 16	8. 3	10. −1

Exercise 5i Page 41

1.

x	–3	0	4
y	–2	1	5

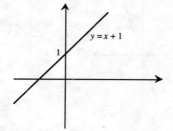

$y = x + 1$

1

2.

x	0	–1	6
y	–2	–3	4

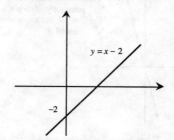

$y = x - 2$

–2

3.

x	–2	2	6
y	–1	1	3

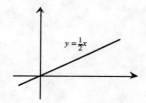

$y = \frac{1}{2}x$

4.

x	–2	2	6
y	–1	1	3

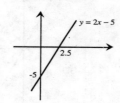

$y = 2x - 5$

2.5

-5

Chapter 6   Approximations

Exercise 6a Page 42

	a)	b)	c)			a)	b)	c)
1.	3430	3400	3000		**9.**	92,400	92,400	92,000
2.	6200	6200	6000		**10.**	23,980	24,000	24,000
3.	5620	5600	6000		**11.**	14,590	14,600	15,000
4.	7810	7800	8000		**12.**	26,760	26,800	27,000
5.	8190	8200	8000		**13.**	30,500	30,500	30,000
6.	72,980	73,000	73,000		**14.**	28,460	28,500	28,000
7.	16,720	16,700	17,000		**15.**	96,510	96,500	97,000
8.	24,190	24,200	24,000					

208

Exercise 6b Page 43

	a)	b)	c)
1.	8.2	8.24	8.236
2.	9.0	9.02	9.017
3.	43.2	43.21	43.213
4.	35.7	35.66	35.657
5.	0.2	0.24	0.238
6.	21.7	21.67	21.671
7.	1.9	1.88	1.880
8.	45.4	45.35	45.352

	a)	b)	c)
9.	213.0	213.00	213.002
10.	65.9	65.88	65.882
11.	3.5	3.50	3.499
12.	9.0	8.99	8.985
13.	0.0	0.03	0.027
14.	0.6	0.62	0.619
15.	6.0	6.00.	6.000
16.	121.4	121.39	121.390

Exercise 6c Page 43

	a)	b)	c)
1.	5000	5100	5120
2.	50,000	47,000	46,900
3.	5000	5500	5490
4.	9000	9500	9480
5.	200,000	220,000	216,000
6.	900,000	870,000	875,000
7.	600,000	650,000	646,000
8.	2,000,000	2,000,000	2,000,000

	a)	b)	c)
9.	2	2.5	2.45
10.	10	15	14.6
11.	400	420	422
12.	9000	8800	8790
13.	0.2	0.16	0.157
14.	0.005	0.0055	0.00547
15.	0.0009	0.00088	0.000870
16.	0.10	0.100	0.0999

Exercise 6d Page 44

1. 10.2	4. 3.7	7. 278.5	10. 0.26	13. 439.0
2. 124.5	5. 1.54	8. 1.03	11. 0.02	14. 156.50
3. 12.70	6. 11.8	9. 63.6	12. 0.461	15. 25.853

Exercise 6e Page 45

1. 4.3	4. 5.4	7. 0.08	10. 1.75	13. 3.643
2. 6.3	5. 26.7	8. 5.89	11. 70.927	14. 125.549
3. 2.6	6. 0.82	9. 5.56	12. 3.286	15. 821.752

Exercise 6f Page 45

1. 3	4. 59	7. 11.4	10. 0.1	13. 0.05
2. 21	5. 405	8. 369.4	11. 0.08	14. 15.92
3. 16	6. 3.2	9. 0.1	12. 5.52	15. 0.41

Chapter Seven Practice and Revision 1

Exercise 7a Page 46

1. 7.1	**5.** 3.67	**9.** 143	**13.** 5	**17.** -17
2. 2.7	**6.** 360	**10.** 91	**14.** -56	**18.** 3577
3. 171	**7.** 21	**11.** 3	**15.** -7	**19.** 6089
4. 401	**8.** 146	**12.** -7	**16.** -1	**20.** 28.609

Exercise 7b Page 46 (Strokes are included for ease of marking.)

1. 95/06	**7.** 107/12	**13.** 100/98	**19.** 104/04	**25.** 0.000625
2. 77/90	**8.** 122/08	**14.** 1010/958	**20.** 116/64	**26.** 20/21
3. 45/12	**9.** 1139/924	**15.** 12339/5316	**21.** 20/25	**27.** 12/24
4. 989/024	**10.** 12138/0660	**16.** 8798/6388	**22.** 12/25	**28.** 42/16
5. 9988/0035	**11.** 94/86	**17.** 96/04	**23.** 132/25	**29.** 56/09
6. 8163/3670	**12.** 101/76	**18.** 92/16	**24.** 0.4225	**30.** 90/16

Exercise 7c Page 46 (Strokes separate quotient from remainder.)

1. 12/4	**6.** 1/16	**11.** 12/279	**16.** 23/21	**21.** 26/2
2. 1135/6	**7.** 11/44	**12.** 133/505	**17.** 13/20	**22.** 49/284
3. 14/0	**8.** 12/55	**13.** 21/873	**18.** 13/33	**23.** 38/123
4. 1149/1	**9.** 1/236	**14.** 12254/87	**19.** 11/18	**24.** 1351/23
5. 1/25	**10.** 2/4357	**15.** 210/531	**20.** 111/24	

Exercise 7d Page 47

1. $6b$	**4.** $5k + 3n$	**7.** $2p$	**10.** $18cd$
2. $3n + t$	**5.** $2d + 4$	**8.** $8b$	**11.** $12mp$
3. $2k + 3m$	**6.** $h + 5g$	**9.** $4hk$	**12.** $30vwx$

13. $3c + 3d$	**18.** $ab + 3a$	**23.** $14nt + 6nu$	**28.** $5x + 11$	**33.** $10a + 6b$
14. $7e + 7f$	**19.** $5g - gh$	**24.** $2p^2 - 10p$	**29.** $6y - 2$	**34.** $2x + 10y + 3$
15. $6n - 6p$	**20.** $8c - 12$	**25.** $m^2 + m$	**30.** $3a - 14$	**35.** $18a - 12b - 15$
16. $ab + ac$	**21.** $18 + 12h$	**26.** $4x^2 - 8xy$	**31.** $3x + 33$	**36.** $16a + 7b$
17. $de - df$	**22.** $2ab + 10a$	**27.** $8a - 6ab$	**32.** $8 - 9z$	**37.** $2x - y$

Exercise 7e Page 47

1. 5	**5.** 4	**9.** 6	**13.** $-\frac{7}{5}$	**17.** 3	**21.** 2
2. 5	**6.** 5	**10.** 2	**14.** 0	**18.** 3	
3. 11	**7.** 5	**11.** 4	**15.** 0	**19.** 7	
4. 12	**8.** 6	**12.** 6	**16.** 2	**20.** 9	

Exercise 7f Page 48

1.

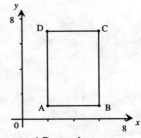

a) Rectangle
b) 24 sq.cm

2.

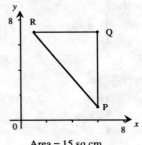

Area = 15 sq.cm

3.

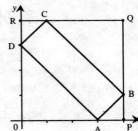

b) Area OPQR = 64 sq.cm
c) Area OAD = 18 sq.cm
   Area APB = 2 sq.cm
d) Area ABCD = 24 sq.cm

4.

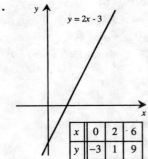

$y = 2x - 3$

x	0	2	6
y	-3	1	9

5.

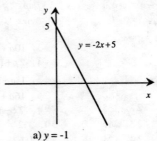

$y = -2x + 5$

a) $y = -1$
b) $x = 1/2$
c) $(0, 5)$ and $(2 1/2, 0)$

6. a) At $x = 8$, $y = 4 \times 8 - 3$
$$= 32 - 3 = 29$$
$\therefore (8, 29)$ does lie on the line.

b) At $x = 2$, $y = 4 \times 2 - 3$
$$= 8 - 3 = 5$$
$\therefore (2, -3)$ does not lie on the line.

c) $y = 4x - 3$
$y + 3 = 4x$
$4x = y + 3$
$$x = \frac{y + 3}{4}$$

Chapter 8 Geometry 1

Exercise 8a Page 57

1. $a = 30°$ **4.** $d = 41°$ **7.** $g = 60°$ **10.** $j = 78°$ **13.** $m = 70°$ **16.** $q = 29°$
2. $b = 45°$ **5.** $e = 37.5°$ **8.** $h = 30°$ **11.** $k = 128°$ **14.** $n = 27°$
3. $c = 62°$ **6.** $f = 32°$ **9.** $i = 25°$ **12.** $l = 64°$ **15.** $p = 70°$

Exercise 8b Page 59

1. $x = 28°$ **4.** 60°   **7.** 33°   **10.** 70°   **13.** $\angle A = 52°$, $\angle C = 60°$
2. $y = 15°$ **5.** isosceles   **8.** 53°   **11.** 30°,60°,90°   **14.** 30°
3. $z = 20°$ **6.** 80°   **9.** 55°   **12.** $\angle PQR = 62°$ **15.** $\angle AQC = 100°$
                                                $\angle PMQ = 84°$ $\angle ACB = 80°$

Exercise 8c Page 64

1. $a = 72°$ **5.** $e = 55°$ **7.** $h = 95°$ **8.** $l = 56°$ **9.** $q = 60°$ **11.** $w = 116°$
2. $b = 123°$ **6.** $f = 45°$ $i = 95°$ $m = 124°$ $r = 48°$ $x = 64°$
3. $c = 67°$ $g = 135°$ $j = 95°$ $n = 124°$ $s = 72°$ **12.** $y = 69°$
4. $d = 104°$ $k = 85°$ $p = 56°$ **10.** $t = 57°$ $z = 42°$
                                                            $u = 50°$ $a = 111°$
                                                            $v = 73°$

Exercise 8d Page 64

1. $x = 40°$ **5.** $g = 33°$ **8.** $p = 30°$ **9.** 65°   **13.** $x = 62°$ **14.** $a = 49°$
2. $f = 56°$ **6.** $y = 28°$ $q = 120°$ **10.** 40°, 60°, $y = 62°$ $b = 84°$
3. 60°   **7.** $b = 41°$ $r = 60°$ 80° $z = 56°$ $c = 47°$
4. 45° $s = 60°$ **11.** $s = 67°$ $d = 131°$
                          $t = 60°$ **12.** $t = 44°$ $e = 131°$
                                        $u = 136°$ $f = 84°$

Chapter 9 Arithmetic Practice

Exercise 9a Page 67

1. 51   **8.** 922   **15.** 25   **22.** 235   **29.** 2873
2. 36   **9.** 474   **16.** 68   **23.** 266   **30.** 332
3. 68   **10.** 509   **17.** 63   **24.** 124   **31.** 1162
4. 99   **11.** 39   **18.** 37   **25.** 4999   **32.** 2287
5. 65   **12.** 32   **19.** 135   **26.** 40468
6. 144   **13.** 17   **20.** 234   **27.** 638
7. 523   **14.** 36   **21.** 422   **28.** 6664

Exercise 9b Page 67

1. 46	**5.** 1328	**9.** 3708	**13.** 268576
2. 144	**6.** 1688	**10.** 2394	**14.** 43967
3. 244	**7.** 1725	**11.** 4336	**15.** 25712
4. 434	**8.** 1416	**12.** 10263	**16.** 37.488
17. 3.789	**21.** 16.536	**25.** 3616.9	**29.** 48.2296
18. 162.029	**22.** 217.784	**26.** 1185928	**30.** 2.8287
19. 544.96	**23.** 2.305	**27.** 565704	**31.** 0.315
20. 28.2735	**24.** 2571.2	**28.** 10333.08	**32.** 21.33

Exercise 9c Page 67

1. 124	**7.** 293	**13.** 806	**19.** 35	**25.** 6.35
2. 82	**8.** 4921	**14.** 801	**20.** 63	**26.** 0.0504
3. 232	**9.** 782	**15.** 0.618	**21.** 823	**27.** 1.28
4. 131	**10.** 2141	**16.** 84.6	**22.** 134	**28.** 1.67
5. 154	**11.** 806	**17.** 1.042	**23.** 373	**29.** 0.623
6. 2438	**12.** 506	**18.** 64	**24.** 0.92	**30.** 19.128

Exercise 9d Page 68

1. 4320	**7.** 20730	**13.** 577440	**19.** 371610	**25.** 55.89
2. 12440	**8.** 14480	**14.** 114030	**20.** 2769600	**26.** 1668
3. 20460	**9.** 68160	**15.** 230090	**21.** 56.2	**27.** 125.68
4. 11460	**10.** 49860	**16.** 257340	**22.** 173.6	**28.** 267.6
5. 6360	**11.** 48720	**17.** 296580	**23.** 439.6	**29.** 49.44
6. 29890	**12.** 128600	**18.** 2081640	**24.** 12	**30.** 29.477

Exercise 9e Page 68

1. 24	**7.** 0.8	**13.** 0.9	**19.** 24.1	**25.** 30.7
2. 12	**8.** 0.8	**14.** 0.8	**20.** 3.2	**26.** 76.8
3. 16	**9.** 0.7	**15.** 9	**21.** 64.2	**27.** 108.7
4. 4	**10.** 2.7	**16.** 28.2	**22.** 106.2	**28.** 94.5
5. 327	**11.** 0.9	**17.** 12.225	**23.** 154.8	**29.** 3147.7
6. 2.4	**12.** 0.7	**18.** 10.45	**24.** 164.3	**30.** 24282.3

Exercise 9f Page 69

1. 450	**7.** 1.23	**13.** 48.9	**19.** 7
2. 76	**8.** 345.2	**14.** 30	**20.** 6.5
3. 677	**9.** 40	**15.** 0.003	**21.** 200
4. 68	**10.** 57.6	**16.** 2	**22.** 0.3847
5. 0.03	**11.** 4570	**17.** 57000	**23.** 23990
6. 0.0072	**12.** 1290	**18.** 354000	**24.** 75

Exercise 9g Page 70

1. 14.4	**7.** 8.52	**13.** 1200	**19.** 201000
2. 8.6	**8.** 25.76	**14.** 2200	**20.** 105000
3. 7.4	**9.** 65.68	**15.** 1000	**21.** 62000
4. 230	**10.** 2300	**16.** 4.84	**22.** 5.368
5. 420	**11.** 14200	**17.** 12.48	**23.** 32.52
6. 1170	**12.** 18550	**18.** 24.44	**24.** 247.764

Exercise 9h Page 70

1. $\frac{3}{5}$	**9.** 7	**17.** $3\frac{1}{2}$	**25.** $16\frac{5}{7}$	**33.** 71
2. 30	**10.** $6\frac{2}{3}$	**18.** $18\frac{3}{4}$	**26.** $40\frac{1}{2}$	**34.** $68\frac{4}{7}$
3. 32	**11.** $13\frac{1}{3}$	**19.** 5	**27.** $21\frac{3}{4}$	**35.** $47\frac{1}{3}$
4. 32	**12.** $21\frac{1}{3}$	**20.** 20	**28.** $67\frac{2}{3}$	**36.** 380
5. 25	**13.** $12\frac{2}{3}$	**21.** $19\frac{1}{5}$	**29.** $10\frac{2}{3}$	**37.** 37
6. 48	**14.** $13\frac{1}{3}$	**22.** 80	**30.** $1\frac{1}{25}$	**38.** 250
7. 4	**15.** 5	**23.** $2\frac{1}{2}$	**31.** $2\frac{1}{2}$	**39.** $467\frac{2}{3}$
8. 5	**16.** 8	**24.** 5	**32.** $15\frac{3}{8}$	**40.** $429\frac{1}{2}$

Exercise 9i Page 71

1. 143	**7.** 484	**13.** 902	**19.** 4.836	**25.** 1601052
2. 154	**8.** 322	**14.** 989	**20.** 2.184	**26.** 231.7933
3. 168	**9.** 276	**15.** 8.16	**21.** 35200	**27.** 4.276665
4. 480	**10.** 231	**16.** 12.19	**22.** 22.032	**28.** 28381.5
5. 240	**11.** 312	**17.** 377.52	**23.** 6.804	**29.** 1672000
6. 441	**12.** 651	**18.** 247.53	**24.** 3808	**30.** 5097444

Chapter 10 Compound arithmetic

Exercie 10a Page 73

1. 9 yr 4 m
2. 43 yr 7 m
3. 12 min 23 sec
4. 22 min 20 sec
5. 14 hr 12 min

6. 7 hr 54 min
7. 13 hr 3 min
8. 15 d 6 hr
9. 16 d 16 hr
10. 13 d 21 hr

11. 10 ft 1 in
12. 23 ft 7 in
13. 43 ft 5 in
14. 14 yd 1 ft
15. 10 lb 8 oz

16. 62 lb 9 oz
17. 13 lb 7 oz
18. 21 st 5 lb
19. 21 st 2 lb
20. 10 mi 318 yd

Exercie 10b Page 74

1. 8 ft 8 in
2. 2 ft 8 in
3. 34 ft 9 in
4. 3 st 12 lb
5. 7 st 10 lb

6. 1 lb 12 oz
7. 4 lb 8 oz
8. 25 lb 6 oz
9. 1 yr 7 m
10. 3 yr 7 m

11. 6 yr 8 m
12. 3 hr 47 min
13. 1 hr 27 min
14. 4 hr 36 min
15. 7 hr 22 min

16. 1 d 17 hr
17. 4 d 16 hr
18. 7 d 13 hr

Exercie 10c Page 74

1. 10 ft 9 in
2. 68 ft 6 in
3. 22 ft
4. 65 ft 8 in
5. 39 yd 2 ft
6. 39 yd

7. 13 lb 2 oz
8. 9 lb 12 oz
9. 23 lb 3 oz
10. 74 lb
11. 76 st 1 lb
12. 33 st 6 lb

13. 45 st 7 lb
14. 26 st 6 lb
15. 26 hr
16. 7 hr 42 min
17. 54 hr 36 min
18. 57 min 45 sec

19. 22 min
20. 115 min 4 sec
21. 50 min
22. 16 d 9 hr
23. 123 d 2 hr
24. 89 d 9 hr

Exercise 10d Page 75

1. 24, 96, 36, 108, 144
2. 4, 5, 6, $7\frac{1}{2}$, $8\frac{1}{3}$
3. 2, 4, 3
4. 5280, 2640
5. 48, 96, 896, 1120

6. 3, 5, $\frac{1}{2}$, $\frac{1}{4}$
7. 180, 420, 600, 1800, 3600
8. 120, 240, 720, 1440
9. 86,400; 604,800; 31,536,000

Exercie 10e Page 76

1. 3 ft 1 in
2. 3 ft 10 in
3. 2 ft 11 in
4. 3 ft 8 in
5. 2 ft 7 in

6. 3 hr 6 min
7. 2 hr 20 min
8. 5 hr 37 min
9. 1 hr 47 min
10. 1 hr 58 min

11. 3 min 1 sec
12. 2 min 29 sec
13. 3 min 12 sec
14. 2 min 8 sec
15. 2 min 14 sec

16. 2 lb 4 oz
17. 3 lb 3 oz
18. 5 lb $11\frac{1}{2}$ oz
19. 4 st 10 lb
20. 2 st 10 lb

Exercie 10f Page 76

1. 43 in	**6.** 3880 yd	**11.** 305 min	**16.** 87 oz
2. 86 in	**7.** 158 hr	**12.** 740 sec	**17.** 154 oz
3. 191 in	**8.** 91 hr	**13.** 227 sec	**18.** 61 lb
4. 47 ft	**9.** 203 min	**14.** 835 sec	**19.** 44 lb
5. 40 ft	**10.** 478 min	**15.** 35 oz	**20.** 123 lb

Exercie 10g Page 77

1. 7 oz	**4.** 5 lb	**7.** 2 in	**10.** 4 ft	**13.** 23 sec
2. 6 oz	**5.** 10 oz	**8.** 4 in	**11.** 19 min	**14.** 16 min
3. 10 lb	**6.** 6 in	**9.** 1 ft	**12.** 51 min	**15.** 4 hr

Exercie 10h Page 77

1. 4 oz	**4.** 6 oz	**7.** 4 in	**10.** 12 sec	**13.** 9 sec
2. 9 in	**5.** 7 lb	**8.** 2 ft 3 in	**11.** 45 min	**14.** 36 min
3. 6 in	**6.** 3 lb	**9.** 8 in	**12.** 25 min	**15.** 1 sec

Exercise 10i Page 78

1. 106 mm	**7.** 8 g	**13.** 2275 ml	**19.** 0.6135 km
2. 90 cm	**8.** 4200 mg	**14.** 1.25 m	**20.** 0.25 g
3. 140 cm	**9.** 0.7 kg	**15.** 36.4 mm	**21.** 10.5 tonnes
4. 6 m	**10.** 7850 g	**16.** 4.5 km	**22.** 950 cm
5. 8300 m	**11.** 3500 kg	**17.** 2900 m	**23.** 0.7 cm
6. 2.5 km	**12.** 0.5 tonnes	**18.** 600 g	**24.** 2400 kg

Exercise 10j Page 79

1. 2000, 500, 230, 4320	**6.** 1,000,000
2. 200, 70, 205, 0.8, 2.3	**7.** 100
3. 4, 1.72, 0.58, 0.04	**8.** 10,000
4. 400, 368, 80, 22	**9.** 10,000,000,000
5. 40, 38.5, 3.86, 0.1	

Exercise 10k Page 79

1. 1.7 cm	**6.** 3.12 m	**11.** 7.1 cm	**16.** 2.5 kg	**21.** 9.6 cm
2. 1.28 m	**7.** 24.1 cm	**12.** 0.25 m	**17.** 3.24 tonnes	**22.** 2.38 cm
3. 1.218 km	**8.** 58.4 g	**13.** 1.1 cm	**18.** 450 kg	**23.** 20.64 m
4. 1.3 g	**9.** 7.15 kg	**14.** 6.77 g	**19.** 5.65 l	**24.** 2.334 m
5. 0.39 tonnes	**10.** 1.65 m	**15.** 4 g	**20.** 2654 ml	**25.** 2.72 km

26. 0.75 g	**29.** 2.43 l	**32.** 6.3 m	**35.** 6.75 km
27. 2.9 kg	**30.** 2.9 cm	**33.** 175 cm	**36.** 500 kg
28. 5.75 tonnes	**31.** 12 mm	**34.** 490 m	**37.** 150 ml

Exercise 10l Page 80

1. 2.6 km	**3.** 20,640 l	**5.** 0.1 mm
2. 30 cm	**4.** 170 g	**6.** 5 boxes

Chapter 11   Indices

Exercise 11a Page 81

1. 2^4	**7.** 7^3	**13.** c^2	**19.** 5^2	**25.** b
2. 3^3	**8.** 9^5	**14.** d^5	**20.** 8	**26.** c
3. 4^4	**9.** $2^3 \times 5^2$	**15.** a^2b^2	**21.** 9^2	**27.** y^3
4. 10^2	**10.** $3^2 \times 7^3$	**16.** b^3c^2	**22.** a^2	
5. 2^2	**11.** a^3	**17.** x^3y^2	**23.** b^2	
6. 6^5	**12.** b^4	**18.** m^3n	**24.** x	

Exercise 11b Page 83

1. 2^5	**7.** 3^{14}	**13.** 6^3	**19.** a^7	**25.** p^2
2. 3^8	**8.** 2^{10}	**14.** 9^4	**20.** y^8	**26.** z^9
3. 2^{10}	**9.** 6^{25}	**15.** 1	**21.** x^5	**27.** x^{-3}
4. 5^5	**10.** 3^3	**16.** 4	**22.** b^6	
5. 7^7	**11.** 2^2	**17.** 5	**23.** d^{20}	
6. 9^9	**12.** 4	**18.** 1	**24.** m^6	

Exercise 11d Page 85

1. 2^{-4}	**5.** 4^{-1}	**9.** a^{-4}	**13.** $c^{-3}d^{-1}$	**17.** c^2b^{-2}
2. 3^{-2}	**6.** 9^{-5}	**10.** p^{-1}	**14.** $m^{-1}n^{-3}$	**18.** $x^3y^{-3}z^{-1}$
3. 5^{-3}	**7.** x^{-2}	**11.** $p^{-2}q^{-2}$	**15.** $2x^{-2}y^{-1}$	
4. 8^{-4}	**8.** y^{-3}	**12.** $a^{-2}b^{-1}$	**16.** ab^{-2}	

Exercise 11e Page 85

1. b	**3.** $\dfrac{1}{b}$	**5.** $\dfrac{1}{a}$	**7.** 1	**9.** $\dfrac{a}{b}$
2. a	**4.** a	**6.** x^2	**8.** y	**10.** ab

11. $\dfrac{c}{d}$ **13.** $\dfrac{1}{n}$ **15.** $2a$ **17.** $\dfrac{2}{3a^2}$ **19.** $\dfrac{a^2b}{2c}$

12. ac **14.** $\dfrac{1}{xy^2}$ **16.** $\dfrac{3x}{2}$ **18.** $\dfrac{3}{2y}$ **20.** $\dfrac{yz^2}{3}$

Exercise 11f Page 86

1. 169 cm²	**3.** 375 m²	**5.** 1836 m²	**7.** 64 cm²	**9.** 1050 cm²
2. 256 cm²	**4.** 504 mm²	**6.** 297 km²	**8.** 424 cm²	**10.** 392 cm²
				11. 48 mm²

Exercise 11g Page 88

1. 120,000 cm³	**3.** 12,600 cm³	**5.** 1.728 m³	**7.** 840 mm³	**9.** 0.064 mm³
2. 30 cm³	**4.** 512 mm³	**6.** 2880 cm³	**8.** 0.09 m³	**10.** 1512 cm³
				11. 14,500 cm³

Chapter 12   Further division

Exercise 12a Page 90

1. 21/0	**9.** 4/55	**17.** 223/1	**25.** 20/34
2. 21/30	**10.** 6/36	**18.** 131/0	**26.** 43/51
3. 25/11	**11.** 17/0	**19.** 114/36	**27.** 241/20
4. 11/19	**12.** 16/30	**20.** 128/14	**28.** 74/50
5. 12/35	**13.** 30/2	**21.** 108/71	**29.** 102/48
6. 5/60	**14.** 7/39	**22.** 152/30	**30.** 50/38
7. 24/5	**15.** 9/29	**23.** 170/18	**31.** 170/14
8. 24/0	**16.** 15/7	**24.** 61/23	**32.** 222/17

Exercise 12b Page 90

1. 27/3	**6.** 43	**11.** £31	**16.** £115
2. 24	**7.** 1140	**12.** 1370	**17.** 42 m
3. 24	**8.** 111	**13.** 26	**18.** 122
4. 17 and 6 cm	**9.** 3214/2	**14.** 12	**19.** 116
5. 250 mins	**10.** 53	**15.** 2700	**20.** 4432

Exercise 12c Page 92

1. 4/1
   3/5
   2/9
   1/13

2. 5/1
   4/4
   3/7
   2/10

3. 10/1
   9/3
   8/5
   7/7

4. 4/4
   3/9
   2/14
   1/19

5. 6/1
   5/5
   4/9
   3/13

6. 5/1
   4/7
   3/13
   2/19

7. 6/1
   5/4
   4/7
   3/10

8. 4/4
   3/11
   2/18
   1/25

9. 3/5
   2/13
   1/21
   0/29

10. 20/2
    19/5
    18/8
    17/11

11. 13/1
    12/5
    11/9
    10/13

12. 5/0
    4/1
    3/2
    2/3

13. 9/4
    8/9
    7/14
    6/19

14. 7/4
    6/13
    5/22
    4/31

15. 4/7
    3/15
    2/23
    1/31

Exercise 12d Page 93

1. 18/21
2. 18/15
3. 10/58
4. 24/33
5. 26/1
6. 4/83
7. 17/15
8. 26/9

9. 21/0
10. 18/9
11. 23/10
12. 47/10
13. 19/8
14. 14/9
15. 15/24
16. 4/0

17. 161/23
18. 42/9
19. 238/23
20. 117/13
21. 5/17
22. 250/27
23. 26/77
24. 202/9

25. 180/1
26. 89/88
27. 114/12
28. 36/57
29. 142/20
30. 165/20
31. 41/46
32. 588/4

Exercise 12e Page 94

1. 30
2. 27/1
3. 10

4. 83/8
5. 33/2
6. 24

7. 75 m
8. £120
9. 25

10. 30
11. £46
12. 18 and 14 cm

13. £3750
14. 6944 tons

Chapter 13 Factors and multiples

Exercise 13a Page 97

1. 456, 850
2. 531, 777, 13482
3. 344, 788, 464
4. 4500, 210
5. 8264, 5200

6. 7353, 361368
7. 34000, 564050
8. 612, 426
9. 7188, 924
10. 435, 765, 675

11. 522, 6804
12. 640
13. 13152, 1032
14. 450

15. 1331, 48202, 4669874, 845574323

Exercise 13b Page 98

1. 2×3	18. $3^2 \times 5$	35. $2 \times 3 \times 5 \times 7$	52. $3^2 \times 5 \times 7 \times 11$
2. 3^2	19. 2^4	36. $3 \times 7 \times 11$	53. $3 \times 5^2 \times 7^2$
3. 2×5	20. $2^3 \times 3$	37. $2^2 \times 3^2 \times 7$	54. $2^3 \times 3^4 \times 7$
4. 2×7	21. $2^4 \times 3$	38. $2^3 \times 3 \times 7$	55. $2^2 \times 3 \times 5 \times 7 \times 11$
5. 3×7	22. $2^3 \times 7$	39. $3^2 \times 5 \times 7$	56. $3^2 \times 7^2 \times 11$
6. 3×11	23. $2^2 \times 3 \times 5$	40. $3 \times 11 \times 13$	57. $2 \times 3 \times 5^3 \times 7$
7. 5×7	24. 2	41. $3 \times 5^2 \times 7$	58. $3^2 \times 7 \times 11^2$
8. 2×19	25. $2^3 \times 3^2$	42. $2 \times 3^3 \times 11$	59. $3^2 \times 5^2 \times 7^2$
9. 7^2	26. $2^4 \times 5$	43. $2^2 \times 3^2 \times 17$	60. $3^2 \times 11^2 \times 13$
10. 2^3	27. 3^4	44. $3^2 \times 7 \times 11$	61. $3^2 \times 7 \times 11 \times 41$
11. $2^2 \times 3$	28. $2^5 \times 3$	45. $5 \times 11 \times 13$	62. $2 \times 3^2 \times 5 \times 7^2 \times 11$
12. $3^2 \times 2$	29. $2 \times 3 \times 17$	46. $2^3 \times 3 \times 5 \times 7$	63. $5^2 \times 11^2 \times 17$
13. $2^2 \times 5$	30. 3×5^2	47. $2 \times 7 \times 61$	64. $2^4 \times 3^2 \times 7 \times 89$
14. 3^3	31. $2 \times 3 \times 13$	48. $3^2 \times 11^2$	65. $7^4 \times 13^2$
15. $2^2 \times 7$	32. 2×7^2	49. 11^3	66. $2^2 \times 3 \times 11^3 \times 47$
16. $2 \times 3 \times 5$	33. $2^3 \times 13$	50. $2 \times 5 \times 11 \times 13$	67. $2 \times 3 \times 5^3 \times 7 \times 11 \times 13$
17. $2 \times 3 \times 7$	34. $3 \times 5 \times 7$	51. $2^4 \times 7 \times 13$	68. $2^5 \times 3^3 \times 5^3 \times 11^2 \times 43$

Exercise 13c Page 99

1. 5	5. 7	9. 20	13. Coprime	17. 3
2. 6	6. 9	10. Coprime	14. 4	18. 18
3. 2	7. 6	11. 7	15. 15	19. Coprime
4. 2	8. Coprime	12. 1	16. 50	20. 25

Exercise 13d Page 100

1. 10	5. 9	9. 6	13. 6	17. 55
2. 8	6. 9	10. 21	14. 13	18. 112
3. 5	7. 2	11. 35	15. 54	19. 42
4. 12	8. 7	12. 63	16. 42	20. 252

Exercise 13e Page 100

1. 12	7. 4	13. 4	19. 7	25. 90	31. 1428
2. 8	8. 4	14. 75	20. 16	26. 4	32. 68
3. 16	9. 4	15. 8	21. 24	27. 96	
4. 15	10. 12	16. 18	22. 32	28. 72	
5. 18	11. 9	17. 12	23. 1	29. 64	
6. 30	12. 18	18. 28	24. 35	30. 48	

Exercise 13f Page 102

1. 24	**7.** 60	**13.** 216	**19.** 440	**25.** 648	**31.** 11209
2. 42	**8.** 120	**14.** 150	**20.** 819	**26.** 3640	**32.** 58608
3. 60	**9.** 96	**15.** 490	**21.** 105	**27.** 4470	
4. 36	**10.** 120	**16.** 420	**22.** 1680	**28.** 825	
5. 60	**11.** 210	**17.** 504	**23.** 5250	**29.** 1800	
6. 143	**12.** 144	**18.** 132	**24.** 1564	**30.** 1943	

Exercise 13g Page 102

1. 72	**3.** £1.75	**5.** 14.4 m	**7.** 30	**9.** 9" × 9", 105 tiles
2. 315	**4.** 7' 6"	**6.** 3.6 sec	**8.** 112, 126	**10.** 40

Exercise 13h

Number, n	6 × n	6n + 1	Prime?	6n − 1	Prime?
1	6	7	√	5	√
2	12	13	√	11	√
3	18	19	√	17	√

Chapter 14   Triangles

Exercise 14a Page 108

1. (a) ∠A = 32.5°
(b) ∠B = 51°

2. (a) ∠PQR = 68.5°
(b) ∠PRQ = 67°

3. (a) ∠EDF = 56°
(b) ∠DFE = 77°

4. (a) BC = 7.6 cm
(b) ∠B = 53°

5. (a) PR = 10.8 cm
(b) ∠R = 43°

6. (a) YZ = 9.0 cm
(b) ∠XYZ = 60.5°

7. (a) AC = 6.35 cm
(b) BC = 4.7 cm

8. (a) PR = 4.5 cm
(b) QR = 3.4 cm

9. (a) LN = 2.45 cm
(b) MN = 3.2 cm

10. (a) AC = 4.05"
(b) BC = 2.1"

11. (a) XZ = 3.8 cm
(b) XY = 3.5 cm

12. (a) AB = 2 or 8.5 cm
(b) ∠B = 13.5° or 83°

13. AD = 4.85 cm

14. RS = 2.44"

15. EP = 4.0 cm

16. LP = 4.6 cm

Exercise 14b Page 109

1. Both 2.45 cm

6. 4.45 cm

7. 9 cm

8. BC = 5.6 cm

11. PQ = 3.2 cm

12. KJ = 1.23", KJ = 5.7"

221

Chapter 15 Vulgar fractions: addition and subtraction

Exercise 15a Page 112

1. $\frac{2}{3}$ 6. $\frac{3}{4}$ 11. $\frac{2}{9}$ 16. $\frac{1}{6}$ 21. $\frac{14}{33}$

2. $\frac{1}{3}$ 7. $\frac{2}{5}$ 12. $\frac{3}{7}$ 17. $\frac{7}{30}$ 22. $\frac{1}{2}$

3. $\frac{3}{4}$ 8. $\frac{1}{5}$ 13. $\frac{1}{4}$ 18. $\frac{3}{5}$ 23. $\frac{3}{5}$

4. $\frac{1}{8}$ 9. $\frac{1}{3}$ 14. $\frac{5}{14}$ 19. $\frac{8}{45}$ 24. $\frac{1}{3}$

5. $\frac{11}{15}$ 10. $\frac{4}{5}$ 15. $\frac{6}{11}$ 20. $\frac{1}{3}$ 25. $\frac{19}{61}$

Exercise 15b Page 113

1. 8   5. 12   9. 77   13. 42   17. 35   21. 45

2. 10   6. 16   10. 35   14. 22   18. 96   22. 20

3. 10   7. 32   11. 18   15. 20   19. 10   23. 24

4. 12   8. 20   12. 15   16. 54   20. 28   24. 64

Exercise 15c Page 113

1. $1\frac{1}{4}$ 4. $4\frac{1}{2}$ 7. $1\frac{3}{7}$ 10. $4\frac{1}{7}$ 13. $33\frac{1}{3}$ 16. $\frac{11}{4}$

2. $2\frac{2}{3}$ 5. $4\frac{1}{3}$ 8. $3\frac{1}{6}$ 11. $6\frac{3}{7}$ 14. $8\frac{1}{3}$ 17. $\frac{13}{4}$

3. $3\frac{3}{5}$ 6. $6\frac{2}{3}$ 9. $4\frac{1}{4}$ 12. $4\frac{2}{9}$ 15. $14\frac{3}{5}$ 18. $\frac{22}{5}$

19. $\frac{31}{5}$ 21. $\frac{23}{3}$ 23. $\frac{55}{8}$ 25. $\frac{41}{19}$ 27. $\frac{75}{11}$ 29. $\frac{107}{20}$

20. $\frac{43}{8}$ 22. $\frac{65}{12}$ 24. $\frac{74}{17}$ 26. $\frac{80}{43}$ 28. $\frac{81}{23}$ 30. $\frac{209}{25}$

Exercise 15d Page 114

1. $\frac{1}{2}$ 5. $\frac{1}{2}$ 9. $\frac{9}{16}$ 13. $\frac{1}{2}$ 17. $\frac{5}{36}$

2. $\frac{7}{9}$ 6. $\frac{2}{3}$ 10. $\frac{4}{5}$ 14. $1\frac{9}{16}$ 18. $\frac{1}{40}$

3. $\frac{3}{8}$ 7. $\frac{27}{32}$ 11. $\frac{1}{4}$ 15. $\frac{8}{45}$ 19. $\frac{1}{64}$

4. $\frac{13}{15}$ 8. $\frac{5}{16}$ 12. $\frac{5}{8}$ 16. $\frac{34}{35}$ 20. $\frac{2}{21}$

Exercise 15e Page 115

1. $\frac{19}{20}$ 4. $\frac{14}{45}$ 7. $\frac{1}{6}$ 10. $\frac{8}{21}$ 13. $\frac{1}{24}$

2. $\frac{11}{20}$ 5. $\frac{13}{30}$ 8. $\frac{21}{80}$ 11. $\frac{15}{88}$ 14. $\frac{37}{60}$

3. $\frac{2}{15}$ 6. $\frac{5}{12}$ 9. $\frac{17}{24}$ 12. $\frac{29}{30}$ 15. $\frac{11}{60}$

16. $\frac{9}{77}$ **18.** $\frac{11}{30}$ **20.** $\frac{5}{88}$ **22.** $\frac{74}{105}$ **24.** $\frac{37}{340}$

17. $1\frac{19}{72}$ **19.** $1\frac{29}{48}$ **21.** $\frac{29}{72}$ **23.** $\frac{53}{150}$ **25.** $\frac{43}{150}$

Exercise 15f Page 116

1. $\frac{7}{18}$ **6.** $\frac{7}{12}$ **11.** $\frac{19}{40}$ **16.** $\frac{19}{96}$ **21.** $\frac{1}{10}$

2. $\frac{23}{24}$ **7.** $\frac{5}{18}$ **12.** $\frac{13}{50}$ **17.** $\frac{27}{40}$ **22.** $\frac{37}{126}$

3. $\frac{1}{12}$ **8.** $\frac{47}{60}$ **13.** $\frac{13}{20}$ **18.** $\frac{29}{72}$ **23.** $\frac{13}{42}$

4. $\frac{1}{2}$ **9.** $\frac{29}{36}$ **14.** $\frac{29}{36}$ **19.** $1\frac{23}{80}$ **24.** $\frac{47}{54}$

5. $\frac{5}{24}$ **10.** $\frac{7}{12}$ **15.** $\frac{12}{35}$ **20.** $\frac{11}{42}$ **25.** $\frac{7}{500}$

Exercise 15g Page 117

1. $5\frac{5}{12}$ **5.** $9\frac{1}{24}$ **9.** $7\frac{25}{48}$ **13.** $35\frac{11}{40}$ **17.** $8\frac{59}{112}$

2. $5\frac{13}{24}$ **6.** $11\frac{41}{60}$ **10.** $11\frac{11}{36}$ **14.** $10\frac{17}{144}$ **18.** $3\frac{81}{200}$

3. $8\frac{7}{15}$ **7.** $20\frac{11}{24}$ **11.** $14\frac{1}{16}$ **15.** $5\frac{15}{28}$ **19.** $\frac{19}{150}$

4. $1\frac{7}{12}$ **8.** $14\frac{13}{30}$ **12.** $6\frac{19}{60}$ **16.** $66\frac{7}{120}$ **20.** $96\frac{43}{144}$

Exercise 15h Page 117

1. $7\frac{7}{12}$ **3.** $7\frac{1}{4}$ **5.** $6\frac{1}{6}$ **7.** $42\frac{1}{2}$ **9.** $8\frac{53}{165}$

2. $8\frac{11}{30}$ **4.** $5\frac{1}{14}$ **6.** $12\frac{1}{12}$ **8.** $11\frac{2}{15}$ **10.** $12\frac{1}{8}$

11. $11\frac{11}{60}$ **13.** $10\frac{83}{420}$ **15.** $1\frac{1}{3}$ **17.** $2\frac{23}{44}$ **19.** $5\frac{2}{27}$

12. $6\frac{13}{30}$ **14.** $2\frac{1}{4}$ **16.** $9\frac{47}{77}$ **18.** $17\frac{7}{9}$ **20.** $30\frac{23}{100}$

Exercise 15i Page 118

1. $2\frac{2}{3}$ **5.** $2\frac{1}{13}$ **9.** $9\frac{8}{15}$ **13.** $1\frac{5}{12}$ **17.** $11\frac{43}{50}$

2. $4\frac{3}{5}$ **6.** $2\frac{7}{12}$ **10.** $24\frac{5}{24}$ **14.** $\frac{5}{18}$ **18.** $13\frac{1}{105}$

3. $3\frac{1}{4}$ **7.** $1\frac{2}{7}$ **11.** $5\frac{4}{9}$ **15.** $3\frac{3}{16}$ **19.** $12\frac{25}{28}$

4. $5\frac{6}{17}$ **8.** $6\frac{5}{19}$ **12.** $4\frac{19}{30}$ **16.** $4\frac{13}{36}$ **20.** $7\frac{91}{100}$

Exercise 15j Page 118

1. $\frac{7}{16}$ 4. $1\frac{59}{80}$ in   7. 3   10. 264 l   13. $4\frac{4}{5}$ days

2. $4\frac{15}{16}$ lb   5. $2\frac{3}{4}$ cm   8. $4\frac{1}{24}$ 11. $\frac{1}{6}$, $\frac{1}{3}$, $\frac{1}{2}$, 2 min   14. $1\frac{9}{20}$

3. $5\frac{5}{8}$ in   6. $\frac{1}{12}$ m   9. 800 acres   12. 6 min

Exercise 15k Page 120

1. $\frac{2}{5}$ 7. equal   13. $\frac{11}{15}$ 19. $\frac{7}{8}$ 25. $\frac{4}{5}$

2. $\frac{2}{3}$ 8. $\frac{7}{8}$ 14. $\frac{13}{16}$ 20. $\frac{1}{2}$ 26. $\frac{9}{16}$

3. $\frac{7}{9}$ 9. $\frac{5}{16}$ 15. $\frac{3}{15}$ 21. $\frac{5}{6}$ 27. $\frac{7}{10}$

4. $\frac{2}{7}$ 10. $\frac{11}{20}$ 16. $\frac{3}{7}$ 22. $\frac{2}{5}$ 28. $\frac{4}{7}$

5. $\frac{5}{6}$ 11. $\frac{11}{12}$ 17. $\frac{7}{9}$ 23. $\frac{8}{9}$ 29. $\frac{7}{18}$

6. $\frac{8}{9}$ 12. $\frac{5}{12}$ 18. $\frac{4}{5}$ 24. $\frac{5}{12}$ 30. $\frac{7}{40}$

Chapter 16   Vulgar fractions: mutliplication and division

Exercise 16a Page 121

1. $1\frac{1}{2}$ m   7. $\frac{3}{4}$ lb   13. $3\frac{3}{4}$ 19. $3\frac{1}{2}$ 25. $\frac{2}{21}$ 31. $\frac{1}{4}$

2. 4 min   8. $1\frac{7}{8}$ oz   14. $5\frac{1}{3}$ 20. $2\frac{1}{2}$ 26. $\frac{1}{3}$ 32. $\frac{3}{4}$

3. $2\frac{1}{4}$ cm   9. $1\frac{7}{8}$ ft   15. £4   21. £$1\frac{1}{4}$ 27. $\frac{1}{6}$

4. 3 in   10. $\frac{9}{10}$ 16. ^{42} 22. $\frac{3}{4}$ 28. $\frac{2}{21}$

5. $2\frac{2}{3}$ km   11. $1\frac{1}{2}$ 17. ^{9} 23. $1\frac{3}{5}$ 29. $\frac{4}{9}$

6. $10\frac{1}{2}$ sec   12. 1   18. $7\frac{1}{2}$ 24. $1\frac{2}{3}$ 30. 1

Exercise 16b Page 122

1. $\frac{6}{35}$ 7. $\frac{4}{9}$ 13. $\frac{1}{8}$ 19. $\frac{5}{27}$ 25. $\frac{5}{8}$ 31. $2\frac{2}{5}$

2. $\frac{3}{10}$ 8. $\frac{1}{21}$ 14. 6   20. 1   26. $5\frac{1}{2}$ 32. 1

3. $\frac{4}{15}$ 9. $\frac{2}{15}$ 15. 15   21. $\frac{1}{3}$ 27. $6\frac{2}{3}$

4. $\frac{5}{14}$ 10. 1   16. $\frac{1}{24}$ 22. $2\frac{1}{7}$ 28. $4\frac{2}{7}$

5. 5   11. ^{12} 17. $\frac{3}{7}$ 23. $3\frac{27}{40}$ 29. $\frac{60}{61}$

6. $\frac{9}{16}$ 12. 12   18. $\frac{1}{24}$ 24. 10   30. $10\frac{1}{2}$

Exercise 16c Page 123

1. $\frac{1}{6}$, $\frac{1}{8}$, $\frac{1}{10}$ 6. $\frac{1}{2}$, $\frac{3}{8}$, $\frac{1}{4}$ 11. 6   16. $1\frac{1}{2}$ 21. 1

2. $\frac{1}{6}$, $\frac{1}{9}$, $\frac{1}{18}$ 7. $\frac{3}{4}$, $\frac{3}{8}$, $\frac{1}{4}$ 12. 20   17. $\frac{2}{3}$ 22. $1\frac{2}{3}$

3. $\frac{1}{4}$, $\frac{3}{16}$, $\frac{3}{20}$ 8. $1\frac{1}{2}$ 13. 35   18. $\frac{2}{3}$ 23. $\frac{15}{16}$

4. $\frac{2}{9}$, $\frac{4}{27}$, $\frac{1}{27}$ 9. $\frac{2}{9}$ 14. 3   19. 2   24. $\frac{15}{16}$

5. $\frac{3}{25}$, $\frac{12}{125}$, $\frac{3}{50}$ 10. 6   15. 10   20. $\frac{3}{4}$ 25. $\frac{1}{6}$

Exercise 16d Page 123

1. $3\frac{1}{3}$ 5. $\frac{4}{11}$ 9. $\frac{8}{65}$ 13. $1\frac{1}{2}$ 17. $\frac{1}{35}$

2. $\frac{4}{7}$ 6. 1   10. 1   14. $\frac{8}{15}$ 18. $1\frac{1}{2}$

3. $\frac{8}{15}$ 7. $2\frac{7}{10}$ 11. $\frac{3}{22}$ 15. $1\frac{1}{2}$ 19. $\frac{2}{7}$

4. $\frac{3}{20}$ 8. $\frac{2}{15}$ 12. $1\frac{1}{3}$ 16. $1\frac{2}{5}$ 20. $1\frac{1}{3}$

Exercise 16e Page 124

1. $\frac{7}{12}$ 6. $\frac{5}{12}$ 11. $\frac{1}{20}$ 16. $\frac{2}{9}$ 21. $2\frac{1}{4}$

2. $\frac{5}{24}$ 7. $\frac{1}{4}$ 12. $\frac{11}{60}$ 17. $\frac{1}{6}$ 22. $7\frac{5}{21}$

3. $\frac{1}{4}$ 8. $1\frac{2}{5}$ 13. $\frac{1}{20}$ 18. $\frac{3}{10}$ 23. $\frac{3}{4}$

4. $\frac{1}{9}$ 9. $1\frac{1}{10}$ 14. 0   19. 0   24. $\frac{4}{27}$

5. $\frac{1}{3}$ 10. $\frac{13}{60}$ 15. $\frac{1}{18}$ 20. $\frac{15}{23}$ 25. $3\frac{4}{5}$

Exercise 16f Page 125

1. $\frac{18}{25}$ 7. $\frac{71}{96}$ 13. $9\frac{3}{5}$ days   19. £7.00   25. £2375

2. $\frac{1}{4}$ 8. $1\frac{7}{27}$ 14. $9\frac{1}{2}$ mins   20. 54 mins   26. (a) 56 yrs

3. $\frac{15}{16}$ lb   9. $50\frac{17}{32}$ cu.in.   15. $\frac{5}{19}$ 21. 15 mins   (b) $\frac{2}{3}$

4. $9\frac{5}{8}$ sq.ft.   10. 30 ft   16. £13.50   22. $\frac{3}{10}$ (c) 14 yrs

5. 8   11. 128 sec   17. 1000 tons   23. 225,000 galls   (d) $\frac{2}{13}$

6. $\frac{2}{27}$ 12. 9   18. 36   24. £27,500

Chapter 17 Discrimination in division

Exercise 17a Page 128

1. 89	11. 6570/7	21. 123/1	31. 31/5
2. 121/1	12. 5979/8	22. 211/3	32. 200
3. 1696/2	13. 6721/2	23. 202	33. 211
4. 248/2	14. 16140/3	24. 21/7	34. 20
5. 925	15. 97023/4	25. 11/4	35. 21/1
6. 302/2	16. 51341/5	26. 22/3	36. 240
7. 1095/5	17. 219007/1	27. 212/8	37. 206/24
8. 1216	18. 47250	28. 212/10	38. 505
9. 974/3	19. 27492/7	29. 312/2	39. 300
10. 10863/3	20. 27272/8	30. 10/10	40. 311

Exercise 17b Page 128

1. 2/7	9. 5/8	17. 4/2	25. 13/5	33. 38/1
2. 3/4	10. 2/7	18. 9/5	26. 13/8	34. 17/3
3. 46/7	11. 9	19. 8/6	27. 14/8	35. 30
4. 5/6	12. 3	20. 11	28. 24/6	36. 21/1
5. 7/8	13. 2	21. 11/5	29. 36/7	37. 31/4
6. 4/7	14. 5	22. 12/4	30. 46/0	38. 52/3
7. 1/3	15. 7	23. 13/7	31. 88/8	39. 124/5
8. 3/8	16. 8/3	24. 15/7	32. 78/0	40. 137/1

Exercise 17c Page 129

1. 11/56	5. 31/55	9. 1/71	13. 125/73	17. 11/464
2. 21/87	6. 1/55	10. 2/35	14. 233/76	18. 3/648
3. 14/75	7. 2/89	11. 124/76	15. 227/0	19. 11/164
4. 22/55	8. 1/75	12. 216/93	16. 12/366	20. 1/145

Exercise 17d Page 130

1. 2/5	9. 5/3	17. 3/9	25. 71/2	33. 62/10
2. 3/3	10. 2/6	18. 5/6	26. 42/7	34. 22/9
3. 4/4	11. 9/0	19. 6/6	27. 11/7	35. 61/9
4. 5/0	12. 1/1	20. 8/3	28. 30/6	36. 35/7
5. 6/3	13. 2/3	21. 10/1	29. 26/0	37. 42/9
6. 2/1	14. 3/1	22. 12/2	30. 31/6	38. 112/2
7. 3/5	15. 6/4	23. 23/1	31. 20/10	39. 1234/5
8. 4/5	16. 2/10	24. 31/0	32. 41/0	40. 9/1

Exercise 17e Page 131

1. 131/7	10. 10/46	19. 23/24	28. 111/14
2. 1125/3	11. 12/21	20. 31/40	29. 22/127
3. 2133/6	12. 13/40	21. 34/12	30. 123/104
4. 132/4	13. 21/32	22. 11/10	31. 201/201
5. 15/49	14. 21/15	23. 121/23	32. 11/213
6. 14/21	15. 21/01	24. 212/22	33. 230/2327
7. 11/01	16. 20/33	25. 121/13	34. 12/424
8. 11/24	17. 22/21	26. 300/51	35. 321/024
9. 11/40	18. 22/00	27. 12/10	36. 720/79

Exercise 17f Page 131

1. 4.6	5. 46.2	9. 21.8	13. 1665	17. 0.646
2. 8.4	6. 87.4	10. 87.8	14. 1206.4	18. 1.2422
3. 12.8	7. 124.2	11. 206.8	15. 8649	19. 11.2426
4. 7.6	8. 147.6	12. 426.6	16. 2.48	20. 0.004842

Exercise 17g Page 132

1. 10	8. 0.032	15. 0.0012	22. 7	29. 0.3
2. 6	9. 50	16. 852	23. 7	30. 68
3. 6	10. 50	17. 0.00075	24. 0.2	31. 0.015
4. 115	11. 625	18. 457	25. 30	32. 35
5. 200	12. $83\frac{1}{3}$	19. 496	26. 8	
6. 28	13. $\frac{9}{1250}$	20. 36	27. 2	
7. 6.24	14. 0.27	21. 7	28. 110	

Exercise 17h Page 133

1. 13/7	9. 103/51	17. 355/5	25. 20698/17
2. 14/22	10. 226/34	18. 1716/7	26. 12517/23
3. 16/18	11. 241/2	19. 2347/25	27. 14893/29
4. 19/27	12. 75/56	20. 1634/3	28. 5252/68
5. 6/63	13. 14/81	21. 1765/22	29. 4632/5
6. 12/41	14. 191/0	22. 149/45	30. 12371/27
7. 19/33	15. 101/71	23. 632/29	31. 5763/6
8. 47/17	16. 145/30	24. 1785/16	32. 18046/2

Exercise 17i Page 134

1. 85/16	**9.** 176/37	**17.** 26395/10	**25.** 568/15
2. 158/18	**10.** 2669/15	**18.** 16666/12	**26.** 823/9
3. 15/62	**11.** 349/44	**19.** 6143/5	**27.** 1577/25
4. 45/23	**12.** 442/42	**20.** 11876/26	**28.** 10859/52
5. 127/18	**13.** 626/38	**21.** 12346/25	**29.** 2531/51
6. 137/25	**14.** 1462/29	**22.** 6398/46	**30.** 9567/45
7. 146/18	**15.** 297/22	**23.** 9582/42	**31.** 37684/4
8. 82/41	**16.** 617/68	**24.** 15645/25	**32.** 526315/15

Exercise 17j Page 135

1. 77/0	**9.** 3503/14	**17.** 351/0	**25.** 271/0
2. 235/0	**10.** 217/0	**18.** 14231/0	**26.** 156/81
3. 10525/0	**11.** 1157/11	**19.** 31910/20	**27.** 13859/8
4. 94/0	**12.** 216/52	**20.** 222/45	**28.** 614/0
5. 63/0	**13.** 100/45	**21.** 38557/15	**29.** 592/24
6. 343/4	**14.** 4495/5	**22.** 624/0	**30.** 26491/6
7. 527/0	**15.** 13837/5	**23.** 264/02	**31.** 45/854
8. 12/48	**16.** 1261/4	**24.** 243/0	**32.** 971/0

Chapter 18 Further algebra

Exercise 18a Page 136

1. $4a$	**4.** 0	**7.** $6y$	**10.** $8f$	**13.** $13b$	**16.** $9k$
2. $5b$	**5.** $3e$	**8.** $5p$	**11.** $5w$	**14.** $3a$	**17.** $2n$
3. d	**6.** $5x$	**9.** r	**12.** $6c$	**15.** b	**18.** 0

19. a	**23.** $4a + 3b$	**27.** $8p - 4q + 4$	**30.** $2j$	**33.** $5a + 3b - 5$
20. $2t$	**24.** $8c + d$	(n.p.)	**31.** $x - 6y - 5z$	**34.** $1 + x + 3y$
21. $2x + 2y$	**25.** $6m - 8n$	**28.** $4k + 3$	**32.** $5r + s - 6 + 7t$	**35.** $x + 4y$
22. $3f + g$	**26.** $4x - 5y$	**29.** $7v + 10w$	(n.p.)	**36.** $7g + 2h + 7$

Exercise 18b Page 137

1. $20d$	**10.** $49yz^2$	**19.** n	**28.** $3\frac{1}{2}v^2$	**37.** $\dfrac{d}{e}$
2. $49b$	**11.** $12b^2cd$	**20.** 1	**29.** n^2	**38.** rs
3. $9f$	**12.** $4u^2v^2$	**21.** $\dfrac{4y}{3}$	**30.** d	**39.** $\dfrac{4b}{3c}$
4. 0	**13.** $36x^2yz^2$	**22.** $\dfrac{3h}{2}$	**31.** $\dfrac{7h}{2}$	**40.** $\dfrac{4a}{b}$
5. $25x^2$	**14.** $2x$	**23.** $\dfrac{3a}{2}$	**32.** $\dfrac{c}{d}$	**41.** $\dfrac{2r^2}{3s^2}$
6. $24rs$	**15.** $8m$	**24.** $\dfrac{5a^2}{8}$	**33.** $\dfrac{1}{g}$	**42.** $\dfrac{10i}{9j}$
7. gh^2	**16.** n	**25.** $\dfrac{7b^2}{2}$	**34.** $\dfrac{1}{k}$	**43.** $\dfrac{3t^2}{2s}$
8. $2pqt$	**17.** $3p$	**26.** $10k$	**35.** y	**44.** 1
9. $25m^2n^2$	**18.** $\dfrac{1}{2x}$	**27.** $10z$	**36.** q	

Exercise 18c Page 138

1. 10	**5.** 5	**9.** 0	**13.** $10a+15$	**17.** $de-df$
2. 16	**6.** 1	**10.** 24	**14.** $12c-8d$	**18.** $abc-abd$
3. 9	**7.** 6	**11.** 20	**15.** $15a-5b$	**19.** $12gh-3g$
4. 55	**8.** 1	**12.** 0	**16.** $17p-51q$	**20.** $14d-21e+7$

21. $24a-40b-8$	**25.** $11k+4$	**29.** 50	**33.** 8
22. $ab+ac-2ad$	**26.** $ax-2bx+9ay+3by$	**30.** 34	**34.** $2\frac{6}{7}$
23. $11x-9$	**27.** $5ab+3ac-bc$	**31.** 35	**35.** 121
24. $6px+3py+4ap+2bp$	**28.** 23	**32.** 19	**36.** 49

Exercise 18d Page 139

1. $3(2a+b)$	**3.** $z(3x-y)$	**5.** $2x(y-3z)$
2. $4(3f-e)$	**4.** $\dfrac{(a+b+c)}{2}$ or $\div 2$	**6.** $\dfrac{(2a+3b-5)}{7}$

7. $\frac{1}{2}(3m + 7n)$

13. $y^2 + z^2 - (x + y)^2$

18. (i) $\dfrac{10 - x}{3}$

8. $(2c - d) - (a - 2b)$

14. $n(n + 1)$

(ii) $\dfrac{2(10 - x)}{3}$

9. $(r - s)(r + s)$

15. $(m - 1)(m)(m + 1)$

(iii) $x + \dfrac{2(10 - x)}{3}$

10. $b - (d - c)$

16. $x - y, \quad p(x - y)$

19. (i) $(y - x)$ kg

11. $\frac{1}{5}(3f + 5g)$

17. $10 - n, \quad 20n + 10(10 - n)p$

(ii) $\left(x + \dfrac{y - x}{3}\right)$ kg

12. $2(2c + d) - 5(2b + 3)$

Exercie 18e Page 141

1. $3(x - y)$

6. $3(2x - 3y - 4z)$

11. $u(t - v - w)$

16. $2y(4x - 6 + 7z)$

2. $3(2a + 3b)$

7. $a(b + d)$

12. $3a(b + c)$

17. $x(x + 1)$

3. $4(r - 2s)$

8. $b(x - y)$

13. $2x(y - z)$

18. $a(a - 3)$

4. $8(2a - 3b)$

9. $c(a + b)$

14. $4c(b - d)$

19. $b(3 + 2b)$

5. $3(a + b + c)$

10. $p(q + r - s)$

15. $2m(2n + 3p)$

20. $2y(2y^2 - 3)$

21. $5a(2a^2 + 3a - 1)$

Exercise 18f Page 142

1. $x^2 + 4x + 3, \ 143$

10. $x^2 + 4x + 4$

19. $x^2 - 6x + 9$

28. $x^2 + 11x + 24$

2. $x^2 + 6x + 8, \ 168$

11. $x^2 + 6x + 9$

20. $x^2 - 2x - 8$

29. $x^2 - 14x + 49$

3. $x^2 + 7x + 12, \ 182$

12. $x^2 - 6x + 8$

21. $x^2 - 2x - 3$

30. $x^2 - x - 42$

4. $x^2 + 2x + 1$

13. $x^2 - 9x + 20$

22. $x^2 - 2x - 15$

31. $x^2 - 4x - 32$

5. $x^2 + 3x + 2$

14. $x^2 - 10x + 9$

23. $x^2 - 4$

32. $x^2 + 7x + 6$

6. $x^2 + 9x + 18$

15. $x^2 - 15x + 56$

24. $x^2 - 36$

33. $x^2 - 7x + 6$

7. $x^2 + 8x + 7$

16. $x^2 - 14x + 45$

25. $x^2 + 6x - 7$

34. $x^2 + 5x - 6$

8. $x^2 + 17x + 72$

17. $x^2 - 2x + 1$

26. $x^2 + x - 72$

35. $x^2 - 5x - 6$

9. $x^2 + 10x + 21$

18. $x^2 - 4x + 4$

27. $x^2 - 1$

36. $x^2 - x - 132$

Exercise 18g Page 143

1. $x^2 + 10x + 25$

2. $x^2 + 12x + 36$

3. $x^2 + 20x + 100$

4. $x^2 - 16x + 64$

5. $x^2 - 8x + 16$

6. $x^2 - 18x + 81$

7. $2x^2 + 5x + 2$

8. $2x^2 + 3x + 1$

9. $2x2 + 5x + 3$

10. $2x2 + 7x + 3$

11. $2x^2 + 15x + 7$

12. $3x^2 + 14x + 16$

13. $4x^2 + 31x + 21$

14. $2x^2 - 9x + 7$

15. $2x^2 - 13x + 15$

16. $2x^2 - 17x + 18$

17. $5x^2 - 17x + 6$

18. $2x^2 - 9x + 9$

19. $3x2 + 11x - 20$

20. $6x2 + x - 1$

21. $9x^2 + 6x + 1$

22. $16x^2 + 12x + 2$

23. $10x^2 + 36x + 18$

24. $6x^2 + 23x + 7$

25. $9x^2 + 80x + 64$

26. $4x^2 + 20x + 21$

27. $3x^2 + 19x - 72$

28. $7x^2 - 6x - 1$

29. $10x2 + 31x + 24$

30. $6x2 - 35x + 49$

31. $7x^2 - 8x - 12$

32. $15x^2 - 4x - 32$

33. $7x^2 + 13x + 6$

34. $2x^2 + 9x + 4$

35. $45x^2 + 23x + 2$

36. $3x^2 + 25x + 42$

37. $10x^2 + 37x + 7$

38. $6x^2 + 25x + 11$

39. $21x2 + 58x + 21$

Exercise 18h Page 143

1. 32 cm

2. $p = 2(l + w)$ cm

3. 4 cm

4. $p = (2a + b)$ cm

5. 53 mph

6. $v = \dfrac{s}{t}$

7. $V = 4xy$

8. $V = 294$ cm^3

9. $V = b^2h$ cm^3

10. $A = 266$ cm^2

11. $A = 2b^2 + 4bh$

12. £1700

13. $T = £(D + nC)$

14. $C = \frac{5}{9}(F - 32)$

15. $V = hl^2$

Exercise 18i Page 145

1. 19

2. 7

3. 2

4. 21

5. 45

6. 36

7. 32

8. 30

9. 15

10. 21

11. 8

12. 7

13. 0

14. 0

15. -5

16. 45

17. 15

18. $\frac{5}{6}$

19. 3

20. $\frac{1}{2}$

21. $\frac{2}{15}$

22. $\frac{8}{15}$

23. $\frac{5}{6}$

24. 1

25. $2\frac{9}{10}$

26. $\frac{17}{20}$

27. $1\frac{1}{52}$

28. $\frac{1}{2}$

29. $1\frac{9}{16}$

30. $6\frac{1}{4}$

31. $\frac{1}{4}$

32. $\frac{1}{5}$

33. $3\frac{1}{8}$

34. $\frac{16}{25}$

35. $2\frac{1}{2}$

36. $5\frac{9}{20}$

Exercise 18j Page 146

1. £960

2. 78.4 m

3. 40 km

4. 270 kg

5. $75\frac{3}{7}$ cm

6. 154 cm^2

7. (i) 6 in

   (ii) $7\frac{1}{2}$ in

8. (i) 212° F

   (ii) 32° F

   (iii) 59° F

Chapter 19   Ratio and proportion

Exercise 19a   Page 147

1. 4 : 7	**5.** 1 : 4	**9.** 5 : 4	**13.** 85 : 9	**17.** 2 : 9 : 16
2. 1 : 2	**6.** 4 : 1	**10.** 1 : 6	**14.** 1 : 3	**18.** 3 : 18 : 5
3. 3 : 2	**7.** 2 : 1	**11.** 9 : 16	**15.** 21 : 43	**19.** 13 : 24 : 40
4. 3 : 1	**8.** 5 : 1	**12.** 104 : 41	**16.** 1 : 3 : 13	**20.** 4 : 8 : 1

Exercise 19b Page 148

1. 21	**5.** $\frac{5}{8}$	**9.** 10	**13.** $3\frac{1}{3}$	**17.** 192	**21.** $8\frac{4}{7}$
2. 60	**6.** 3	**10.** $\frac{1}{3}$	**14.** 50	**18.** 360	**22.** $1\frac{1}{2}$
3. $\frac{1}{5}$	**7.** $\frac{6}{7}$	**11.** $\frac{11}{15}$	**15.** 36	**19.** $\frac{3}{8}$	**23.** $\frac{11}{20}$
4. $\frac{2}{5}$	**8.** 5	**12.** $1\frac{1}{2}$	**16.** $\frac{3}{5}$	**20.** $4\frac{2}{3}$	**24.** 2016

Exercise 19c   Page 149

1. 40 km	**6.** £12.46	**11.** 15	**16.** 600 lbs
2. 4000 g	**7.** £56.25	**12.** £336	**17.** 2,072,000,000
3. £800	**8.** $16\frac{2}{3}$ m/s	**13.** £3.15	**18.** 11,340,000
4. £10.50	**9.** £32	**14.** 25	
5. 20 gallons	**10.** 80 kg	**15.** £72.18	

Exercise 19d   Page 151

1. 9 journeys	**6.** 18 loaves	**11.** 90 bunches
2. 4 days	**7.** 36 days	**12.** 25 mins
3. 3 hrs	**8.** 24 days	**13.** 8 days
4. 6 glasses	**9.** 48 boxes	**14.** $1\frac{1}{2}$ hrs
5. 200 pages	**10.** 40 days	**15.** 32 tiles

Exercise 19e   Page 153

1. 21, 35	**5.** 160°, 200°; difference 40°	**11.** 0.2 m, 0.3 m, 0.5 m
2. £200, £150	**6.** 16 cm, 24 cm, 40 cm	**12.** £15, £5
3. (i) £24, £36	**7.** 240, 400, 640	**13.** $2400, $4000, $4800
(ii) £25, £35	**8.** 31500, £2000, £4000	**14.** £762
(iii) £48, £12	**9.** £28, £36, £48	
4. 10.5 kg, 9.5 kg	**10.** 16 cm, 20 cm, 28 cm	

15. Length, 400 m;
Breadth, 200 m;
Area, 80,000 m²

16. £42, £56

17. 32, 64, 128

18. £150,000; £250,000; £350,000

Exercise 19f Page 155

1. 25%
2. 90%
3. 2.5%
4. 20%
5. 40%
6. 15%
7. 2.5%
8. 16%
9. 150%
10. 200%

11. 66.5%
12. 300%
13. 45
14. 35p
15. 3.92 m
16. 1.08 kg
17. 0.72 m
18. 105.8
19. 624
20. £38

21. 67.2 m
22. 1.488 km
23. £70
24. £2520
25. 65%
26. 80%
27. 75% have bicycles
28. 94%
29. 12%
30. 45%

31. 4.8%
32. £600
33. (i) £8400
(ii) £15600
(iii) £1300
34. £18.80
35. 8,225,000
36. 16,640

Exercise 19g Page 157

1. £437.50
2. 320
3. 78

4. 72
5. £19,440
6. £23.40

7. £5.40
8. £496.80
9. 32.4°C

10. 62.5%
11. 19%
12. 16,960,000

Exercise 19h Page 158

1. European, 750,000
Japanese, 1,375,000
American, 500,000
Others, 375,000

2. Manual labour, 73
Secretaries, 23
Directors, 6
Managers, 18

3. Lawn, 225°
Patio, 45°
Path, 31.5°
Flower-beds, 58.5°

4.

5.

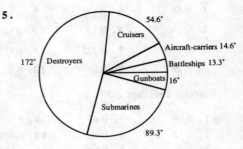

6. Earth 1, Mars 2, Jupiter 12, Saturn 10, Uranus 5, Neptune 2

233

Chapter 20   Fractions to decimals

Exercise 20a   Page 163

1. $0.\dot{0}52\,631\,578\,947\,368\,42\dot{1}$
2. $0.\dot{1}05\,263\,157\,894\,736\,84\dot{2}$
3. $0.\dot{8}94\,736\,842\,105\,263\,15\dot{7}$
4. $0.\dot{0}34\,482\,758\,620\,689\,655\,172\,413\,793\,\dot{1}$
5. $0.\dot{0}25\,64\dot{1}$
6. $0.\dot{2}63\,157\,894\,736\,842\,10\dot{5}$
7. $0.\dot{5}78\,947\,368\,421\,052\,63\dot{1}$
8. $0.\dot{0}14\,492\,753\,623\,188\,405\,797\,\dot{1}$

Exercise 20b   Page 163

1. $0.\dot{2}$
2. $0.539\dot{5}$
3. $2.\dot{3}\dot{2}$
4. $0.00\dot{7}$
5. $0.472\dot{3}$
6. $0.\dot{0}\dot{1}$
7. $4.321\dot{9}$
8. $0.79\dot{1}$

Exercise 20c   Page 164

1. $0.\dot{6}$
2. 0.75
3. 0.4
4. $0.8\dot{3}$
5. $0.\dot{4}2857\dot{1}$
6. 0.875
7. $0.\dot{4}$
8. 0.7
9. $0.5\dot{4}$
10. $0.41\dot{6}$

Exercise 20d   Page 165

1. 0.85
2. $0.4\dot{3}$
3. 0.475
4. 0.42
5. $0.2\dot{3}$
6. 0.15
7. 0.225
8. 0.86
9. $0.98\dot{3}$
10. 0.925
11. 0.8375
12. $0.9\dot{6}$
13. $0.88\dot{3}$
14. $0.4\dot{5}$
15. $0.4\dot{7}1428\dot{5}$
16. $0.28\dot{3}$
17. 0.37
18. $0.7\dot{1}\dot{8}$
19. 0.0875
20. $0.58\dot{}$

Exercise 20e   Page 165

1. 0.06
2. 0.52
3. 0.8
4. 0.38
5. 0.92
6. 0.06
7. 0.55
8. 0.28
9. 0.062
10. 0.405
11. 0.224
12. 0.18
13. 0.555
14. 0.164
15. 0.426
16. 0.024
17. 0.5105
18. 0.6438
19. 0.4964
20. 0.8888

Exercise 20f Page 166

1. $0.\dot{4}\dot{6}$
2. $0.\dot{7}\dot{3}$
3. $0.\dot{5}\dot{3}$
4. $0.0\dot{6}$
5. $0.5\dot{1}$
6. $0.0\dot{6}$
7. $0.6\dot{8}$
8. $0.0\dot{2}$
9. $0.0\dot{2}8571\dot{4}$
10. $0.0\dot{8}5714\dot{2}$
11. $0.01\dot{8}$
12. $0.87\dot{2}$
13. $0.9\dot{3}$
14. $0.4\dot{8}5714\dot{2}$
15. $0.03\dot{6}$
16. $0.0\dot{5}7142\dot{8}$
17. $0.1\dot{7}14285$
18. $0.7\dot{1}$
19. $0.8\dot{6}$
20. $0.2\dot{1}\dot{8}$

Exercise 20g Page 167

1. $0.08\dot{3}$
2. $0.0\dot{7}1428\dot{5}$
3. $0.0\dot{6}$
4. 0.0625
5. 0.05
6. $0.0\dot{4}761\dot{9}$
7. $0.04\dot{5}$
8. $0.041\dot{6}$
9. 0.04
10. $0.03\dot{7}$
11. $0.03\dot{5}7142\dot{8}$
12. $0.0\dot{3}$
13. 0.03125
14. $0.0\dot{3}$
15. $0.0\dot{2}8571\dot{4}$
16. $0.02\dot{7}$
17. 0.025
18. $0.02\dot{2}\dot{7}$
19. $0.0\dot{2}$
20. $0.01\dot{8}\dot{5}$

Chapter 22   Practice and revision 2

Consolidation Test 1 Page 183

1. 824
2. 5.04
3. 2
4. 248
5. 2.35
6. 5864
7. 483
8. 9506
9. 700
10. 16.8
11. 284
12. 104 r 49
13. 12 r 23
14. 23
15. 1630 r 14
16. 7
17. 30
18. Yes
19. $\frac{2}{5}$
20. $1\frac{1}{5}$
21. $\frac{8}{3}$
22. $\frac{8}{21}$
23. $1\frac{1}{6}$
24. $1\frac{3}{10}$
25. $\frac{1}{10}$
26. 9 kg
27. 5
28. 21
29. y^3z^2
30. $5a-3b$
31. $4:9$
32. $x=8$
33. $x=7$
34. 3 kg
35. 30%

Consolidation Test 2 Page 184

1. 1284
2. 8.43
3. 3
4. 386
5. 3.88
6. 32778
7. 448
8. 8928
9. 1560
10. 62.4
11. 1644
12. 11 r 42
13. 22 r 16
14. 9
15. 2041 r 14
16. 15
17. 48
18. Yes
19. $\frac{3}{4}$
20. $2\frac{1}{4}$
21. $\frac{10}{3}$
22. $\frac{1}{4}$
23. $2\frac{7}{9}$
24. $1\frac{2}{15}$
25. $\frac{8}{15}$
26. 70 m
27. 16
28. 10
29. m^4n^2
30. $6c-9d$
31. $4:1$
32. $x=20$
33. $x=10$
34. 18 cm
35. 20%

Consolidation Test 3 Page 185

1. 1443	**8.** 8740	**15.** 1830 r 19	**22.** $\frac{1}{6}$	**29.** a^2b^3
2. 11.16	**9.** 1950	**16.** 32	**23.** $3\frac{3}{8}$	**30.** $3a - 5b + 10$
3. $_{-3}$	**10.** 40.8	**17.** 63	**24.** $\frac{35}{36}$	**31.** $3:5$
4. 2308	**11.** 533	**18.** No	**25.** $\frac{19}{36}$	**32.** $x = 27$
5. 47.8	**12.** 12 r 66	**19.** $\frac{3}{4}$	**26.** 42 min	**33.** $x = 6$
6. 3714	**13.** 11 r 4	**20.** $1\frac{2}{7}$	**27.** 14	**34.** 8 km
7. 364	**14.** 5 r 64	**21.** $\frac{27}{5}$	**28.** 19	**35.** 80%

Consolidation Test 4 Page 186

1. 1002	**8.** 7372	**15.** 6457 r 31	**22.** $\frac{3}{11}$	**29.** p^3q^2
2. 3.818	**9.** 68000	**16.** 16	**23.** 2	**30.** $6c - 10d$
3. $_{-2}$	**10.** 3.4	**17.** 112	**24.** $4\frac{7}{20}$	**31.** $3:1$
4. 3784	**11.** 782	**18.** No	**25.** $2\frac{5}{16}$	**32.** $x = 48$
5. 54.7	**12.** 12 r 79	**19.** $\frac{1}{2}$	**26.** 48 m	**33.** $x = 8$
6. 3402	**13.** 21 r 11	**20.** $4\frac{1}{3}$	**27.** 7	**34.** £300
7. 476	**14.** 170	**21.** $\frac{61}{8}$	**28.** 0	**35.** 15%

Consolidation Test 5 Page 187

1. 1892	**8.** 984064	**15.** 12311 r 33	**22.** $\frac{3}{8}$	**29.** a^3b^2
2. 99.7	**9.** 128 000	**16.** 16	**23.** $\frac{5}{24}$	**30.** $2a + 5b$
3. $_{-3}$	**10.** 0.267	**17.** 336	**24.** $13\frac{14}{15}$	**31.** $3:5$
4. 322	**11.** 822	**18.** No	**25.** $1\frac{11}{15}$	**32.** $x = 4$
5. 5.6	**12.** 112 r 53	**19.** $\frac{11}{18}$	**26.** 120 miles	**33.** $x = 5$
6. 45610	**13.** 13 r 30	**20.** $3\frac{3}{11}$	**27.** 35	**34.** 12.5 litres
7. 2091	**14.** 50	**21.** $\frac{49}{9}$	**28.** $_{-32}$	**35.** 40%

Exam Paper 1 (1 hour) Page 188

1. 1892	**4.** 322	**7.** 2091	**10.** 0.0267	**13.** 13 r 30
2. 99.7	**5.** 5.6	**8.** 984064	**11.** 822	**14.** 50
3. 7	**6.** 45610	**9.** 128000	**12.** 112 r 53	**15.** 12311 r 33

16. 16

17. 336

18. No

19. $\frac{11}{18}$

20. $3\frac{3}{11}$

21. $\frac{49}{9}$

22. $\frac{3}{8}$

23. $1\frac{23}{27}$

24. $13\frac{14}{15}$

25. $1\frac{11}{15}$

26. 120 miles

27. 35

28. -32

29. a^3b^2

30. $2a+5b$

31. $3:5$

32. $4\frac{1}{2}$

33. $x=5$

34. 12.5 litres

35. 40%

38. AD = 4.8 cm, $\angle$DAC = 28.7°

Exam Paper 2 (1$\frac{1}{2}$ hours) Page 189

1. $4\frac{1}{2}$

2. 2.0272

3. (i) 20, (ii) 19.8

4. $\frac{13}{40}$

5. 24402 r 5

6. (i) $42 = 2 \times 3 \times 7$

$ 63 = 3^2 \times 7$

(ii) 21

7. 81 kg

8. £240

9. (i) $5a+10b$

(ii) $\dfrac{6c^2}{d}$

10. $3x^2y^2(1-2y)$

11. (i) $x=8$

(ii) $a=4\frac{1}{5}$

12. (i) $C = £(5y+15)$

(ii) $y = \dfrac{C-15}{5}$

13. 10 cm, 15 cm, 20 cm

14. 18

15. 70%

16. AC = 9.05 cm,

BC = 7.9 cm h = 7.5 cm,

Area = 28.1 cm^2

17. (i) 74°, (ii) 74°, (iii) 106°

18.

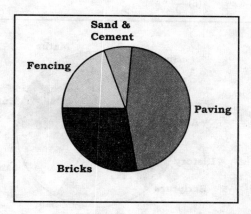

237

19.

x	0	–1	6
y	–2	–3	4

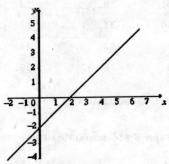

20. (a) 15 km/h, (b) He is not moving, (c) $13\frac{1}{3}$ km/h, (d) 35 km, (e) 5:15

Exam Paper 3 ($1\frac{1}{2}$ **hours) Page 191**

1. 2

2. 4.352

3. 2.36

4. 21

5. $\frac{21}{100}$

6. 154 r 438

7. 8 stone

8. (i) $72 = 2^3 \times 3^2$

               $64 = 2^6$

  (ii) 8

9. £294

10. 18%

11. (i) $14a + 27b$

  (ii) $\dfrac{2c}{d}$

12. $2y(4x - 6 + 7z)$

13. $x^2 + 17x + 72$

14. (i) $y = 3$

  (ii) $y = 23$

15. 6 months

16. 44.1 m

17. (i) $4:5$

  (ii) length = 15 cm,

  breadth = 12 cm

18. £40

19. OK = 4.2 cm

20. (i) 34°, (ii) 73°,

  (iii) 39°, (iv) 146°

21.

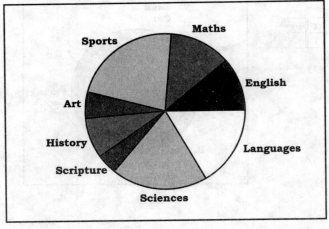

22.

x	0	2	5
y	–3	1	7

At $y = 4$, $x = 3\frac{1}{2}$

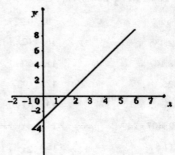

23. (a) 30 min, (b) 1 hr, (c) 100 mph, (d) 250 miles

Exam Paper 4 ($1\frac{1}{2}$ hours) Page 193

1. 6

2. 17.584

3. 17.486

4. 10

5. $\frac{17}{20}$

6. 1201 r 52

7. 1.47 m

8. 57 min 45 sec

9. 0.36

10. £$p - q - r$

11. £716.80

12. $84 = 2^2 \times 3 \times 7$

$24 = 2^3 \times 3$

168

13. (i) $4b + 21c$

(ii) $\dfrac{y^3}{2x}$

14. $4ab(2b - a + 3)$

15. $2x^2 + 13x + 15$

16. $x = 10$

17. 12

18. £3806

19. (a) £$7x$

(b) £$11y$

(c) £$C = 7x + 11y$

(d) £665

20. 6.2 cm

21. Carbohydrate, 15g;
Fat, 10 g;
Protein, 3g;
Additives, 2g

22.

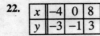

x	–4	0	8
y	–3	–1	3

At $y = -1\frac{1}{2}$, $x = -1$

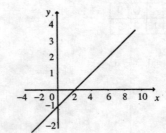

23. (i) 68°, (ii) 44°, (iii) 44°

24. (a) 15 km/h, (b) $13\frac{1}{3}$ km/h, (c) 25 km, (d) 4:52:30

239

Exam Paper 5 ($1\frac{1}{2}$ hours) Page 195

1. $2\frac{1}{2}$

2. 2.485

3. 8.10

4. 26

5. $\frac{5}{24}$

6. 23407 r 24

7. 11.8 s

8. 55 mins

9. 0.225.

10. $12x + 15y$ pence

11. 6%

12. 192

13. (i) $20n$ (ii) $2ab$

14. $4xy(3x + 4y - 1)$

15. $2x^2 + 11x - 21$

16. $x = 10$

17. $4\frac{1}{2}$

18. 60 runs

19. (a) 2390, (b) 478

20. Inscribing circle

21. $P = 2l + 2w$

22. Find, (a) 75°, (b) 75°, (c) 75°

23.

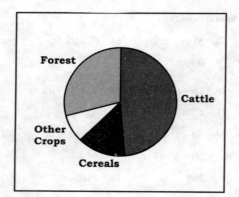

24.

x	-3	0	9
y	1	2	5

At $y = 0$, $x = -6$

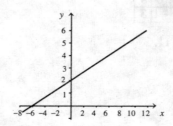

25. (a) 16 km/h, (b) 20 km/h, (c) 15 km, (d) Aprox 12:11 and 1:15